The World Directory of Scottish Associations

Michael Brander

Neil Wilson Publishing • Glasgow • Scotland

Published by Neil Wilson Publishing Ltd
303a The Pentagon Centre
36 Washington Street
GLASGOW
G3 8AZ

Tel: 0141-221 1117
Fax: 0141-221 5363
E-mail: *nwp@cqm.co.uk*
URL — *http://www.nwp.co.uk/*

The moral right of the author has been asserted. A catalogue record
for this book is available from the British Library.
ISBN 1-897784-27-9

Typeset in 10.5/11pt Bembo by The Write Stuff, Glasgow
Tel: 0141-339 8279
E-mail: *wilson_i@cqm.co.uk*

Printed by Interprint Ltd., Malta

Contents

New Zealand

Africa

Middle East

Indian Subcontinent

South-East Asia

Far East

Pacific Rim

Preface

WITH the number of Scots, or those claiming Scots descent, living outside Scotland variously estimated at between 40 and 50 million in number, it is not surprising that there are a very considerable number of societies, clubs and associations throughout the world, as well as in Scotland itself, connected with Scottish heritage in one way or another.

The names, addresses and information contained in this book are as accurate and up-to-date as possible, but inevitably some of the information and particularly the names and addresses of officials will already have changed by the time of publication. These will, of course, be brought up-to-date regularly and the information amended as required. It is, however, up to the officers of the associations included and any others which may have been overlooked or omitted, to contact Neil Wilson Publishing Ltd and provide full and updated information for further editions. Co-operation in this way will ensure that all the information and addresses given in each forthcoming edition are to the ultimate benefit of all concerned.

It is my publisher's intention to create a website for the information included in this book, and details of this can be found on the NWP website (http://www.nwp.co.uk/). When this website goes live, updating information will be carried out on a constant basis and links to other Scottish organisations will be created. Any amendments or new information can be e-mailed directly to nwp@cqm.co.uk.

Michael Brander

Introduction

The population of Scotland has never exceeded six million, yet around the world there are almost ten times that number who lay claim to Scottish descent. A glance at Scotland's history and geography will help to explain this anomaly. Geography has always played a vital part in Scotland's development as a nation. The remote and barren Highlands, beautiful though they might be, provided little in the way of sustenance, and the nature of the terrain impeded communications and commerce. With the exception of the lowland coastal belt with its fertile soil and mild climate, stretching from Stonehaven round to Dornoch, life in the Highlands of Scotland was always a constant battle against the elements.

The more fertile Central Lowlands, by contrast, was excellent agricultural and grazing land, rich in minerals, with long rivers which provided both fish and a ready means of transport to facilitate commerce and industry. The Southern Uplands stretching from the Ayrshire coast in the west to Dunbar in the east, formed a natural border, impeding invasion from the south.

Those living in the Scottish Border counties were subject to almost continuous warfare for centuries as were their fellow Borderers in Northumberland and Cumberland. Other outlying areas, such as Galloway in the south-west and the Inner and Outer Hebrides were also difficult to defend and the latter especially were for long under the rule and domination of Norway. For many centuries the country was thus divided into three separate and distinct regions, the remoter Highlands and Islands, the Central Lowlands and the buffer region of the Borders.

It was indeed the wild nature of the terrain, rather than the undoubted fighting abilities of the various northern tribes uniting against the invading Romans from the south, which prevented them being conquered. The Romans were forced to withdraw behind Hadrian's Wall and the northern tribes were thus spared the benefits of civilisation. Even so, for centuries thereafter, the country was subjected to invasion and colonisation from other points of the compass. Early in the sixth century the Scots, a Celtic people from Ireland, settled in Dalriada in Argyll, warring bitterly with the Picts to the east. A century later the Angles from Northumbria held much of the south-east of the country.

It was only in the ninth century when Kenneth MacAlpin, King of the Scots, defeated the Picts that the first sign of an emergent nation appeared. By 1034 Malcolm II was known as the 'King of Scotia' ruling over the Britons in the south-west as well as the Angles in the south-east. Throughout this entire period there were frequent invasions by Norsemen in their long boats and the Norwegian Kings remained a constant threat to Scottish political and economic stability until 1263 when King Hakon's invasion fleet was decisively defeated in the Battle of Largs.

Thereafter it was England which became the main threat. The largely unprovoked onslaught of Edward I, the self-styled 'Hammer of the Scots,' brought Scotland under the English yoke until Sir William Wallace led a spontaneous revolt against his bloody and tyrannical rule. After Wallace's death Robert the Bruce continued the struggle. By this time the Scots had been welded into a united nation on the anvil of hatred and were determined to fight and to survive. The Battle of Bannockburn in 1314, when the English were finally decisively defeated, established Scotland's total independence.

The Declaration of Arbroath in 1320 sent by a group of Scottish Barons to the Pope proclaimed: 'For so long as a hundred of us are left alive, we will yield in no least way to English dominion. We fight not for glory nor for wealth nor honours; but only and alone we fight for freedom, which no good man surrenders, but with his life.'

Throughout the Hundred Years War (1337-1453) Scotland remained more or less permanently allied to France against England. The unity of the country was, however, impaired by constant feuding amongst the nobility and amongst the clans for several centuries. On occasion, when economic and social stability appeared to have been achieved, it was Scotland's fate to lose an able king and have an infant succeed to the throne, with inevitable intrigue and political and social upheaval resulting. Religious strife was added with the coming of the Reformation to Scotland during Mary's reign in the first half of the 16th century, a period which also saw the ending of the 'Auld Alliance' with France and a move towards union with England instead.

Perhaps because of a need for community in the remote and inaccessible glens and islands, the Highland Scots always identified themselves with a clan, or a family, or with a place, as well as with their nation. A system of clan loyalties developed which had no hierarchical distinctions, but accepted an alliegance to a chosen leader, or chief, usually distinguished by his boldness in battle. It was a bond of dignity and pride, not of servility or humbleness. Indeed each clansmen felt himself in most ways the equal of his chieftain and free to speak his mind in his presence. It was thus that ties of kinship and territory came to mean a great deal to the Scots.

Hence, while often aggressively nationalistic when away from Scotland, they are still generally prepared to welcome remote clan or family connections, or even those of locality, as deserving of friendship and loyalty, or even as proof of kinship. It is possibly this 'clannishness' of the Scot abroad which constitutes his most prominent characteristic.

Born in a land where it was hard to earn a living and often forced to emigrate out of necessity, the Scots have always been prepared to seek their fortunes abroad. Always hardy fighting men, they earned a reputation in Europe as fine mercenary soldiers. As merchants they came to be recognised as shrewd and honest traders who knew how to strike a hard bargain but stood by their word once given. They were used to a frugal living at home or abroad and were prepared to work or fight hard to survive.

From the Middle Ages until the end of the 17th century the steadily flourishing ports of the Firth of Forth kept up a regular trade with Scandinavia, the Low Countries and France. It was from there and the east coast ports as far north as Aberdeen and Fraserburgh that the steady movement of Scots to and from Europe continued. As traders, merchants, mercenaries, and scholars, the Scots penetrated everywhere from the Papal courts at Rome to the wild hinterlands of Finland. Indeed as early as the 13th century a certain James Tait of East Lothian, in the service of Finnish nobility, founded a family which so prospered that today Tait is a well-known name in Finland,

In France, during the Hundred Years War, the Scots served willingly against the English and formed, amongst other regiments, The Scottish Archers Guard, Les Gardes du Corps Ecossoises, the personal bodyguard of the French Kings, as well as the most elite of all the French Forces, Les Gens d'Armes Ecossoises, The Scottish Men-at-Arms. Although by the end of the 16th century these regiments were almost entirely manned by Frenchmen they still used the old Scots commands. Doubtless, many forming these corps were third and fourth generation Franco-Scots, for the Scots have always had a way of absorbing themselves into a country while retaining their own native characteristics. In this way such names as Dougal changed to Duval, Douglas to du Glas, Drummond to Dromont, Leslie to de Lisle, Ramsay to de Ramezay and many more; such corruptions are sometimes the only evidence of a Scottish ancestry.

Scotland has also always had close links with Scandinavia; successive Viking invasions left their mark and fishermen and whalers inevitably met frequently on common fishing grounds and in ports. Nor was it only fishermen and sailors who moved between Scotland and Scandinavia, but also merchants and mercenary soldiers. In Sweden especially there are still numerous families tracing their ancestry to Scottish forebears as far back as the 17th century, even today bearing their family names with pride and sometimes also wearing the family tartan, despite the fact that they often speak only Swedish. A good example of this is the Thorburn-MacFie Family Society, open to all related by blood or marriage to the descendants of two merchants named Thorburn, one of whom married a MacFie and settled on an estate in Sweden near Gothenburg. There are now over 200 members of this society which prides itself on its links with Scotland and holds regular meetings.

Due largely to successive years of famine in Scotland in the early 17th century, Poland and East Prussia (where there were already established communities of wealthy Scottish merchants) saw a particularly large influx of young Scots, many little more than penniless pedlars or 'Kremers'. 'As poor as a Scot's pedlar's pack', became a well-known Polish saying and at one time, around 1630, it was estimated that there were over 30,000 Scots in Poland. Inevitably the same process of absorption took place as it had in other parts of Europe. Corruptions of Scottish names into Polish included Czamer for Chalmers, Driowski for Drew, Zlott for Scott, Brun for Brown, Grim for Graham, Rusek for Ross and many more. In East Prussia some of the corruptions included Allt for Auld, Bruisz for Bruce, Duncken for Duncan, Kaubrun for Cockburn, Etzbeld for Archibald, Nickel for Nichol, and Schotte for Scott. Since the Second World War the Scots have returned the compliment of this hospitality and absorbed many Poles who fought in the Free Polish Forces and felt unable to return to Poland. Their descendants in the third and fourth generation are now very truly Scots, even if retaining a natural feeling for their homeland.

A certain measure of stability was achieved under the Union of the Crowns in 1603 when James VI of Scotland succeeded Elizabeth I as James I of Great Britain and Ireland. Throughout the remainder of his reign, however, James only visited Scotland once and was the first to introduce government from Whitehall. It was his proud boast that he had at last brought law and order to the Borders, even if he remained less successful in the Highlands. His reign was followed by a century of religious and political strife which engulfed most of Europe.

The only successful Scottish colonisation scheme, however, took place in the first half of the 17th century in Northern Ireland where James VI and I conceived the idea of forming 'plantations' on the lines of those already formed in North America. The Scots took to the scheme enthusiastically and considerable numbers moved to Ulster. It was also seen as a convenient repository for those Borderers who still clung to their old habits of cattle and horse thieving. Be that as it may, between 1609 and 1639 some 40,000 Scots were estimated to have settled in Ulster and by the turn of the century the figure had risen to almost 100,000. It was notable, however, that many of these moved to the New World, where they became distinguished from their fellow Scots by the description 'Irish-Scots' and were noted for their quarrelsome nature.

Amongst the earliest emigrants from Scotland to the New World, albeit involuntary ones, were those unfortunates taken prisoner when opposing Cromwell's forces at the Battle of Dunbar in 1650, who were sent to America as indentured servants. Soon a small number of Scottish emigrants began to trickle out to the New World, mostly centred in New Jersey. At the same time an increasing number of merchants also fought to establish themselves in the face of English opposition and successfully flouted the Customs stranglehold enjoyed by the English by trans-shipping tobacco from Virginia and rum, molasses and sugar from the West Indies at fishing ports in Newfoundland. The goods were then sent direct to Glasgow. From Glasgow French silks, brandy and lace were shipped back to Newfoundland to be trans-shipped to the Colonies in complete defiance of the Customs laws and English trade embargo. The Scots merchants in Glasgow in a position to benefit from this trade became extremely wealthy and it was from these beginnings that Glasgow's wealth and ultimate claim to be the 'Second City of the Empire' developed.

The Civil Wars in the mid-17th century saw Montrose's brief year of glory in 1645 when, with a small army of Highlanders, he literally conquered the whole of Scotland for Charles II. Unfortunately his victories only succeeded in establishing a lasting fear of the Highlanders in many leading Lowland minds. Cromwell, at the head of his New Model Army, was soon established as undisputed ruler of both England and Scotland. For the first time Scotland enjoyed parity of trade, even if she was also heavily taxed.

Despite determined efforts to subdue the Highlands, even Cromwell's deputies had little success beyond causing a lasting resentment of southern rule exacerbated by the fact that the Highlanders, for the most part, only spoke Gaelic which was not understood in the Lowland south. Mutual dislike and misunderstanding between Lowlands and Highlands were accentuated during the reign of William III by further draconian acts such as the notorious Massacre of Glencoe.

In 1707 the Act of Union was passed, uniting the Parliaments of both England and Scotland under one Crown. The Act, however, was only passed as the result of considerable political chicanery by the English Whig politicians and the wholesale bribery of Scottish nobility with the result that there remained immense popular opposition to the Union within Scotland. Despite the Union of the Parliaments, however, Scotland retained her own legal and educational systems and her separate Presbyterian church.

At the time of the Union in 1707 there was an estimated population in Scotland of around one million and also 100,000 Scots in Ulster. It can reasonably be accepted that there were already then about 50,000 Scots permanently settled in North America. In Scandinavia and Europe there must also have been in the region of 100,000 Scots, or people of Scots descent. The sum total of Scots outside Scotland at this time must therefore have been at least a quarter of the country's total population and from this date onwards the population of Scotland was to remain relatively static while the numbers of overseas Scots grew progressively greater.

Without roads, without effective control and with a separate language of their own the Highlands were effectively cut off from the rest of the country and posed a problem to successive governments from James VI and I onwards. It was largely the strains of economic union and discontent with Hanoverian rule in the Highlands, rather than any great longing for the return of the Stuarts, which led to the Jacobite risings of 1715 and 1745.

So nearly successful was the latter ill-led rising under 'Bonnie Prince Charlie' which ended on the fateful battle of Culloden Moor in 1746, that repressive measures were introduced to ensure the Highlanders never took up arms again. These included banning the carrying of arms, the wearing of tartan and severely curbing the powers of the chieftains. The socio-economic effects of turning the chieftains from hereditary rulers into dispossessed tenants valued on a par with cattle and sheep, eventually resulted in the notorious Clearances during the latter part of the 18th and 19th centuries.

The most effective measure to control the Highlanders, however, was the principle of allowing them to form Highland regiments to fight overseas, introduced by Prime Minister William Pitt. During the years from 1715 to 1815 no less than 85 regiments were raised from the Highlands of Scotland alone. Many Scots soldiers died overseas, in battle or from disease, but many remained as emigrants. Of those who returned, many found their homes burned during the Clearances to make way for sheep, and it was clear that the land could not support the numbers clamouring for food from it. It was this inability of the land to provide along with the introduction of the Cheviot sheep which accelerated the movement of people off the land.

First introduced in the 1780s the sheep were soon found to be very profitable. Whole townships living near the poverty line and subject to appalling hardships in periodic famines due to crop failure, were cleared to make way for them, which now replaced the traditional but less profitable black cattle.

Highlanders emigrated in great numbers throughout the 18th and 19th centuries, or moved down to swell the numbers of low-paid workers or unemployed in Glasgow, Edinburgh, or even further south. Sometimes whole communities emigrated together. Amongst the earliest notable emigrations from the Highlands was a group from Argyll of some 90 families who settled in the Cross Creek region of Cape Fear in North Carolina as early as 1739. After Culloden many more followed their example. A feature of the early Highland emigrations was a tendency to remain in the region first settled and a preference for staying amongst people of a similar culture and background, wearing the kilt and speaking Gaelic.

By the mid-18th century many Scots were spreading out around the world taking full advantage of the lifting of trade barriers. In many cases their first step was to move southwards to England, most probably to London. Because of the parish educational facilities available in Scotland, which were much superior to those of England, these emigrants were at a considerable advantage. Many entered the East India Company, or emigrated to North America or the West Indies, or wherever British influence offered a foothold. They were suddenly everywhere, much to the discomfort of the English mob who made their dislike plain in graffiti.

The Scots in America also took every opportunity available to them after the Act of Union of 1707, when for the first time they were offered the same opportunities for trading as the English merchants. Within 50 years they had established themselves everywhere. As in England they were prominent in the professions, in commerce, banking, politics and law.

Although they played a prominent part on both sides during the American War of Independence, the Scots remaining in America afterwards tended to play down their origins rather more than previously. The main ethnic settlements retaining the Gaelic language and Highland dress had departed either at the start of the war or when it was over. Those Scots remaining tended to adapt more readily to the American way of life, still maintaining their St Andrews Societies and similar institutions but no longer as obtrusively as before. Thus it is that the kilt is not as common in the USA today as it is in Canada, where, as in Australia, there were numerous kilted regiments raised to fight in the First World War.

During this period considerable numbers of Scots left North Carolina and New York State where they had settled in large numbers and emigrated to Canada. At the end of the war a further 30,000 Scottish loyalists moved from North Carolina, New York and Pennsylvania to Halifax, Nova Scotia. There was also a fresh spate of emigration from Scotland to Canada, when word was received of the opportunities available.

With the outbreak of war with France in 1793, however, emigration to North America tailed off and for the first time there was emigration instead to Australia, some of it involuntary. Between 1788 and 1820 some 26,000 convicts were transported to New South Wales and Tasmania, or Van Diemen's Land as it was then known. How many of these were Scots is not recorded, but there were numerous Scots amongst the administrators.

The record of the Scots as administrators and as merchants in India during the 18th and 19th centuries was outstanding. They were also prominent in Africa throughout the 19th century as explorers, hunters, merchants and in the professions and as Kirk missionaries. Their long-established ties with the Low Countries proved useful when Scottish Clerics in the Presbyterian Church proved acceptable to the Boers in the Cape, who vehemently rejected any ties with the English. A number of the Boer leaders were proud to admit Scottish blood through inter-marriage with a Presbyterian minister's family.

In the Crimean War and the Indian Mutiny the Scottish regiments, notably the Highland Brigade under its valiant commander Sir Colin Campbell, fought magnificently. Yet on their return to Scotland there was still little enough for such men to live on and more often than not, like many earlier veterans from Waterloo, they had to look overseas to earn their living. Canada, New Zealand, Australia and the United States of America all received a steady flow of Scottish emigrants during the 19th century and the steady drain of Scots into England also continued.

In the Highlands in the latter half of the 19th century the depopulation caused by the Clearances had virtually ended. The glens were empty of men. The sheep which had displaced them began to make way in their turn for deer and grouse as the sporting value of the Highland estates was appreciated by new owners from England, who had in many cases replaced the original chieftains. Following the example of Queen Victoria, the English aristocracy flocked to the Highlands for the deer stalking and salmon fishing. The

Balmoralisation of the Highlands had begun. The glorious landscape, now devoid of humanity, became the sporting playground of the wealthy English.

Throughout the 19th century the importance of Glasgow increased as the main port of access for North America. The population of the Lowlands was concentrated in the region of the Forth and Clyde central industrial belt where coal mining and the heavy industries dependent on Clydeside developed. The successful introduction of modern farming methods further depopulated the countryside. Yet again the tendency was for the younger sons to emigrate, taking their skills with them. During the farming depressions of the 1870s and 1880s many Scottish farmers moved south to take over farms in England which were no longer considered economic by their former tenants and owners, but which seemed to these Scots infinitely superior to those they had farmed in Scotland.

In the 20th century the Scots have achieved prominence throughout the world. Wherever they have spread they have provided leaders in every field. Their ability, integrity and shrewdness are known and envied in every world centre and this guide is a manifestation of the success of this world family of Scots who have settled in every corner of the globe and maintained their own links with their culture and the mother country.

Michael Brander, 1996

Key to symbols

✍	Name of principal contacts
☎	Telephone (including international codes. Check access numbers in your own country of residence. In the UK, these numbers are 00)
ℭ	Fax (including international codes. Check access numbers in your own country of residence. In the UK, these numbers are 00)
E	E-mail address

SCOTLAND

ABERDEEN

ABERDEEN BRANCH OF THE ROYAL SCOTTISH COUNTRY DANCE SOCIETY

Aims & Activities: See the RSCDS on page 47.
✍ Secretary: Dr R. Drummond
363 Gt. Western Road, Aberdeen.
AB1 6NU
☎ 01224 322316 (home)
☎ 01224 663131 extn 51513 (business)

ABERDEEN BURNS CLUB

Founded: 1872.
Aims & Activities: To encourage an interest in Robert Burns and Scottish literature. Educational. Historical. Charitable and Social. Annual Meeting.
Affiliations: The Burns Federation, No. 40.
✍ Secretary: Mrs Irene Fraser
4 Ramsay Crescent, Barthdee, Aberdeen.
AB1 7BN

ABERDEEN HIGHLAND GAMES

Aims & Activities: To organise annual professional Highland Games and sports in the area of Aberdeen. Regarded as a considerable tourist attraction.
Affiliations: The Scottish Games Association, (page 74).
✍ Secretary: City Arts Officer
St Nicholas House, Broad St, Aberdeen.
AB9 1XJ
☎ 01224 522475

ABERDEEN UNIVERSITY SCOTTISH COUNTRY DANCE SOCIETY

Aims & Activities: See the RSCDS on page 47.
✍ Secretary: Helen Whittle
c/o SRC Luthuli House, 50/2 College Bounds, Old Aberdeen.

NORTHERN SCOTTISH COUNTIES ASSOCIATION OF BURNS CLUBS

Aims & Activities: Social. Annual Dinner to promote interest in Robert Burns.
Affiliations: The Burns Federation, No. 921.
✍ Secretary: Miss Ethel Hall
280 Whitehall Place, Aberdeen.
AB2 4PA

ABERDEENSHIRE

ABOYNE HIGHLAND GAMES

Founded: 1867.
Aims & Activities: To organise an annual gathering and professional Highland Games and sports in the area of Aboyne, 11 miles east of Ballater. These are one of the classic Deeside Games and are usually held on the first Saturday in August.
Affiliations: The Scottish Games Association, (page 74).
✍ Secretary: William Kelman
Craigmore, Logie Coldstone.
AB34 5PQ
☎ 01339 881057

BALLATER HIGHLAND GAMES

Aims & Activities: To organise annual professional Highland Games and sports in the area of Ballater, 17 miles east of Braemar, and the nearest railway station to Balmoral. Amongst the first of the notable Deeside Games, usually held soon after those at Aboyne.

Affiliations: The Scottish Games Association, (page 74).

✍ Chieftain: Farquharson of Invercauld

✍ Secretary: Edward Anderson PO Box 2, Ballater. AB35 5RZ

☎ 01339 755771

BANFFSHIRE BRANCH OF THE ROYAL SCOTTISH COUNTRY DANCE SOCIETY

Aims & Activities: See the RSCDS on page 47.

Membership: 68.

✍ Secretary: Mrs A. Archibald 26 Mackay Road, Macduff. AB44 1XL

☎ 01261 832154 (home)

☎ 01261 812267 (afternoon)

BRAEMAR GATHERING

Founded: 1800.

Aims & Activities: The Braemar Royal Highland Society, open only to natives of the parish and those who have resided there for three years, organise these world-famous annual professional Highland Games and sports in the area of Braemar. Royal patronage dates from 1848 when Queen Victoria first attended these notable Games held in a natural bowl in the hills eight miles from Balmoral. Usually held in the first Saturday in September and the last of the big Deeside Games, they form a worthy climax to the Games season.

Affiliations: The Scottish Games Association, (page 74).

Publications: Annual Programme of Events, available at the Games.

✍ Secretary: W. A. Meston

Coilacreich, Ballater. AB35 5UH

☎ 01339 755377

BRAEMAR ROYAL HIGHLAND SOCIETY

Founded: 1817.

Aims & Activities: The Society organises the famous Braemar Gathering at which the Royal family put in an annual appearance from nearby Balmoral. Overseas links. Charitable.

Membership: Open only to natives of Braemar and district, or those who have resided there for at least three years.

✍ Secretary: W. A. Meston Coilacreich, Ballater. AB35 5UH

☎ 01338 755377

CLAN BUCHAN SOCIETY

Aims & Activities: To promote awareness of the clan and family history, background and connections and the part they have played in Scottish history. To strengthen overseas links.

Membership: Open to the families and connections of the Buchan clan and family.

✍ Chieftain: The Lord Kilmarnock Auchmacoy House, Ellon. AB4 9RB

CLAN BURNETT

Aims & Activities: To foster the clan spirit worldwide. To collect clan and genealogical records. To encourage overseas links.

Membership: Open to those named Burnett, in its various spellings, and to those related by marriage or descent.

✍ Chieftain: J. C. A. Burnett of Leys Crathes Castle, Crathes. AB3 3QJ

CLAN FARQUHARSON

Aims & Activities: To promote awareness of the clan history.

Membership: Open to members of the Farquharson clan and family and those bearing that name, or variants of it.

✍ Capt. A. C. C. Farquharson
Invercauld, Braemar.
AB3 5XB

CLAN FRASER

Aims & Activities: To promote awareness of the clan history.

Membership: Open to members of the Fraser clan and family and those bearing that name, or variants of it.

✍ The Lady Saltoun
Cairnbulg Castle, Fraserburgh.
AB4 5TN

CLAN LESLIE

Aims & Activities: To promote awareness of the clan history.

Membership: Open to members of the Leslie clan and family and those bearing that name, or variants of it.

✍ David Leslie
Insch.
AB52 6NX

CLAN MACTHOMAS SOCIETY

Founded: 1954.

Aims & Activities: To develop interest in the clan and to promote its welfare. To strengthen overseas links. Charitable. Educational. Social. Historical. Annual Gathering.

Affiliations: Branches in Australia, Canada, New Zealand, South Africa and U. S. A.

Publications: Clach A'Choilich, Newsletter (both annual).

Membership: Open to all connected with the clan surnames: Combe, Combie, McCombe, McCombie, McColm, McComb, McComas, McComish, NcComie, MacOmie, MacOmish, Tam, Thom, Thoms, Thomas, Thomson (of the last two, only those originating from Fife, Grampian and Tayside Regions).

✍ Secretary: Roslin Cottage
Pitmedden, Ellon.
AB41 0NY

CLAN SEMPILL

Aims & Activities: To promote awareness of the clan history.

Membership: Open to members of the Sempill clan and family and those bearing that name, or variants of it.

✍ The Lady Sempill
Drumminor Castle, Rhynie.
AB5

DRUMTOCHTY HIGHLAND GAMES

Aims & Activities: To organise annual professional Highland Games and sports in the area of Laurencekirk, a small market town 25 miles south of Aberdeen in the old county of Kincardineshire. The Games are generally held in late June in the grounds of Drumtochty Castle.

Affiliations: The Scottish Games Association, (page 74).

✍ Secretary: A. Reid
Brodie House, 21 Garvock Street, Laurencekirk.
AB30 1HD
☎ 01561 377252

FATHERLAND BURNS CLUB

Founded: 1926.

Aims & Activities: Social. Annual Gathering. To foster appreciation of the work of Robert Burns.

Affiliations: The Burns Federation, No. 458.

✍ Secretary: Mrs Elizabeth Petrie
Ashley Cottage, 23 Slug Road, Stonehaven.
AB3 2EX

FORBES SOCIETY

Aims & Activities: To promote awareness of the clan and family history,
background and connections and
their part in Scottish history. To
strengthen overseas links.
Membership: Open to the families and
connections of the Forbes clan and
family.
✍ The Master of Forbes
  Castle Forbes, Alford.
  AB53 8BL

FRASERBURGH BURNS CLUB

Founded: 1928.
Aims & Activities: Social. Annual din-
ner. To encourage interest in the work
of Burns.
Affiliations: The Burns Federation,
No. 403.
✍ Secretary: W. J. Smith
  31 Brodick Road, Fraserburgh.
  AB43 5TU

HUNTLY ROTARY CLUB

Aims & Activities: Social. Annual din-
ner.
Affiliations: The Burns Federation,
No. 1111.
✍ Secretary: H. Stuart Jolly
  Winds Eye, Green Road, Huntly.

LONACH GATHERING

Founded: 1822.
Aims & Activities: To organise annual
professional Highland Games and
sports in the area of Upper Donside.
Amongst the earlier of the established
Highland Games, a prominent feature
of the day is the 'March of the
Clansmen' when the Forbes, Gordons
and Wallaces march six miles round
the neighbouring large houses before
marching past at the Games, a feature
much copied in the USA.
Affiliations: The Scottish Games
Association, (page 74).
✍ Secretary: John Barbour

Torrancroy, Strathdon.
AB36 8UG
☎ 01975 651233

OLDMELDRUM HIGHLAND GAMES

Aims & Activities: To organise annual
professional Highland Games and
sports in the area of Oldmeldrum,
four miles north of Inverurie in
Aberdeenshire.
Affiliations: The Scottish Games
Association, (page 74).
✍ Secretary: Robert A. Forsyth
  2 Rosebank, Oldmeldrum.
  AB51 0BE
☎ 01651 873909

PETERHEAD BRANCH OF THE ROYAL SCOTTISH COUNTRY DANCE SOCIETY

Aims & Activities: See the RSCDS on
page 47.
✍ Secretary: Miss E. Downie
  32 Strawberry Bank, Peterhead.
  AB42 6AT
☎ 01779 479114

PETERHEAD BURNS CLUB

Founded: 1826.
Aims & Activities: Social. Charitable
and educational. To encourage inter-
est in the poetry of Robert Burns.
Annual meeting.
Affiliations: The Burns Federation,
No. 336.
✍ Secretary: Mr J. A. MacRitchie
  Broad House, Broad Street,
  Peterhead.
  AB42 6JA

STONEHAVEN BRANCH OF THE ROYAL SCOTTISH COUNTRY DANCE SOCIETY

Aims & Activities: See the RSCDS on
page 47.
Membership: 58.

✍ Secretary: Mrs M. Lillie
120 Forest Park, Stonehaven.
AB3 2GE
☎ 01569 764941

STONEHAVEN HIGHLAND GAMES

Aims & Activities: To organise annual professional Highland Games and sports in the area of Stonehaven, the attractive old seaport and county town of Kincardineshire.
Affiliations: The Scottish Games Association, (page 74).
✍ Secretary: Mrs Audrey Lockhead
iewmount, Arduthie Road.
AB3 2DQ

TOMINTOUL HIGHLAND GAMES

Founded: 1842.
Aims & Activities: To organise annual professional Highland Games and sports in the area of Tomintoul, one of the highest villages in Scotland, 12 miles south of Ballindalloch. These Games are traditionally held on the third Saturday in July.
Affiliations: The Scottish Games Association, (page 74).
✍ Secretary: P. E. Grant
Monriack, 18 Main Street,
Tomintoul.
AB37 9EX
☎ 01807 580407

ANGUS

ARBROATH BURNS CLUB

Founded: 1888.
Aims & Activities: Social. Educational. Annual Gathering. To promote knowledge of the work of Robert Burns.
Affiliations: The Burns Federation, No. 82.
✍ Secretary: Mr G. J. M. Dunlop

Brothockbank House, Arbroath.
DD11 1MJ

ARBROATH HIGHLAND GAMES

Aims & Activities: To organise annual professional Highland Games and sports in the area of Arbroath.
Affiliations: The Scottish Games Association, (page 74).
✍ Secretary: George Mitchelson
3 Addereley Terrace, Monifieth.
DD5 4DQ
☎ 01382 532858

ARBUTHNOTT FAMILY ASSOCIATION

Aims & Activities: To promote awareness of the family history.
Membership: Open to members of the Arbuthnott family and those bearing that name, or variants of it.
✍ Secretary: Cairnhill
Forfar.
DD8 3TG

CARNEGIE CLAN

Aims & Activities: To promote awareness of the clan history.
✍ The Earl of Southesk
Kinnaird Castle, Brechin.
DD9 6TZ

CARNOUSTIE BRANCH OF THE ROYAL SCOTTISH COUNTRY DANCE SOCIETY

Aims & Activities: See the RSCDS on page 47.
Membership: 33.
✍ Secretary: Mrs J. MacIntosh
1 North Brown Street,
Carnoustie.
DD7 7PX
☎ 01241 832707

CLAN NEWLANDS

Aims & Activities: To promote aware-ness of the clan history.
Membership: Open to members of the Newlands clan and family and those bearing that name, or variants of it.
✍ Secretary: Lauriston Castle
St Cyrus.
DD10 0DJ

CLAN OGILVY

Aims & Activities: To promote aware-ness of the clan history.
Membership: Open to members of the Ogilvy clan and family and those bearing that name, or variants of it.
✍ The Earl of Airlie
Cortachy Castle, Cortachy,
Kirriemuir.
DD8 4LX

EAST ANGUS BRANCH OF THE ROYAL SCOTTISH COUNTRY DANCE SOCIETY

Aims & Activities: See the RSCDS on page 47.
Membership: 45.
✍ Secretary: Mrs K. Skea
39 Elliot Street, Arbroath.
DD11 3BZ
☎ 01241 873078

FORFAR BRANCH OF THE ROYAL SCOTTISH COUNTRY DANCE SOCIETY

Aims & Activities: See the RSCDS on page 47.
Membership: 72.
✍ Secretary: Miss C. Rigby
Rockhead Cottage, Guthrie,
Forfar.
DD8 2TL
☎ 01241 828447

FORFAR HIGHLAND GAMES

Aims & Activities: To organise annual professional Highland Games and sports in the area of Forfar, the small and attractive county town of Angus. The games are generally held in mid-June in the Lochside Park.
Affiliations: The Scottish Games Association, (page 74).
✍ Secretary: Mrs E. Webster
5 Jeanfield Crescent, Forfar.
DD8 1JR
☎ 01307 465605

GLENBERVIE BURNS MEMORIAL ASSOCIATION

Aims & Activities: Social and to pro-mote the memory of Robert Burns. Annual Dinner.
Affiliations: The Burns Federation, No. 897.
✍ Secretary: Mr George F. Watt
1a Seagate, Montrose.
DD10 8BA

MONTROSE BURNS CLUB

Aims & Activities: Social and to encourage interest in the poetical works of Robert Burns. Annual Dinner.
Affiliations: The Burns Federation, No. 242.
✍ Secretary: Nicholas Bradford
4 Queen's Close, 113 High Street, Montrose.
DD10 8QR

MONTROSE HIGHLAND GAMES

Aims & Activities: To organise annual professional Highland Games and sports in the area of North-east Angus around the Royal Burgh and port of Montrose at the mouth of the river Esk.
Affiliations: The Scottish Games Association, (page 74).
✍ Secretary: Mrs R. Beedie
14 Angus Drive, Montrose.
DD10 9DZ
☎ 01674 674885

RAMSAY FAMILY

Aims & Activities: To promote awareness of the family history.
Membership: Open to members of the Ramsay family and clan and those bearing that name, or variants of it.
✍ The Earl of Dalhousie
Brechin Castle, Brechin.
DD9 6SH

ARGYLL AND BUTE

APPIN SCOTTISH COUNTRY DANCE CLUB

Aims & Activities: See the RSCDS on page 47.
✍ Secretary: Mrs M. Toole
1 Shuna View, Port Appin.
PA38 4DG
☎ 01631 730533

BLAIRMORE COUNTRY DANCE CLUB

Founded: 1983.
Aims & Activities: Social. Classes taught by Miss Madalene Lee.
The Royal Scottish Country Dance Society, (page 47).
✍ Secretary: Ms V. Archbold
Ar Tigh Beag, Creggandarroch Lodge, Shore Road, Blairmore, Dunoon.
PA23 8TJ
☎ 01369 840569

CLAN CAMPBELL SOCIETY

Aims & Activities: To promote awareness of the clan, its background and its place in Scottish history. To strengthen overseas links. Genealogical. Social. Annual Gathering.
Membership: Open to anyone with the name Campbell or that of one of the clan septs, also their descendants and those related by marriage.
✍ Secretary: Argyll Estates Office

Charry Park, Inveraray.
PA32 8XE

CLAN COCHRANE

Aims & Activities: To promote awareness of the clan history.
Membership: Open to members of the Cochrane clan and family and those bearing that name, or variants of it.
✍ Chieftain: The Earl of Dundonald
Lochnell Castle, Ledaig, Mull.
PA34 1QT

CLAN LIVINGSTONE SOCIETY

Aims & Activities: To encourage interest in the history of the clan. To strengthen overseas links. Genealogical. Social.
Membership: Open to any members of the Livingstone clan and family, and those related by marriage or descent.
✍ Secretary: Bachuil, Lismore
Oban.
PA34 5UL

CLAN MACDOUGALL SOCIETY

Aims & Activities: To promote the clan spirit. To increase awareness of the clan and family history and their part in Scottish history. To stengthen overseas links. Genealogical. Social.
Membership: Open to all those bearing the name MacDougall and its various derivatives, also those of the various clan septs.
✍ Secretary: Dunollie Castle
Oban.
PA34 5TT

CLAN MALCOLM AND MACCALUM SOCIETY

Aims & Activities: To encourage interest in the clan history. To promote the clan spirit. To strengthen overseas links. Social. Genealogical.
Membership: Open to anyone with the names Malcolm or MacCalum, their

descendants, or those related by marriage.

✍ Secretary: Duntrune Castle
Kilmartin.
PA31 8GG

CLAN McALISTER SOCIETY

Aims & Activities: To encourage awareness of the clan and family history. To strengthen overseas links. Genealogical. Social.
Membership: Open to anyone named McAlister, or variants of that name, or of the clan septs.
✍ Secretary: Glenbarr Abbey
Kintyre.

COWAL HIGHLAND GATHERING

Founded: 1894.
Aims & Activities: To organise annual amateur Highland Games in the area of Dunoon the principal holiday centre on the Cowal pensinsula which has a regular ferry service from Gourock. Usually held in late August, these well attended and popular Games feature one of the Five Pipe Band Championships, qualifying for the Champion of Champions League.
✍ Manager: Stuart Donald
Cowal Highland Gathering Ltd,
2 Hanover Street, Dunoon.
PA23 7AB
☎ 01369 703206

COWAL SCOTTISH COUNTRY DANCE CLUB

Aims & Activities: See the RSCDS on page 47.
✍ Secretary: Mrs J. Rennie
Lower Netherby, Hunter Street,
Kirn, Dunoon.
PA23 8DT
☎ 01369 705453

INELLAN SCOTTISH COUNTRY DANCE CLUB

Aims & Activities: See the RSCDS on page 47.
✍ Secretary: Christine Walpole
Schoolhouse, Toward.
PA23 7UG

INVERARAY HIGHLAND GAMES

Founded: 1866 (revived 1956 after lapsing during the Second World War).
Aims & Activities: To organise annual professional Highland Games and sports in the area of Inveraray, the small attractive county town of Argyll situated at the end of Loch Fyne and close to Inveraray Castle, the seat of the Duke of Argyll, the hereditary Chieftain of the Clan Campbell. The Games are held in the Winterton Park in the Castle grounds around mid-July. A particular feature is the solo piping.
Affiliations: The Scottish Games Association, (page 74).
✍ Chieftain: Duke of Argyll
✍ Secretary: Mrs M. Mather
16 Upper Riochan, Inveraray.
PA32 8WR
☎ 01499 302458

ISLE OF ISLAY BRANCH OF THE ROYAL SCOTTISH COUNTRY DANCE SOCIETY

Aims & Activities: See the RSCDS on page 47.
Membership: 32.
✍ Secretary: Mrs G. McAuslan
Failte, Bruichladdich.
IPA43 7LE
☎ 01496 850558

KILMORE AND KILBRIDE HIGHLAND GAMES

Aims & Activities: To organise annual professional Highland Games and sports in the united parishes of Kilmore and Kilbride, including

Oban and the Isle of Kerrera on the Firth of Lorne. The Games are customarily held in Oban in early July.
Affiliations: The Scottish Games Association, (page 74).
✍ Secretary: D. A. Ferguson
Dalantobair, Musdale Road,
Kilmore, Oban.
☎ 01631 770241

KYLES COUNTRY DANCE CLUB

Aims & Activities: See the RSCDS on page 47.
✍ Secretary: Mrs Picken
Springbank, Tighnabruaich.
PA21 2JE
☎ 01700 811611

LOCHGOILHEAD BURNS CLUB

Aims & Activities: Social and to perpetuate the memory of Robert Burns.
Affiliations: The Burns Federation, No. 831.
✍ Secretary: Mr Donald McGregor
The Schoolhouse, Lochgoilhead.
PA24 8AG

LOCHGOILHEAD SCOTTISH COUNTRY DANCE CLUB

Aims & Activities: See the RSCDS on page 47.
✍ Secretary: Mrs Byrnes
Lettermay, Lochgoilhead.
PA24 8AE

LORN BRANCH OF THE ROYAL SCOTTISH COUNTRY DANCE SOCIETY

Aims & Activities: See the RSCDS on page 47.
Membership: 107.
✍ Secretary: Mrs S. Porter
Schiehallion, Crinach Gardens,
Oban.
PA34 4LB
☎ 01631 563103

MID-ARGYLL BRANCH OF THE ROYAL SCOTTISH COUNTRY DANCE SOCIETY

Aims & Activities: See the RSCDS on page 47.
Membership: 41.
✍ Secretary: Mrs M. Strathie
10 Fernoch Drive, Lochgilphead.
PA31 8PZ
☎ 01546 602132

MULL HIGHLAND GAMES

Aims & Activities: See Tobermory Highland Games.

NORTH CONNEL COUNTRY DANCE CLUB

Aims & Activities: See the RSCDS on page 47.
✍ Secretary: Mrs V. MacKellar
Seaview, Keil, Benderloch, Oban.

OBAN HIGHLAND GAMES

Founded: 1871.
Aims & Activities: To organise annual professional Highland Games and sports in the area of Oban, the well-known west-coast sea port, tourist centre opposite the Island of Mull on the Firth of Lorne. Customarily held towards the end of August.
Affiliations: The Scottish Games Association, (page 74).
✍ Chieftain: The Duke of Argyll
✍ Secretary: Mrs P. McKiernan
Lyndon, Lonan Drive, Oban.
PA34 4NN
☎ 01631 562671

SOUTH ARGYLL BRANCH OF THE ROYAL SCOTTISH COUNTRY DANCE SOCIETY

Aims & Activities: See the RSCDS on page 47.
Membership: 101.
✍ Secretary: Mrs R. McDonald
Cruachan Mhor, 35a Pilot Street,

Dunoon.
PA23 8BY
☎ 01369 703303

STRACHUR AND DISTRICT SCOTTISH COUNTRY DANCE CLUB

Aims & Activities: See the RSCDS on page 47.
✍ Secretary: Mrs E. Shipley
8 Clachan Beag, Strachur.
PA27 8DG
☎ 01369 860419

TARBERT SCOTTISH COUNTRY DANCE CLUB

Aims & Activities: See the RSCDS on page 47.
✍ Secretary: Mr E. S. Clark
Northlea, 1 Leene Road, Tarbert.
PA29 6TT
☎ 01880 820793

TOBERMORY HIGHLAND GAMES

Founded: 1926.
Aims & Activities: To organise annual professional Highland Games and sports in the area of the well-known seaport of Tobermory on the Isle of Mull. The Games are generally held in mid-July on Tobermory Golf Course with the spectators seated on a steep bank overlooking the Sound of Mull with a wonderful view as far as the Morvern Hills on the mainland, a setting which is hard to beat anywhere in Scotland. As a considerable tourist attraction they are usually well attended.
Affiliations: The Scottish Games Association, (page 74).
✍ Secretary: Games Office
c/o Mishnish Hotel, Tobermory, Mull.
PA75 6PN

AYRSHIRE, EAST

AFTON LILY BURNS CLUB

Founded: 1969.
Aims & Activities: Social. Annual dinner. To encourage the enjoyment of the poetry of Robert Burns.
Affiliations: The Burns Federation, No. 1079.
✍ Secretary: Alex McGinn
38 Loch View, New Cumnock.
KA18 4DL

AYRSHIRE ASSOCIATION OF BURNS CLUBS

Founded: 1908.
Aims & Activities: To further the spirit of Robert Burns by education and encouragement.
Affiliations: The Burns Federation, No. 192.
✍ Secretary: Mr Harry Bull
49 Annanhill Avenue, Kilmarnock.
KA1 2NX

BURNS FEDERATION

Founded: 1885.
Aims & Activities: To encourage Burns Clubs and kindred societies who honour the memory of Robert Burns and his works. To strengthen the bond of fellowship among members of Burns Clubs and kindred societies throughout the world. To keep alive the old Scots tongue. To encourage and arrange schoolchildren's competitions. To stimulate the teaching of Scottish literature, history, art and music. To conserve buildings and places associated with Robert Burns and his contemporaries. Committees: Finance, Schools' Competitions, Literature, Memorials, Publicity.
Affiliations: Federated Societies: There are currently 1,119 Federated Societies each of which is allocated a

number which lapses if the society is dissolved or ceases to exist, but which may be renewed if it resumes operations. The number of the Federated Society is thus an indication of the age of that Federated Society or Club.

Publications: Burns Chronicle (quarterly, free to members); A Scots Kišt; Robert Burns & Edinburgh; The Burns Federation Song Book.

🖎 Honorary Treasurer: Joseph J. Brown

🖎 Honorary Secretary: John Inglis c/o The Dick Institute, Elmbank Avenue, Kilmarnock, Ayrshire. KA1 3BU.

☎ 01475 521442 (home)

☎ 01563 526401 (business)

CRONIES BURNS CLUB KILMARNOCK

Founded: 1948.

Aims & Activities: Social. Annual dinner. To enjoy the spirit of Robert Burns.

Affiliations: The Burns Federation, No. 681.

🖎 Secretary: J. F. Richardson 45 Rowallan Drive, Kilmarnock. KA3 1TU

CUMNOCK BURNS CLUB

Founded: 1887.

Aims & Activities: Social. Charitable. Educational. Annual gathering.

Affiliations: The Burns Federation, No. 45.

🖎 Secretary: Mr Robin D Hunter 1 The Square, Cumnock. KA18 1BQ

CUMNOCK CRONIES BURNS CLUB

Founded: 1910.

Aims & Activities: Social. Annual meeting. To savour the spirit of Robert Burns and his poetry.

Affiliations: The Burns Federation, No. 773.

🖎 Secretary: A. C. Rutherford 18 Coila Place, Cumnock. KA18 1LK

CUMNOCK JOLLY BEGGARS BURNS CLUB

Founded: 1948.

Aims & Activities: Social. Annual dinner. To promote greater enjoyment of Burns.

Affiliations: The Burns Federation, No. 682.

🖎 Secretary: John Goudie 23 Barrhill Road. Cumnock. KA18 1PJ

KILMARNOCK AND DISTRICT BRANCH OF THE ROYAL SCOTTISH COUNTRY DANCE SOCIETY

Aims & Activities: See the RSCDS on page 47.

Membership: 58.

🖎 Secretary: Mrs O. Cameron 16 Bunting Place, Kilmarnock. KA1 3LE

KILMARNOCK BURNS CLUB

Aims & Activities: To encourage study of the works of Robert Burns. Annual meeting.

Affiliations: The Burns Federation, No 0.

🖎 Secretary: Mrs Ligat 25 Charles Street, Kilmarnock. KA1 1RZ

KILMARONOCK BURNS CLUB

Founded: 1949.

Aims & Activities: Social. Annual dinner. To keep alive the memory of Robert Burns.

Affiliations: The Burns Federation, No. 695.

🖎 Secretary: Mrs Katherine M. E.

Liston
Rock Cottage, Gartocharn.
G83 8RX

LOGANGATE BURNS CLUB

Founded: 1957.
Aims & Activities: Social. Annual dinner.
Affiliations: The Burns Federation, No. 811.
✍ Secretary: Hugh Mitchell
4 McQueen Avenue, Cumnock.

MAUCHLINE BURNS CLUB

Founded: 1923.
Aims & Activities: To study the works of Burns and Scottish life and culture. Educational. Historical. Social.
Affiliations: The Burns Federation, No. 310.
✍ Secretary: Mr D. I. Lyell
MA. FSA (Scot), 9 East Park Avenue, Mauchline.
KA5 5BG

NEW CUMNOCK BURNS CLUB

Founded: 1923.
Aims & Activities: Social. Historical. Educational. To study the works of Robert Burns.
Affiliations: The Burns Federation, No. 500.
✍ Secretary: Wm McA Hastie
16 Greenbraes Drive, New Cumnock.
KA18 4AB

TRYSTING THORN BURNS CLUB

Aims & Activities: Social and to promote interest in the work of Robert Burns. Annual Dinner.
Affiliations: The Burns Federation, No. 920.
✍ Secretary: John Prott
8 Hannahston Avenue, Drongan.

AYRSHIRE, NORTH

AYRSHIRE NORTH-WEST BRANCH OF THE ROYAL SCOTTISH COUNTRY DANCE SOCIETY

Aims & Activities: See the RSCDS on page 47.
Membership: 83.
✍ Secretary: Mrs E. Fulton
3 Kerr Place, Irvine.
KA12 0JJ
☎ 01294 279875

BARRMILL JOLLY BEGGARS BURNS CLUB

Founded: 1944.
Aims & Activities: To perpetuate the spirit of Robert Burns. Social. Annual Gathering.
Affiliations: The Burns Federation, No. 593.
✍ Secretary: James L. Conn
Parkview, 3 Braehead, Dalry.
KA24 5EX

BEITH CALEDONIA BURNS CLUB

Founded: 1974.
Aims & Activities: Social. Annual Dinner. To enjoy the poetry of Robert Burns.
Affiliations: The Burns Federation, No. 931.
✍ Secretary: Jack G. D. Robertson
60 George Street, Ayr.
KA8 0BW

BOYLE FAMILY

Aims & Activities: To promote awareness of the family history.
Membership: Open to members of the Boyle family and those bearing that name, or variants of it.
✍ Chieftain: Earl of Glasgow
Kelburn, Fairlie.
KA30 0BE

BRODICK HIGHLAND GAMES

Aims & Activities: To organise annual amateur Highland Games in the area of Brodick on the Isle of Arran.

✍ Secretary: J. A. N. Dinwoodie
 Kilreen, Brodick, Isle of Arran.
 KA27 8AF

BUSBIEHILL BURNS CLUB

Founded: 1974.
Aims & Activities: Social. Annual Meeting.
Affiliations: The Burns Federation, No. 933.

✍ Secretary: James F. Craig
 9 Parkhill Avenue, Crosshouse.
 KA2 0JF

CLAN HUNTER ASSOCIATION

Aims & Activities: To foster clan and family ties throughout the world and to strengthen overseas links. To collect and preserve records and traditions of the clan. Genealogical. Social.
Affiliations: Clan Hunter Association, NSW, Australia. The Clan Hunter Association, Canada.
Membership: Open to all bearing the name Hunter and also to all those connected by descent or marriage.

✍ Secretary: Hunterston Castle
 West Kilbride.
 KA23 9GL

CLAN KEITH SOCIETY

Founded: 1971.
Aims & Activities: To promote the clan spirit worldwide. To research into genealogies. To hold an annual Gathering. To improve overseas links. Social. Historical and Educational.
Membership: Open to all connected to the Keith clan by descent or marriage and to all interested in the aims of the clan.

✍ Secretary: North Dukes
 Geirston, Kilbirnie.
 KA25 7LG

CUMBRAE BURNS CLUB

Founded: 1896.
Aims & Activities: Social. Annual gathering.
Affiliations: The Burns Federation, No. 580.

✍ Secretary: James Meechan
 3 Copeland Crescent, Millport,
 Isle of Cumbrae.
 KA28 0BP

DALRY BURNS CLUB

Founded: 1884.
Aims & Activities: Social. Educational. To encourage the study of Scottish literature, particularly the work of Robert Burns.
Affiliations: The Burns Federation, No. 35.

✍ Secretary: Mr James Clark
 13 Braehead, Dalry.
 KA24 5EX

EGLINTON BURNS CLUB

Aims & Activities: Social. Annual Dinner.
Affiliations: The Burns Federation, No. 851.

✍ Secretary: Mr Stan Robertson
 7 Heatherstane Bank,
 Bourtreehill, Irvine.
 KA11 1DZ

GARNOCK BURNS CLUB

Founded: 1976.
Aims & Activities: Social. Annual meeting.
Affiliations: The Burns Federation, No. 982.

✍ Secretary: James Marney
 'Mayfield', 8 Barrmill Road,
 Beith.
 KA15 1AU

HOWFF BURNS CLUB

Founded: 1925.
Aims & Activities: Social. To promote

the work of Burns. Annual Gathering.
Affiliations: The Burns Federation, No. 349.
✍ Secretary. Sam Hannah
55 Ayr Road, Kilmarnock.
KA1 4UG

IRVINE BURNS CLUB

Founded: 1826.
Aims & Activities: Charitable. Educational. Social. Annual meeting. To encourage interest in the works of Robert Burns.
Affiliations: The Burns Federation, No. 173.
✍ Secretary: Mr George Watson
Townhead Pharmacy, High Street, Irvine.
KA12 0AY

IRVINE LASSES BURNS CLUB

Founded: 1975.
Aims & Activities: Social. Educational. Historical. To foster interest in Scottish culture and to encourage the study of Burns.
Affiliations: The Burns Federation, No. 936.
Membership: Open to all interested in the aims of the club.
✍ Secretary: Mrs Jean Bell
92 Clark Drive, Irvine.
KA12 0NT

IRVINE ROYAL ACADEMY

Aims & Activities: To foster interest in the works of Robert Burns.
Affiliations: The Burns Federation, No. 1090.
✍ Secretary: Richard Fowler
26 Cathkin Place, Whitehirst Park, Kilwinning.
KA13 6TP

KILBIRNIE ROSEBERY BURNS CLUB

Founded: 1906.
Aims & Activities: Social. Annual Gathering. To perpetuate the memory of Robert Burns.
Affiliations: The Burns Federation, No. 377.
✍ Secretary: Ronald G. Thomson
6 Speirs Road, Lochwinnoch.
PA12 4BS

KILBIRNIE SCOTTISH COUNTRY DANCE GROUP

Aims & Activities: See the RSCDS on page 47.
✍ Secretary: Miss B. Whiteford
14 Dipple Court, Kilbirnie.
KA25 7DR
☎ 01505 682463

KILMAURS GLENCAIRN BURNS CLUB

Founded: 1973.
Aims & Activities: To promote interest in the works of Robert Burns. Social.
Affiliations: The Burns Federation, No. 1042.
Membership: Open to those interested in the aims of the club.
✍ Secretary: Robert Beattie
34 East Park Crescent, Kilmaurs.
KA3 2QT

KILWINNING BURNS CLUB

Founded: 1964.
Aims & Activities: Social. Annual meeting. To promote interest in Robert Burns.
Affiliations: The Burns Federation, No. 1029.
✍ Secretary: Peter Filby
Claremont, Newgate, Kilwinning.

LARGS BURNS CLUB

Aims & Activities: Social and to

encourage interest in the poetry of Robert Burns. Annual dinner.
Affiliations: The Burns Federation, No. 1109.
✍ Secretary: Fairlie McGill
  20 John Street, Largs.
  KA30 6HY

LODGE ST ANDREW

Founded: 1962.
Aims & Activities: Social. Annual meeting.
Affiliations: The Burns Federation, No. 996.
✍ Secretary: R. Ghee
  Inglewood, Moscow.
  KA4 8PR

ST ANDREW'S CRONIES BURNS CLUB

Founded: 1947.
Aims & Activities: Social. Annual Gathering. To further and appreciate the works of Burns.
Affiliations: The Burns Federation, No. 671.
Membership: Open to members of the Masonic fraternity.
✍ Secretary: George Duncan
  52 Muirfield Place, Woodside, Kilwinning.

WEST KILBRIDE BURNS CLUB

Founded: 1947.
Aims & Activities: Social. To enhance apprecation of Robert Burns.
Affiliations: The Burns Federation, No. 664.
✍ Secretary: Mrs Mary Milne
  2 Woodside, West Kilbride.
  KA23 9JB

AYRSHIRE, SOUTH

ALLOWAY BURNS CLUB

Founded: 1908.
Aims & Activities: Social. Educational. To promote interest in and appreciation of the work of Robert Burns. Annual dinner.
Affiliations: The Burns Federation, No. 252.
✍ Secretary: Mr James Glass
  M. A., 31 Glenconner Road, Ayr.
  KA7 3HF

AYR BRANCH OF THE ROYAL SCOTTISH COUNTRY DANCE SOCIETY

Aims & Activities: See the RSCDS on page 47.
Membership: 203.
✍ Secretary: Mrs E. Carlyle
  14 Harling Drive, Troon.
  KA10 6NF
☎ 01292 313615

AYR BURNS CLUB

Founded: 1886.
Aims & Activities: Social. Educational. Charitable. Social. To read and enjoy the works of Robert Burns.
Affiliations: The Burns Federation, No. 275.
✍ Secretary: Alex Macpherson
  15 Burnton Road, Dalrymple.
  KA6 6DY

BARR BURNS CLUB

Aims & Activities: Social. Annual dinner. To honour the memory of Robert Burns.
Affiliations: The Burns Federation, No. 1083.
✍ Secretary: W. L. Dunlop
  Glengennet, Barr, nr Girvan.
  KA26 9TY

CLAN KENNEDY

Aims & Activities: To promote awareness of the clan history. To preserve the Kennedy records and archives. To enhance overseas ties and trace genealogical or historical connections.

Membership: Open to all members of the Kennedy clan and family and those claiming descent, or connected by marriage.

✍ The Marquess of Ailsa
   Blanefield, Kirkoswald.
   KA19 8HH

CROSSHILL AND MAYBOLE SCOTTISH COUNTRY DANCE GROUP

Aims & Activities: See the RSCDS on page 47.

✍ Secretary: Mrs S. Staples
   23 Leven Road, Troon.
   KA10 7DX
☎ 01292 316358

DAILLY JOLLY BEGGARS

Aims & Activities: Social. Annual meeting.

Affiliations: The Burns Federation, No. 179.

✍ Secretary: Mr Archie Howie
   71 Hadyard Terrace, Dailly, by Girvan.
   KA26 9SR

DUNDONALD BURNS CLUB

Founded: 1963.

Aims & Activities: Social.

Affiliations: The Burns Federation, No. 370.

✍ Secretary: R. Trotter
   74 Castleview, Dundonald.

NEWTON BURNS CLUB, AYR

Founded: 1962.

Aims & Activities: To promote and study the works of Burns. Charitable. Historical. Social. Annual gathering.

Affiliations: The Burns Federation, No. 854.

Membership: By invitation.

✍ Secretary: Alex Bair
   215 Whitletts Road, Ayr.

PRESTWICK BURNS CLUB

Founded: 1953.

Aims & Activities: Social. To encourage appreciation of the work of Robert Burns.

Affiliations: The Burns Federation, No. 772.

✍ Secretary: Ritchie Bell
   5 Maryborough Avenue,
   Prestwick.
   KA9 1SE

SYMINGTON BURNS CLUB

Founded: 1946.

Aims & Activities: Social. Annual meeting. To encourage appreciation of the work of Robert Burns.

Affiliations: The Burns Federation, No. 632.

✍ Secretary: Mrs Margaret Davidson
   33 Brewlands Drive, Symington.
   KA1 5AD

WILSON SOCIETY

Aims & Activities: Historical. Genealogical. To strengthen overseas links.

Membership: Open to anyone of that name, or able to claim descent on either side, or connected by marriage.

✍ Secretary: 2 Manse Road
   Colmonell.
   KA26 9SA

CLACKMANNAN

ALVA HIGHLAND GAMES

Aims & Activities: To organise annual professional Highland Games and sports in the area of Alva, seven miles east of Stirling, where this small town nestles under the Ochil Hills. They include a hill race to the top of the Dumyat Hill (419m/1375ft) and back.
Affiliations: The Scottish Games Association, (page 74).
✍ Secretary: C. Dunbar
57 Broomridge Road, St Ninians, Stirling.
FK7 0DT
☎ 01786 813523

ASHBURN HOUSE BURNS CLUB

Founded: 1974.
Aims & Activities: Social and to promote general appreciation of the works of Robert Burns.
Affiliations: The Burns Federation, No. 1062.
✍ Secretary: George A. Shepherd
183 Claremont, Alloa.
FK10 2ER

BEN CLEUCH BURNS CLUB

Founded: 1950.
Aims & Activities: To maintain an interest in the works of Burns. Social. Educational. Annual Gathering.
Affiliations: The Burns Federation, No. 725.
✍ Secretary: Douglas F. McEwan
18 Auchinbair, Sauchie, Alloa.
FK10 3HB

CLACKMANNANSHIRE BRANCH OF THE ROYAL SCOTTISH COUNTRY DANCE SOCIETY

Aims & Activities: See the RSCDS on page 47.
Membership: 101.

✍ Secretary: Mrs R. Brown
17 Argyll Street, Dollar.
☎ 01259 743423

CLAN GREGOR SOCIETY

Aims & Activities: To promote awareness of the clan history.
Membership: Open to members of the Gregor clan and those bearing that name, or variants of it.
✍ Secretary: Ishbel McGregor
2 Brae Head, Alloa.

COALSNAUGHTON BURNS CLUB

Founded: 1945.
Aims & Activities: Social. Annual Gathering. To promote enjoyment and understanding of Robert Burns poetry.
Affiliations: The Burns Federation, No. 630.
✍ Secretary: John Pickles
6 The Craigs, Devonside, Tillicoultry.
FK13 6JB

DOLLAR BURNS CLUB

Founded: 1887.
Aims & Activities: Social. Charitable. Historical. Educational. Annual Gathering. To promote greater appreciation of Robert Burns.
Affiliations: The Burns Federation, No. 37.
✍ Secretary: Mr David M. Tait
Thorndean, Strachan Crescent, Dollar.
FK14 7HL

ERSKINE SOCIETY

Aims & Activities: To strengthen overseas links. Genealogical. Historical.
Membership: Open to all bearing that name, or variants of it, also those who are connected by descent or by marriage.
✍ The Earl of Mar & Kellie

Claremont House, Alloa.
FK10 2JF

Kincardine, Alloa.
FK10 4PB

GARTMORN LADIES' BURNS CLUB

Founded: 1947.
Aims & Activities: Social and to implement a greater appreciation and understanding of the works of Robert Burns.
Affiliations: The Burns Federation, No. 665.
✍ Secretary: Mrs Anne Boslem
11 Pitfairn Road, Fishcross, Alloa.
FK10 3HU

ROBERT BRUCE BURNS CLUB

Founded: 1953.
Aims & Activities: Social. Annual Gathering.
Affiliations: The Burns Federation, No. 769.
✍ Secretary: W. Dawson
17 Harland Road, Castletown, Caithness.
KW14 8UB

SAUCHIE BURNS CLUB

Founded: 1929.
Aims & Activities: Social. Educational. Annual Gathering. To provide a deeper understanding of Robert Burns and his work.
Affiliations: The Burns Federation, No. 426.
✍ Secretary: J. Gilmour
3 Ravenswood, Tillicoutry.
FK13 6PT

TULLIALLAN BURNS CLUB

Aims & Activities: Social and to encourage interest in the works of Robert Burns. Annual Gathering.
Affiliations: The Burns Federation, No. 1093.
✍ Secretary: R. Millar
27 Kellywood Crescent,

UNITED GLASS JOLLY BEGGARS BURNS CLUB

Founded: 1972.
Aims & Activities: Social. Annual Gathering.
Affiliations: The Burns Federation, No. 1000.
✍ Secretary: John Smith
3 Muircot Place, Coalsnaughton.
FK13 6LP

DUMFRIES AND GALLOWAY

ANNAN BRANCH OF THE ROYAL SCOTTISH COUNTRY DANCE SOCIETY

Aims & Activities: See the RSCDS on page 47.
Membership: 27.
✍ Secretary: Mrs W. Adams
Kirtledene, Kirtlebridge, Lockerbie.
DG11 3LR
☎ 01461 500250

ANNAN LADIES BURNS CLUB

Founded: 1928.
Aims & Activities: Social and to promote a greater appreciation of Robert Burns and his poetry.
Affiliations: The Burns Federation, No. 393.
✍ Secretary: Mrs M. Hyslop
4 Seaforth Avenue, Annan.
DG12 6DX

BRIGEND BURNS CLUB

Founded: 1876.
Aims & Activities: Social. Educational and charitable. Annual Gathering.

Affiliations: The Burns Federation, No. 401.
✍ Secretary: J. MacMillan
45 Terregles Road, Dumfries.
DG2 9HA

CAN-DU BURNS CLUB

Founded: 1976.
Aims & Activities: Overseas links. Social.
Affiliations: The Burns Federation, No. 1076.
✍ Secretary: Mrs Mary J. Urquhart
Glebe House, 39 Glebe Street, Dumfries.
DG1 2LQ

CASTLE DOUGLAS BRANCH OF THE ROYAL SCOTTISH COUNTRY DANCE SOCIETY

Aims & Activities: See the RSCDS on page 47.
Membership: 67.
✍ Secretary: Miss M. McCartney
8 Academy Street, Castle Douglas.
DG7 1AP
☎ 01556 502638

CASTLE DOUGLAS BURNS CLUB

Founded: 1930.
Aims & Activities: Social. Educational. To encourage the study of Burns. Annual Gathering.
Affiliations: The Burns Federation, No. 562.
✍ Secretary: J. C. McLatchie
43 Robb Place, Castle Douglas.
DG7 1LW

CLAN ARMSTRONG SOCIETY

Aims & Activities: To promote awareness of the clan history.
Affiliations: The Armstrong Trust.
Membership: Open to members of the Armstrong clan and those related by descent or marriage, or those in accordance with the aims.

✍ Secretary: Brieryshaw Langholm.
DG13 0HJ

CLAN CUNNINGHAM

Aims & Activities: To promote awareness of the clan history.
Membership: Open to members of the Cunningham clan and those related by marriage or descent, also those bearing variants of the name.
✍ James Cunningham
Flat 12, Dowding House, Moffat.
DG10 9AW

CLAN JARDINE SOCIETY

Aims & Activities: To promote awareness of the clan history, background and connections. To strengthen overseas links. Genealogical. Historical.
Affiliations: Clan Jardine Society of Western Canada. Clan Jardine Society of Southern California.
Membership: Open to anyone bearing the name Jardine, or related by descent or marriage.
✍ Secretary: Braeriach
15 Mile House Crescent, Dumfries.
DG1 1JZ

CLAN JOHNSTONE

Aims & Activities: To organise clan catherings. To research and record the clan history and genealogy. To strengthen overseas links.
Membership: Open to all Johnstones, in the various spellings, and to to those related by descent or marriage.
✍ The Earl of Annandale & Hartfell
Annandale Estates, Estate Office, St Anne's, Lockerbie, Dumfriesshire.
DG11 1HG

DUMFRIES AND DISTRICT ROUND TABLE BURNS CLUB

Founded: 1967.
Aims & Activities: Social. Annual Gathering. To promote interest in the works of Robert Burns.
Affiliations: The Burns Federation, No. 999.
✍ Secretary: Mr John Thomson
  2 East Cluden, Holywood,
  Dumfries.
  DG2 0JA

DUMFRIES BRANCH OF THE ROYAL SCOTTISH COUNTRY DANCE SOCIETY

Aims & Activities: See the RSCDS on page 47.
Membership: 91.
✍ Secretary: Mrs M. Dickson
  19 Montague Street, Dumfries.
  DG1 1HE
☎ 01387 265815

DUMFRIES BURNS CLUB

Founded: 1820.
Aims & Activities: Social. Educational. Charitable. To encourage the study of Scottish literature, particularly the poetry of Robert Burns.
Affiliations: The Burns Federation, No. 226.
✍ Secretary: Mr John A. C. McFadden
  Walker & Sharpe Solicitors, 37 George Street, Dumfries.
  DG1 1EB

DUMFRIES BURNS HOWFF CLUB

Founded: 1889.
Aims & Activities: Social. Annual Gathering. To promote interest in the poetry and literature of Burns.
Affiliations: The Burns Federation, No. 112.
✍ President: Mr David C. Smith
  22 Cargenbridge Avenue,
  Dumfries DG2 8LP

DUMFRIES LADIES' BURNS CLUB

Founded: 1930.
Aims & Activities: To further interest in Burns and Scottish literature. Overseas links. Charitable. Educational. Historical. Social.
Affiliations: The Burns Federation, No. 437.
✍ Secretary: Mrs Elizabeth Haining
  74 Laghall Court,
  Kingholm Quay, Dumfries.
  DG1 4GX

ESKDALE BURNS CLUB

Founded: 1886.
Aims & Activities: Social. Educational. Charitable. To encourage reading of the work of Robert Burns.
Affiliations: The Burns Federation, No. 217.
✍ Secretary: Ms Nicola Weatherstone
  92 Henry Street, Langholm.
  DG13 0AS

FRASER SCOTTISH COUNTRY DANCE GROUP

Aims & Activities: See the RSCDS on page 47.
✍ Secretary: Miss J. Campbell
  14 McConnel Street,
  Kello Holme, Kirkconnel.

GATEHOUSE OF FLEET BRANCH OF THE ROYAL SCOTTISH COUNTRY DANCE SOCIETY

Aims & Activities: See the RSCDS on page 47.
Membership: 51.
✍ Secretary: Dr B. Law
  High Trees, Ramsey Wood,
  Gatehouse of Fleet, Castle Douglas.
  DG7 3HJ
☎ 01557 814489

GATEHOUSE OF FLEET BURNS CLUB

Founded: 1947.
Aims & Activities: Social. Annual Gathering. To promote interest in Robert Burns.
Affiliations: The Burns Federation, No. 1004.
✍ Secretary: George McCullough
4 Carney's Corner,
Gatehouse of Fleet.
DG7 2HW

GLEN ISLA BURNS CLUB

Aims & Activities: Social. To commemorate the memory of Robert Burns.
Affiliations: The Burns Federation, No. 1119.
✍ Secretary: H. Ellis
2 Glen Road, Palnackie,
Castle Douglas.
DG7 1PH

HILLVIEW BURNS CLUB

Aims & Activities: Social and to commemorate the works of Burns. Annual Dinner.
Affiliations: The Burns Federation, No. 1123.
✍ Secretary: Mrs N. E. Mackenzie
6 Hillview Drive, Georgetown,
Dumfries.
DG1 4DS

HOLE I' THE WA' BURNS CLUB

Aims & Activities: Social and to promote interest in the works of Robert Burns. Annual dinner.
Affiliations: The Burns Federation, No. 916.
✍ Secretary: Donald C. McCuaig
70 Pleasance Avenue, Dumfries.
DG2 7JL

KIRKCUDBRIGHT BRANCH OF THE ROYAL SCOTTISH COUNTRY DANCE SOCIETY

Aims & Activities: See the RSCDS on page 47.
Membership: 59.
✍ Secretary: Mrs D. Christie
Aldessan, 10 Mount Pleasant
Avenue, Kirkcudbright.
DG6 4HF
☎ 01557 331108

KIRKCUDBRIGHT BURNS CLUB

Founded: 1918.
Aims & Activities: Social. Annual Gathering. To encourage appreciation of the work of Robert Burns.
Affiliations: The Burns Federation, No. 323.
✍ Secretary: Mr A. Bray
Inglestone, Borgue.
DG6 4UA

LANGHOLM COMMON RIDING

Aims & Activities: To organise annual professional games and sports in the area of Langholm and to organise the Riding of the Marches and the annual celebrations.
Affiliations: The Scottish Games Association, (page 74).
✍ Secretary: A Borthwick
Cronksbank Cottage, Langholm.
DG13 0LL
☎ 013873 80062

LANGHOLM LADIES BURNS CLUB

Founded: 1947.
Aims & Activities: Social. To promote and encourage interest in the work of Burns.
Affiliations: The Burns Federation, No. 660.
✍ Secretary: Miss J. Grace Brown
Glenelg, Walter Street, Langholm.
DG13 0AX

LOCKERBIE BRANCH OF THE ROYAL SCOTTISH COUNTRY DANCE SOCIETY

Aims & Activities: See the RSCDS on page 47.
Membership: 27.
✍ Secretary: Miss M. Brown
   19 Park Place, Lockerbie,
   Dumfriesshire.
   DG11 2HG
☎ 01576 203974

MASONIC BURNS CLUB KIRKCUDBRIGHT

Founded: 1949.
Aims & Activities: Open to members of the Masonic fraternity. Social and to encourage interest in Burns.
Affiliations: The Burns Federation, No. 693.
✍ Secretary: W. J. Davidson
   Flat 2, Salutation Hotel,
   Carsphairn, Castle Douglas.

MOFFAT BRANCH OF THE ROYAL SCOTTISH COUNTRY DANCE SOCIETY

Aims & Activities: See the RSCDS on page 47.
Membership: 22.
✍ Secretary: Cambria Coe
   Dumcrieff, Moffat.
   DG10 9QW
☎ 01683 220474

PAISLEY FAMILY SOCIETY

Aims & Activities: To promote awareness of the family history and connections. Genealogical. To strengthen overseas links.
Membership: Open to all bearing the name of Paisley in its various spellings also to those related by descent or marriage.
✍ Betty L. Paisley
   Glen Annan House, Beechgrove,
   Moffat.
   DG10 9RS

RATTLIN' SQUAD

Founded: 1971.
Aims & Activities: Social. To promote interest in the spirit of Robert Burns works.
Affiliations: The Burns Federation, No. 1071.
✍ Secretary: R. Wilson
   9 Queensberry Square, Sanquhar.
   DG4 6BY

ROSAMOND BURNS CLUB

Founded: 1973.
Aims & Activities: To foster Scottish culture. Social. Charitable. Educational. Historical. To foster overseas links.
Affiliations: The Burns Federation, No. 926.
Membership: Open to all interested in the aims. To perpetuate the memory of Burns.
✍ Secretary: Mrs E. M. Robertson
   68 Annan Road, Gretna, nr
   Carlisle.
   CA6 5DJ

SANQUHAR BLACK JOAN CLUB

Founded: 1945.
Aims & Activities: Social. Annual Gathering. Educational.
Affiliations: The Burns Federation, No. 629.
✍ Secretary: T. A. Johnston
   8 Queensberry Court, Sanquhar.
   DG4 6BY

SCTA BURNS CLUB

Founded: 1939.
Aims & Activities: To foster interest in the works of Robert Burns.
Affiliations: The Burns Federation, No. 924.
✍ Secretary: J. Irving
   Ellisland Farm, by Dumfries,
   Dumfriesshire.

SOLWAY BURNS CLUB

Founded: 1930.
Aims & Activities: Social. Educational. Open to those interested in the poetry of Burns.
Affiliations: The Burns Federation, No. 589.
✍ Secretary: J. Hawkins
Achill, Back-of-The-Hill, Annan.
DG12 6SB

SOUTHERN SCOTTISH COUNTIES BURNS ASSOCIATION

Founded: 1937.
Aims & Activities: To further the works of Burns. Educational. Charitable. Social. Annual Gathering.
Affiliations: The Burns Federation, No. 530.
Membership: Open to Burns Club Associations in the Southern Scottish Counties.
✍ Secretary: Thomas Johnstone
7 Hermitage Crescent, Dumfries.
DG2 7QG

STRANRAER BRANCH OF THE ROYAL SCOTTISH COUNTRY DANCE SOCIETY

Aims & Activities: See the RSCDS on page 47.
Membership: 38.
✍ Secretary: Mrs K. Robertson
14 Academy Street, Stranraer.
☎ 01776 703239 (home)
☎ 01776 702440 (business)

STRANRAER BURNS CLUB

Founded: 1967.
Aims & Activities: Social. Annual Gathering.
Affiliations: The Burns Federation, No. 1058.
✍ Secretary: Mrs Mona M. Paterson
Collieston, 14 Braewood Grove, Stranraer.
DG9 8DF

WHITHORN AND DISTRICT CALEDONIAN SOCIETY

Founded: 1937.
Aims & Activities: Social. Educational. Charitable. To foster interest in the work of Robert Burns and in Scottish literature.
Affiliations: The Burns Federation, No. 536.
✍ Secretary: MacFie & Alexander
58 George Street, Whithorn, Newton Stewart.
DG8 8PA

WIGTOWN BURNS CLUB

Founded: 1905.
Aims & Activities: Educational. To promote interest in Scottish literature and the work of Robert Burns. Social. Annual Gathering.
Affiliations: The Burns Federation, No. 730.
✍ Secretary: Ian M. Thin.
Tramerry
Wigtown.
DG8 9JP

DUNBARTONSHIRE, EAST

BEARSDEN AND MILNGAVIE DISTRICT HIGHLAND GAMES

Aims & Activities: To organise annual amateur Highland Games in the area of Bearsden and Milngavie, north-west of Glasgow. The West of Scotland rugby club ground at Burnbrae is the current venue.
✍ Secretary: C. Wallace
32 Kilmardinny Grove, Bearsden.
G61 3NY
☎ 0141 942 5177

DUNBARTONSHIRE, WEST

ALEXANDRIA BURNS CLUB

Founded: 1884.
Aims & Activities: To preserve and celebrate the memory of Robert Burns. Annual dinner. Social.
Affiliations: The Burns Federation, No. 2.
✍ Secretary: Mr Brian G. Benson
  Edleston, Smollett Street,
  Alexandria.
  G83 0DS

BALLOCH HIGHLAND GAMES

Aims & Activities: To organise annual professional Highland Games and sports in the area of Balloch at the foot of Loch Lomond in mid-July. As they coincide with the Glasgow Trades Holidays and are only 20 miles from Glasgow, they are very well attended.
Affiliations: The Scottish Games Association, (page 74).
✍ Secretary: John Martin
  42 Park Avenue, Balloch.
  G83 8JS
☎ 01389 752288

CLAN COLQUHOUN

Aims & Activities: To strengthen overseas links. Genealogical. Historical.
Membership: Open to members of the Colquhoun clan and all those bearing that name, or variants of it, also those related by descent or marriage.
✍ Chieftain: Sir Ivor Colquhoun of
  Luss
  Camstradden, Luss.

CLAN EWEN SOCIETY

Founded: 1977.
Aims & Activities: To restore places of interest to the clan. To foster interest in clan history. To preserve records. To provide genealogical services. To strengthen overseas links. Annual Gathering.
Publications: Clan Ewen Bulletin (UK), Clan Ewen Newsletter (N. America).
Membership: Open to those bearing the names MacEwen, McEwan, Ewen, Ewing, etc. , and to those connected with the clan by descent or marriage.
✍ Secretary: Bellcairn Cottage
  Cove, Helensburgh.
  G84 0NX

CLAN FORSYTH SOCIETY

Aims & Activities: To research clan history and genealogy. To strengthen overseas links.
Affiliations: Clan Forsyth of North America.
Membership: Open to all bearing the name Forsyth(e) and to those related by descent or marriage.
✍ Secretary: A. A. Forsyth
  68 Oxhill Road, Dumbarton.
  G82 4DG

CLAN McFARLANE

Aims & Activities: Historical. Genealogical. Overseas links.
Membership: Open to members of the McFarlane clan and its septs and to those bearing that name, or variants of it, also to those related by descent or marriage.
✍ Secretary: Arrochar/MacFarlane
  Heritage Trust
  13 West Abercromby Street,
  Helensburgh.
  G84 9LH

DUMBARTON BURNS CLUB

Founded: 1859.
Aims & Activities: Social. Educational. Charitable. To foster interest in

Scottish literature and the works of Robert Burns.

Affiliations: The Burns Federation, No. 10.

✍ Secretary: Mr James Hutton
   Ailsa, 10 Barloan Crescent,
   Dumbarton.
   G82 2AT

DUNBARTONSHIRE WEST BRANCH OF THE ROYAL SCOTTISH COUNTRY DANCE SOCIETY

Aims & Activities: See the RSCDS on page 47.
Membership: 196.
✍ Secretary: Mrs A. Traill
   Greenknowe, 2 West Argyle Street, Helensburgh.
   G84 8UU
☎ 01436 675633

LUSS HIGHLAND GAMES

Aims & Activities: To organise annual professional Highland Games and sports in the area of Luss and Loch Lomondside. Usually held in mid–July on a splendid site on land owned by the Colquhouns of Luss looking across Loch Lomond to Ben Lomond. A special feature is the size of the caber which is always too large to be tossed and has to be sawn down until small enough.
Affiliations: The Scottish Games Association, (page 74).
✍ Chieftain: Colquhoun of Luss
✍ Secretary: J. Fraser Nicol
   14 Chapelacre Grove,
   Helensburgh.
   G84.

ROSNEATH HIGHLAND GAMES

Aims & Activities: To organise annual professional Highland Games and sports in the area of Rosneath and Clynder, two neighbouring villages in West Dumbartonshire on the west side of the Gare Loch. Generally held in mid-July.
Affiliations: The Scottish Games Association, (page 74).
✍ Secretary: Janet Cassie
   3 Ferry Road, Rosneath,
   Helensburgh.
   G84 0RR
☎ 01436 831933

DUNDEE

DUNDEE BRANCH OF THE ROYAL SCOTTISH COUNTRY DANCE SOCIETY

Aims & Activities: See the RSCDS on page 47.
Membership: 368.
✍ Secretary: Mrs Hazel Hall
   The Old Harbour, Tayport, Fife.
   DD6 9AZ
☎ 01382 552239

DUNDEE BURNS CLUB

Founded: 1860.
Aims & Activities: Social. Charitable and educational. Also to encourage further interest in the work of Robert Burns.
Affiliations: The Burns Federation, No. 14.
✍ Secretary: Mr E. R. Bonnar
   29 Bagiebank, Wellbank, Dundee.
   DD5 3PT

DUNDEE HIGHLAND GAMES

Aims & Activities: To organise annual professional Highland Games and sports in the area of Dundee, the fourth largest city in Scotland. The Games are currently held in the Caird Park Stadium early in July and are seen as a major tourist attraction.
Affiliations: The Scottish Games Association, (page 74).
✍ Secretary: Susan Gillan

Leisure and Recreation Department, Earl Grey Place, Dundee.
DD1 4DF
☎ 01382 22729

DUNDEE UNIVERSITY SCOTTISH COUNTRY DANCING SOCIETY

Aims & Activities: See the RSCDS on page 47.
✍ Secretary: Shona Pearmain
38 Roseangle, Dundee.

LOCHEE BURNS CLUB

Founded: 1926.
Aims & Activities: To encourage interest in the poetry of Robert Burns. Annual Gathering. Social.
Affiliations: The Burns Federation, No. 360.
✍ Secretary: Thomas Young
Old Muirton Road, Lochee, Dundee.
DD2 3TY

LODGE CAMPERDOWN 317

Founded: 1968.
Aims & Activities: Social. Annual dinner. To promote greater knowledge of the work of Robert Burns.
Affiliations: The Burns Federation, No. 1049.
✍ Secretary: A. Gowans
22 Invergowrie Drive, Dundee.

ROBERT BURNS LODGE OF DUNDEE

Aims & Activities: Social. Annual dinner to encourage interest on the poetry of Burns.
Affiliations: The Burns Federation, No. 1097.
✍ Secretary: William B. N. Campbell
9 Woodside Terrace, Dundee.
DD4 9AR

EAST LOTHIAN

AIRTS BURNS CLUB, PRESTONPANS

Founded: 1936.
Aims & Activities: Social. Annual Gathering. To encourage interest in the work of Robert Burns.
Affiliations: The Burns Federation, No. 516.
✍ Secretary: Ian G. Telford
73 Polwarth Terrace, Prestonpans.
EH32 9PI

CHARTERIS CLAN

Aims & Activities: Genealogical. Historical. Overseas links.
Membership: Open to members of the Charteris clan and those bearing that name, or variants of it, also to those related by descent or marriage.
✍ Chieftain: The Earl of Wemyss and March
Gosford House, Longniddry.
EH32 0PX

CLAN GLENEIL

Aims & Activities: To encourage worldwide interest in Scottish heritage. To strengthen overseas links. Genealogical. Social.
Publications: The Clan History of the Clan Gleneil. The Highlanders and Their Regiments.
✍ The Clan Secretary
PO Box 13253, Haddington.
EH41 4YA

CLAN GORDON SOCIETY

Founded: 1961.
Aims & Activities: Social. Annual Gathering. To strengthen overseas links. Charitable. Historical.
Publications: Annual newsletter.
Membership: Open to those bearing the name, or one of the septs, and to

those who have served in the Gordon Highlanders.
- Convener: The Earl of Aboyne
- Secretary: Harlaw House
  Harlaw Hill, Prestonpans.
  EH32 9AG.

CLAN HAMILTON SOCIETY

Aims & Activities: To promote knowledge of the clan, its history and antecedents. Genealogical. Social. To strengthen overseas links.
Membership: Open to those bearing the name Hamilton and those related by descent or marriage.
- Secretary: Lord Hugh Douglas-Hamilton
  Lennoxlove, Haddington.
  EH41 4NZ

CLAN MACSPORRAN SOCIETY

Founded: 1975.
Aims & Activities: To promote the family name. To preserve historical records. To establish a family museum in the clan country of Kintyre. To strengthen overseas links. Charitable. Educational. Historical. Social.
Publications: Newsletter.
Membership: Open to all bearing that name or one of its derivatives, or connected with the clan by descent, marriage or adoption.
- Secretary: L. M. MacSporran
  Dalveen, Main Street, Ormiston.
  EH35 5HT

COCKENZIE AND PORT SETON BOWLING AND RECREATION CLUB

Founded: 1958.
Aims & Activities: Social. Annual dinner. To perpetuate the memory of Burns.
Affiliations: The Burns Federation, No. 1067.
- Secretary: A. G. Bellamy
  King George V Park, Port Seton.
  EH32 0BH

EAST LOTHIAN BRANCH OF THE ROYAL SCOTTISH COUNTRY DANCE SOCIETY

Aims & Activities: See the RSCDS on page 47.
Membership: 119.
- Secretary: Mrs M. McCollam
  14 The Beeches, Gullane.
  EH31 2DX
- ☎ 01620 842560

HADDINGTON GOLF CLUB

Founded: 1972.
Aims & Activities: Social. Annual dinner. To foster the memory of Robert Burns.
Affiliations: The Burns Federation, No. 1011.
- Secretary: T. Speirs
  Amsfield Park, Haddington.
  EH41 4PT

HOPETOUN LADDIES BURNS CLUB

Aims & Activities: Social. Annual Gathering. To commemorate Robert Burns.
Affiliations: The Burns Federation, No. 976.
- Secretary: Billy Napier
  Marwood, George Street, Ormiston.
  EH35 5JB

NORTH BERWICK BURNS CLUB

Aims & Activities: Social. To perpetuate the memory of Robert Burns.
Affiliations: The Burns Federation, No. 971.
- Secretary: Mrs M. A. Crawford
  Glenorchy House, Glenorchy Road, North Berwick.

PRESTONPANS HIGHLAND GAMES

Aims & Activities: To organise annual

professional Highland Games and sports in the area of Prestonpans.
Affiliations: The Scottish Games Association, (page 74).
✍ Secretary: James Forster
73 Prestongrange Road,
Prestonpans.
EH32 9DD
☎ 01875 812595

THORNTREE MYSTIC BURNS CLUB

Founded: 1949.
Aims & Activities: Social. Annual dinner. To encourage understanding of the work of Robert Burns.
Affiliations: The Burns Federation, No. 740.
✍ Secretary: Andrew Muir
7 North Grange Grove,
Prestonpans.
EH32 9JP

TRANENT '25' BURNS CLUB

Founded: 1892.
Aims & Activities: Social. Educational. Charitable. To encourage the reading of Scottish literature and the work of Robert Burns.
Affiliations: The Burns Federation, No. 813.
✍ Secretary: George Murdoch
25A Bridge Street, Tranent.
EH33 1AQ

EDINBURGH

ARMSTRONG TRUST LTD

Founded: 1969.
Aims & Activities: To hold clan gatherings (bi-annually). To research and collect information and material on the history and genealogy of the clan. To establish a museum. To acquire, restore and preserve clan property.

Affiliations: The Clan Armstrong Society and numerous others around the world.
Publications: The Armstrong News.
Membership: Open to all connected with the clan by descent or marriage.
✍ President: William A. Armstrong
3 Alnwickhill Road, Edinburgh.
EH16 6LG
☎ 0131 664 3818

CLAN AGNEW SOCIETY

Aims & Activities: To collect genealogical information and promote overseas links. Historical. Social.
Affiliations: Clan Agnew of North America.
Membership: Open to anyone bearing the Agnew name or connected with it.
✍ The Secretary
6 Palmerston Road, Edinburgh.
EH9 1TN

CLAN CHATTAN ASSOCIATION

Founded: 1933.
Aims & Activities: To provide friendly social intercourse among clan members. To encourage interest in and knowledge of clan history and tradition throughout the world. Overseas links.
Publications: Clan Chattan, The Journal of the Clan Chattan Association (Annual).
Membership: Open to all bearing the name of one of the septs of the clan, or connected with it by descent or marriage, or having historical connections with the Clan Chattan country.
✍ The Secretary
74 Tryst Park, Edinburgh.
EH10 7HE

CLAN GAURE

Aims & Activities: Historical. Social. Overseas links.

Membership: Open to all connected with the name, or variants of it (in any of its spellings) by descent or adoption.

✍ Chieftain: Lt Col. Robert Gaure of Gayre & Nigg
1-3, Gloucester Lane, Edinburgh.

CLAN GRAHAM SOCIETY

Aims & Activities: To promote awareness of the clan history, background and connections. To strengthen overseas links. Genealogical. Social.
Affiliations: Clan Graham Society, North Carolina, USA.
Membership: Open to those bearing the name Graham and those related by descent or marriage.

✍ Secretary: 23 Ardmillan Terrace Edinburgh.
EH11 2JW

CLAN GREGOR SOCIETY

Founded: 1822.
Aims & Activities: To encourage interest in and knowledge of the history of the clan, their background, Scottish connections and their part in Scottish history. To strengthen overseas links. Genealogical.
Affiliations: Clan Gregor Societies in Florida, North Carolina and Oklahoma, USA.
Publications: Newsletter.
Membership: Open to descendants of the clan and also to the septs and connections of the Gregor clan.

✍ Chairman: Sheila McGregor
14 Lockharton Avenue,
Edinburgh.
EH14 1AZ
☎ 0131 443 4969
✍ Secretary: 44 St Patrick Square
Edinburgh.
EH8 9ET

CLAN GUNN SOCIETY

Aims & Activities: To encourage interest in clan history, background and connections. To strengthen overseas links. Genealogical.
Affiliations: Clan Gunn Society of North America.
Membership: Open to the descendants and those connected with the Gunn clan.

✍ Secretary: 22 Muirhouse Gardens Edinburgh.
EH4 4SY

CLAN MACNEIL SOCIETY

Aims & Activities: To encourage interest in and knowledge of the clan history, their background and connections inside and outside Scotland. Social. Genealogical. To strengthen overseas links.
Affiliations: Numerous affiliated clan societies around the world.
Membership: Open to all bearing the MacNeil name or that of one of its septs, or related by descent or marriage.

✍ Secretary: 31 Orchardhead Road Edinburgh.
EH16 6HJ

CLAN MACPHEE SOCIETY

Aims & Activities: To promote interest in the clan history, background and connections. Genealogical. Overseas links.
Affiliations: Numerous affiliated clan societies around the world.
Membership: Open to those bearing the name MacPhee (and its varied spellings) or those related by marriage or descent.

✍ Secretary: 75 Buckstone Crescent Edinburgh.
EH10 6TR

CLAN McARTHUR SOCIETY

Aims & Activities: To foster knowledge of the clan and family history, background and connections. To strengthen overseas links. Genealogical. Social.

Membership: Open to those bearing the name Macarthur and all descendants of the clan.

✍ Secretary: 14 Hill Park Place Edinburgh. EH4 7TA

CLAN MENZIES

Aims & Activities: To promote the clan spirit worldwide. To collect and collate clan historical and genealogical records. Social.

Membership: Open to those of the name Menzies, or those of associated septs. or those connected by marriage or descent.

✍ Secretary: Dr A. D. Dewar 1 Belford Place, Edinburgh. EH4 3DH

CLAN MENZIES SOCIETY

Founded: 1892.

Aims & Activities: To foster the clan spirit. To preserve and restore buildings of interest to clan members, including Castle Menzies. To encourage the wearing of Highland dress. Annual Gathering. Charitable. Historical. Social. Genealogical. To strengthen overseas links.

Membership: Open to all bearing the name, or that of one of the septs, and to all connected with the clan by descent. Associate membership open to all interested in the aims.

✍ Secretary: 110 Seaview Terrace Edinburgh. EH15 2HG

CLAN MURRAY SOCIETY

Aims & Activities: To encourage interest in the clan and family history, background and connections. Genealogical. Social. To strengthen overseas links.

Membership: Open to those with the name Murray and to septs of the clan.

✍ Secretary: 67 Dublin Street Edinburgh. EH3 6NS

CLAN ROSS SOCIETY

Aims & Activities: To promote knowledge of the clan and family history, background. Genealogical. Social. To strengthen overseas links.

Membership: Open to any member of the Ross clan.

✍ Secretary 57 Barnton Park View, Edinburgh. EH4 6EL

CLAN WALLACE

Aims & Activities: To promote the clan spirit worldwide. Historical. Genealogical. To encourage overseas links.

Membership: Open to those bearing the name Wallace or related by descent or marriage.

✍ Secretary: Ian F. Wallace 5 Lennox Street, Edinburgh. EH4 1QB

COLINTON BURNS CLUB

Aims & Activities: Annual Gathering. Social and to encourage an interest in the works of Robert Burns.

Affiliations: The Burns Federation, No. 398.

✍ Secretary: Mr Derek G. Cowan 4 Cluny Gardens, Edinburgh. EH10 6BL

CRAMOND BRIG BURNS CLUB

Founded: 1949.

Aims & Activities: Social. To perpetuate the memory of Robert Burns.

Affiliations: The Burns Federation, No. 1031.

✍ Secretary: Duncan Foggon
4 Braepark Road, Cramond,
Edinburgh.
EH4 6DN

DUNEDIN DANCERS

Aims & Activities: See the RSCDS on
page 47.
✍ Secretary: Mrs E Lamb
5 Munro Drive, Edinburgh.
EH13 0EG

EDINBURGH AYRSHIRE ASSOCIATION

Founded: 1914.
Aims & Activities: To foster knowledge
of the works of Robert Burns.
Affiliations: The Burns Federation,
No. 307.
✍ Secretary: Ms Katherine J. Mejka
4 East Parkside, Holyrood Park
Road, Edinburgh.
EH16 5HJ

EDINBURGH BRANCH OF THE ROYAL SCOTTISH COUNTRY DANCE SOCIETY

Aims & Activities: See the RSCDS on
page 47.
Membership: 881.
✍ Secretary: Mrs R. Mulholland
27 Milnacre, Bonnington Mills,
Edinburgh.
EH6 5TD
☎ 0131 553 6113 (home)
☎ 0131 554 6631 (business)

EDINBURGH BURNS CLUB

Founded: 1848.
Aims & Activities: To promote interest
in the works of Robert Burns. Social.
Annual dinner.
Affiliations: The Burns Federation,
No. 22.
✍ Secretary: Mr A. Winton
12 Ventnor Terrace, Edinburgh.
EH9 2BL

EDINBURGH DISTRICT BURNS CLUB ASSOCIATION

Founded: 1925.
Aims & Activities: Social and to foster
interest in the works of Robert
Burns. Annual dinner.
Affiliations: The Burns Federation,
No. 378.
✍ Secretary: Gordon Innes
9 Jeffrey Avenue, Edinburgh.

EDINBURGH FANCY GROUP

Aims & Activities: See the RSCDS on
page 47.
✍ Secretary: Mrs R. Mulholland
27 Milnacre, Bonnington Mills,
Edinburgh.
EH6 5TD
☎ 0131 553 6113

EDINBURGH HIGHLAND GAMES

Aims & Activities: To organise annual
professional Highland Games and
sports in the area of Edinburgh, largely seen as an attraction for tourists.
Affiliations: The Scottish Games
Association, (page 74).
✍ Secretary: J. Anderson
4 Newhalls Road, South
Queensferry.
EH30 9TA
☎ 0131 319 2005

EDINBURGH UNIVERSITY NEW SCOTLAND COUNTRY DANCE SOCIETY

Aims & Activities: See the RSCDS on
page 47.
✍ Secretary: Kathi Branse
EUNSCDS, McEwan Hall, Teviot
Place, Edinburgh.
EH8 9AF
☎ 0131 650 5721

EDINBURGH WEEKEND SCHOOL GROUP

Aims & Activities: See the RSCDS on page 47.

✍ Secretary: Mrs R. Mulholland
27 Milnacre, Bonnington Mills,
Edinburgh.
EH6 5TD
☎ 0131 553 6113

INCORPORATION OF HAMMERMEN OF EDINBURGH

Founded: 1483 under Seal of Cause by Edinburgh City Council
Aims & Activities: Charitable and social, including the administration of a small Trust Fund known as the Hammermen's Award, tenable at Heriot Watt University.
Affiliations: The Convenery of Trades of Edinburgh; The Trades Maiden Hospital.
Membership: Suitably qualified persons interested in promoting public charitable purposes in Edinburgh.

✍ Deacon: Gordon M. Wyllie WS
c/o Biggart Baillie and Gifford,
Dalmore House, 310 St Vincent
St, Glasgow.
G2 5QR
☎ 0141 228 8000
✆ 0141 228 8310

LEITH BURNS CLUB

Founded: 1826.
Aims & Activities: Social. Annual dinner.
Affiliations: The Burns Federation, No. 341.

✍ Secretary: Gerald T. Farmer
CA, ACIS, 34 Cramond Park,
Cramond, Edinburgh.
EH4 6PR

MARCHBANK BURNS CLUB

Founded: 1959.
Aims & Activities: Social and to encourage interest in the works of Robert Burns.
Affiliations: The Burns Federation, No. 992.

✍ Secretary: David Russell
104 Crosswood Crescent,
Balerno.
EH14 7HG

NEWCRAIGHALL WELFARE POOSIE NANSIE BURNS CLUB

Founded: 1921.
Aims & Activities: Annual dinner. Social.
Affiliations: The Burns Federation, No. 293.

✍ Secretary: Mr Stuart Davie
15 Northfield Park, Edinburgh.
EH8 7QU

NINETY BURNS CLUB

Founded: 1890.
Aims & Activities: Social. Annual dinner. To perfect and extend the Burns cult.
Affiliations: The Burns Federation, No. 124.

✍ Secretary: Mr R. M. Armour
213 Braid Road, Edinburgh.
EH10 6NY

PORTOBELLO BURNS CLUB

Founded: 1892.
Aims & Activities: To foster knowledge of the works of Robert Burns. Social. Annual dinner.
Affiliations: The Burns Federation, No. 212.

✍ Secretary: Ms Kathleen
McMichael
22 Seaview Crescent, Edinburgh.
EH15 2LU

ROYAL SCOTTISH COUNTRY DANCE SOCIETY

Founded: 1923.
Aims & Activities: To practise and pre-

serve country dances as danced in Scotland. To collect historic material on them. To publish descriptions of them with diagrams and music. Committees: Finance, General Purposes, Publications and Research, Examinations. Summer School.
Affiliations: 163 branches worldwide. 506 affiliated groups.
Publications: Book of Dances; Bulletin (both annual).
Membership: Open to all interested in the aims of the Society. Apply to the headquarters: 16 Coates Crescent, Edinburgh, EH3 7AF.
✍ President: The Earl of Mansfield Scone Palace, Perth. Chairman: Mr George Lawson. Vice-chairman: Mr Bill Clement. Secretary: Miss Gill S. Parker.

ROYAL SCOTTISH PIPERS' SOCIETY

Aims & Activities: A strictly amateur and private club open by election to gentlemen who are interested in the playing and study of the great highland bagpipe. Members may be playing, or non-playing. The society is strictly amateur and anyone playing professionally or in open competition against professional players is not eligible for membership. The society is managed by a committee of eight members under the Chairmanship of the Hon. Pipe Major, normally a two-year appointment. Patron: Her Majesty the Queen.
✍ Secretary: J. J. Burnet
30 Park Road, Edinburgh.
EH6 4LD
✍ Treasurer: A. W. MacGhie
Springfield Stables, Harvieston Road, Dollar.
FK14 7PT

SAINT ANDREW SOCIETY

Aims & Activities: To uphold Scottish rights. To encourage the celebration

of St. Andrew's Day. To foster Scottish culture and overseas links. Historical. Educational. Social.
Affiliations: Numerous St Andrew Societies worldwide.
Publications: Annual newsletter.
Membership: Open to all of Scottish descent.
✍ Honorary President: The Earl of Wemyss and March. President: Lt Col. M. Muriel Gibson. Vice-president: Dr Farquhar Mackintosh. Secretary: Miss Elizabeth Wark.
✍ Apply to PO Box 84 Edinburgh, Scotland.

SCOTTISH ANCESTRY RESEARCH SOCIETY

Founded: 1945.
Aims & Activities: A non-profit-making organisation to trace Scottish ancestry.
✍ Chairman of the Council: Sir John Clark of Penicuik
✍ Secretary: Alison Munro
29b Albany Street, Edinburgh.
EH1 3QN
☎ 0131 556 4220

SCOTTISH ATHLETICS FEDERATION

Aims & Activities: Overall control and organisation of all Amateur Sport in Scotland including the 25 Amateur Highland Games.
✍ Administrator: Neil Park
✍ General Secretary: R. W. Greenoak
Caledonia House, South Gyle, Edinburgh.
EH12 2DQ
☎ 0131 317 7320/1 (business)
☎ 0131 449 7272 (home)

SCOTTISH BURNS CLUB

Founded: 1920.
Aims & Activities: Social. Annual din-

ner. To encourage interest in Robert Burns and his poetry.
Affiliations: The Burns Federation, No. 314.
✍ Secretary: Mrs Ella Bruce
9 Victor Park Terrace, Edinburgh.

SCOTTISH GENEALOGY SOCIETY

Founded: 1953 (as The Scottish Genealogical Society).
Aims & Activities: To promote research into Scottish family history. To undertake collection, exchange and publication of information relating to this. Overseas links. Educational. Historical. Social.
Publications: The Scottish Genealogist.
Membership: Open to all interested in the aims.
✍ Secretary: Miss J. P. S Ferguson
10 Victoria Terrace, Edinburgh.
EH1 2JL
☎ 0131 220 3677

SCOTTISH OFFICIAL BOARD OF HIGHLAND DANCING

Founded: 1950.
Aims & Activities: To bring about co-operation between the recognised associations, organisations and individuals connected with Highland Dancing without discrimination as to colour, race, nationality, ethnic or national origins.
Affiliations: The Scottish Dance Teachers Alliance, The British Association of Teachers of Dancing, The U. K. Alliance of Teachers and affiliated groups internationally.
✍ President: Dr A. C. Maclaren
TD. Vice President: Miss J.
Stewart. Chairman: Mr W.
Forsyth. Director of
Administration: Miss Marjory
Rowan, 32 Grange Loan,
Edinburgh.
EH9 2NR

STEWART SOCIETY

Aims & Activities: To promote awareness of the clan and family history, their background and connections and their part in Scottish history. To strengthen overseas links.
Membership: Open to anyone with the Stewart name, or variants of it.
✍ Secretary: 17 Dublin Street
Edinburgh.
EH1 3PG

TRINITY ACADEMY FORMER PUPILS COUNTRY DANCE CLUB

Aims & Activities: See the RSCDS on page 47.
✍ Secretary: Mr J. I. Auld
9 Ashley Drive, Edinburgh.
EH11 1RP
☎ 0131 337 4482

FALKIRK

AIRBORNE BURNS CLUB

Aims & Activities: Social. Annual Gathering.
Affiliations: The Burns Federation, No. 1101.
✍ Secretary: C. R. Matheson
44 Randyford Street, Falkirk.
FK2 9DF

AIRTH HIGHLAND GAMES

Aims & Activities: To organise annual professional Highland Games and sports in the area of Airth.
Affiliations: The Scottish Games Association, (page 74).
✍ Secretary: Alex Dettlaff
36 Paul Drive, Airth, by Falkirk.
FK2 8LA
☎ 01324 631712

DENNY CROSS BURNS CLUB

Founded: 1932.
Aims & Activities: Social. Annual Gathering. To perpetuate the name of Robert Burns.
Affiliations: The Burns Federation, No. 469.
✍ Secretary: James Burgess
14 Myott View, Fankerton,
by Denny.
FK6 5HZ

DUNDAS BURNS SOCIETY

Founded: 1968.
Aims & Activities: Social. Annual Gathering.
Affiliations: The Burns Federation, No. 1059.
✍ Secretary: Matthew Gilbert
6 Lumley Place, Grangemouth.
FK3 8BY

FALKIRK BURNS CLUB

Founded: 1866.
Aims & Activities: Educational. Charitable. To promote the study of Scottish literature and the work of Robert Burns.
Affiliations: The Burns Federation, No. 126.
✍ Secretary: Mr William
Cunningham
Northern Rock Building Society,
2 High Street, Falkirk.
FK1 1EZ

FALKIRK HIGHLAND GAMES

Aims & Activities: To organise annual amateur Highland Games in the area of Falkirk, generally in mid-July.
✍ Secretary: Elaine Wond
Falkirk District Council, Leisure Services Dept., Kilns House, Kilns Road, Falkirk.
FK1 5SA

FRIDAY NIGHT BURNS CLUB, FALKIRK

Founded: 1969.
Aims & Activities: Social. Annual Gathering.
Affiliations: The Burns Federation, No. 1069.
✍ Secretary: George Thomson
15 Greenhorns Well Avenue,
Falkirk.
FK1 5HL

WALLACE BURNS CLUB

Aims & Activities: Social.
Affiliations: The Burns Federation, No. 1095.
✍ Secretary: Mrs E. O'Donnell
26 Carmuirs Street, Camelon,
Falkirk.
FK1 4PZ

WHEATSHEAF BURNS CLUB, FALKIRK

Founded: 1974.
Aims & Activities: Social. Annual Gathering. To perpetuate the memory of Robert Burns.
Affiliations: The Burns Federation, No. 930.
✍ Secretary: Peter Lees
63 Webster Avenue, Carronshore,
Falkirk.
FK2 8BA

FIFE

AUCHTERDERRAN JOLLY BEGGARS BURNS CLUB

Founded: 1912.
Aims & Activities: Social. Annual dinner. Charitable. Educational. To encourage study of the work of Robert Burns.
Affiliations: The Burns Federation, No. 768.
✍ Secretary: David Murdoch

2 Craigside Road, Cardenden.

BALMULLO BURNS CLUB

Aims & Activities: Social. To perpetuate the memory of Robert Burns.
Affiliations: The Burns Federation, No. 1013.
✍ Secretary: Mrs J. Milne
3 Lomond Place, Balmullo, St Andrews.

BOWHILL PEOPLE'S BURNS CLUB

Founded: 1940.
Aims & Activities: Social. To further the appreciation of the work of Robert Burns.
Affiliations: The Burns Federation, No. 803.
✍ Secretary: Thomas Hopton
15 Parliament Place, Kinglassie. KY5 0XD

BRUCE FAMILY

Aims & Activities: Genealogical. Historical. Overseas links.
Membership: Open to all members of the Bruce family and those connected by descent or marriage.
✍ Chieftain: The Earl of Elgin & Kincardine
Broomhall, Dumfermline, KY11.

BURNTISLAND HIGHLAND GAMES

Founded: 1635.
Aims & Activities: To organise annual professional Highland Games and sports in the area of Burntisland, a royal burgh and seaport on the north shore of the Firth of Forth. The Games are usually held in late July and as they coincide with the Edinburgh Trades holidays are generally well attended.
Affiliations: The Scottish Games Association, (page 74).
✍ Secretary: Mrs Isa Duncanson

31 Kirkbank Road, Burntisland.
☎ 01592 873234

CLAN ANSTRUTHER

Aims & Activities: Genealogical. Historical. Overseas links.
Membership: Open to all those bearing the name Anstruther and those related by descent or marriage.
✍ Chieftain: Sir Ralph Anstruther
Balcaskie, Pittenweem. KY10 2RD

CLAN LUMSDEN

Aims & Activities: To preserve historical and genealogical records. To strengthen overseas links. Social.
Membership: Open to the those bearing the name Lumsden, or variants of it, also those related by marriage or descent.
✍ Secretary: Mrs S. Asphin
Kilrenny House, Kilrenny. KY10 3JN

CLAN ROLLO SOCIETY

Aims & Activities: To strengthen overseas links. To research and preserve the clan genealogical records. Historical. Social.
Membership: Open to all with the name Rollo and to those claiming relationship by descent or marriage.
✍ Secretary: 25 Blake Street
Broughty Ferry. DD5 3LL

CLAN SCRIMGEOUR

Aims & Activities: To foster clan sentiment and family spirit at home and abroad. To collect and preserve its historical records and traditions and to publish them if deemed advisable. To protect the lands and property associated with the clan, particularly Dudhope Castle. Annual Gathering.

To strengthen overseas links. Social. Annual Gathering.

Publications: The Skirmisher, occasional news bulletin.

Membership: Open to members of the Scrimgeour clan and those bearing that name, or variants of it (in any of its spellings) or connected by marriage or descent.

✍ Hon President: The Earl of
    Dundee
    Birkhill, Cupar.
    KY15 4QN

CLAN WEDDERBURN

Aims & Activities: To preserve historical and genealogical records of the clan. Annual Gathering. To strengthen overseas links. Social.

Membership: Open to members of the Wedderburn clan and those bearing that name, or variants of it, also those related by marriage or descent.

✍ Hon President: Master of Dundee
    Birkhill, Cupar.
    KY15 4QN

CLAN WEMYSS

Aims & Activities: To strengthen overseas links. To preserve all historical and genealogical clan records in the clan archives Annual Gathering.

Membership: Open to members of the Wemyss clan and those bearing that name, or variants of it, including those related by descent or marriage.

✍ The Administrator
    Wemyss Estates, The Red House, East Wemyss.
    KY1 4TE

COWDENBEATH SCOTS WHA' HAE BURNS CLUB

Founded: 1972.

Aims & Activities: Social. Annual Gathering. To preserve the memory of Robert Burns.

Affiliations: The Burns Federation, No. 1040.

✍ Secretary: T. G. Hutton
    36 Clunie Road, Dunfermline.
    KY11 E40

CUPAR BURNS CLUB

Founded: 1884.

Aims & Activities: Social. Educational. Charitable. To promote the reading of Scottish literature especially that of Robert Burns.

Affiliations: The Burns Federation, No. 62.

✍ Secretary: Mr Robert W. M.
    Stewart
    10 Halyburton Place, Cupar.
    KY15 5DZ

DUNFERMLINE BRANCH OF THE ROYAL SCOTTISH COUNTRY DANCE SOCIETY

Aims & Activities: See the RSCDS on page 47.

Membership: 69.

✍ Secretary: Mrs J. MacSporran
    26 High Beveridgewell, Dunfermline.
    KY12 9EP
☎ 01383 724707

DUNFERMLINE UNITED BURNS CLUB

Founded: 1812.

Aims & Activities: To promote interest in and discussion of the works of Robert Burns. Social. Educational.

Affiliations: The Burns Federation, No. 85.

✍ Secretary: Miss F. M. Maclachlan
    26 Viewfield Terrace, Dunfermline.
    KY12 7LB

EARLSFERRY BURNS CLUB

Founded: 1975.

Aims & Activities: Social. Annual

Gathering. To preserve the memory of Burns.
Affiliations: The Burns Federation, No. 967.
✍ The Secretary: The Golf Club House
Elie.

GIFFORDTOWN SCOTTISH COUNTRY DANCE GROUP

Aims & Activities: See the RSCDS on page 47.
✍ Secretary: Mrs S. Watson
50 Whitecraig Road,
Newburgh.
KY14 6BU

GLENROTHES HIGHLAND GAMES

Aims & Activities: To organise annual professional Highland Games and sports in the area of Glenrothes, one of the more successful post-war new towns, originally a mining community until the coal ran out. The Games are currently held towards the end of July in the Warout Stadium.
Affiliations: The Scottish Games Association, (page 74).
✍ Secretary: Adam Crawford
146 Forres Drive, Glenrothes.
KY6 2JY
☎ 01592 753439

INVERKEITHING HIGHLAND GAMES

Aims & Activities: To organise annual professional Highland Games and sports in the area of Inverkeithing, a royal burgh four miles south of Dunfermline on the Firth of Forth. The Games date back to a Lammas Fair in 1652 and include a race of 'a hat and a ribbon'. Usually held in early August.
Affiliations: The Scottish Games Association, (page 74).
✍ Secretary: J. Murray

Inverkeithing.
KY11 1NF
☎ 01383 414469

KIRKCALDY BRANCH OF THE ROYAL SCOTTISH COUNTRY DANCE SOCIETY

Aims & Activities: See the RSCDS on page 47.
Membership: 97.
✍ Secretary: Mrs A. Sweeney
90 Glenorchy Court, Glenrothes.
KY7 6XJ
☎ 01592 742353

KIRKCALDY PATHHEAD PARISH CHURCH SCOTTISH COUNTRY DANCING CLASS

Aims & Activities: See the RSCDS on page 47.
✍ Secretary: Miss J. H. Auld
69 Ravens Craig, Kirkcaldy.
KY1 2PU
☎ 01592 265457

KIRKCALDY-PATHHEAD LADIES' BURNS CLUB

Founded: 1947.
Aims & Activities: Social. To encourage interest in the works of Robert Burns. Annual Gathering.
Affiliations: The Burns Federation, No. 688.
✍ Secretary: Mrs Betsy C. Rodger
10 Durham Crescent, Lower Largo.
KT8 6DN

MARKINCH BURNS CLUB

Founded: 1889.
Aims & Activities: Social. Charitable. Educational. Annual gathering. To promote interest in the work of Robert Burns and to organise competitions in local schools.
Affiliations: The Burns Federation, No. 350.

✍ Secretary: Mrs B. Jolly
   16 Orchard Drive, Glenrothes.

MARKINCH HIGHLAND GAMES

Aims & Activities: To organise annual professional Highland Games and sports in the area of Markinch and Glenrothes. Generally held in early June.
Affiliations: The Scottish Games Association, (page 74).
✍ Secretary: James Duncan
   81 Croft Crescent, Markinch.
   KY7 6EL
☎ 01592 759038

NEWBURGH HIGHLAND GAMES

Founded: 1850 (in the present form).
Aims & Activities: To organise annual professional Highland Games and sports in the area of Newburgh, a small royal burgh with a harbour in the south side of the Firth of Tay, eight miles north-west of Cupar. Generally held in mid-July and originally featuring a pony race, since 1850 the Games have included a coble race on the Firth of Tay and this remains a unique feature of these Games.
Affiliations: The Scottish Games Association, (page 74).
✍ Secretary: Mrs M. Colville
   31 Robertson Crescent,
   Newburgh.
   KY14 6AW
☎ 01337 840691

PITTENWEEM BURNS CLUB

Aims & Activities: Social and to foster the study of Burns. Annual Gathering.
Affiliations: The Burns Federation, No. 1103.
✍ Secretary: A. Guthrie
   14 High Street, Pittenweem.
   KY10 2LA

ST ANDREWS BRANCH OF THE ROYAL SCOTTISH COUNTRY DANCE SOCIETY

Aims & Activities: See the RSCDS on page 47.
Membership: 145.
✍ Secretary: Mrs A. Gibb
   22 High Road, Strathkinness, St Andrews.
   KY6 9SS
☎ 01334 850680 (home)
☎ 01334 463102 (business)

ST ANDREWS BURNS CLUB

Founded: 1869.
Aims & Activities: Social. Educational. Annual Gathering. To encourage interest in the works of Robert Burns.
Affiliations: The Burns Federation, No. 13.
✍ Secretary: Mr Colin McAllister
   140 South Street, St Andrews.
   KY16 9EG

ST ANDREWS HIGHLAND GAMES

Aims & Activities: To organise annual professional Highland Games and sports in the area of St Andrews.
Affiliations: The Scottish Games Association, (page 74).
✍ Secretary: Ian B. Grieve
   54 Crawford Gardens, St Andrews.
   KY16 8XO
☎ 01334 476305

ST ANDREWS UNIVERSITY CELTIC SOCIETY

Founded: 1796 (the oldest Scottish Country Dance Society in the world).
Aims & Activities: See the RSCDS on page 47. Visits to castles, distilleries etc are organised regularly.
Publications: Newsletters
Membership: Open to all students. 225 in 1996.

✍ Secretary: Katrin Jungbeck
21 Fife Park, St Andrews.
KY16.
E celtic@stand.ac.uk

THORNTON HIGHLAND GAMES

Founded: 1864.
Aims & Activities: To organise annual professional Highland Games and sports in the area of Thornton, four miles north of Kirkcaldy. Generally held early in July and featuring pony trotting and cycling.
Affiliations: The Scottish Games Association, (page 74).
✍ Secretary: William Crawford
43 Donald Crescent, Thornton, Kirkcaldy.
KY1 4AS
☎ 01592 774615

GLASGOW

ASSOCIATION OF DEACONS OF THE 14 INCORPORATED TRADES OF GLASGOW

Founded: 1857, and incorporated by Royal Charter in 1910.
Aims & Activities: To encourage membership of the Incorporated Trades of Glasgow and after payment of management expenses to direct its revenue to to the relief of its members, their widows and children when in want or indigent circumstances. Charitable and social, including the visitation of the needy elderly having connections with the Association.
Publications: Quinquennial Report and Annual Accounts
Membership: Past and present Deacons and Visitors of the 14 Incorporated Trades of Glasgow from which a Court of Directors is elected comprising one representative from each Craft.
✍ Clerk: Gordon M. Wyllie WS

310 St Vincent St, Glasgow.
G2 5QR
☎ 0141 228 8000
✆ 0141 228 8310

BLUEVALE BURNS CLUB

Aims & Activities: Social and to encourage interest in the works of Burns.
Affiliations: The Burns Federation, No. 1104.
✍ Secretary: John Willox
101 Culross Street, Glasgow.
G32 9BS

BRIDGETON BURNS CLUB

Founded: 1870.
Aims & Activities: Social. Annual dinner. To promote interest in Robert Burns and his poems.
Affiliations: The Burns Federation, No. 49.
✍ Secretary: Mr Bryan McKirgan
4 Balmoral Drive, Cambuslang, Glasgow.
G72 8BG

BUCHANAN SOCIETY

Founded: 1725.
Aims & Activities: Genealogical. Social. Charitable and Educational. Annual dinner. To strengthen overseas links.
Publications: The Buchanan Society Handbook (issued to members on joining).
Membership: Open to all bearing the names Buchananan, MacAuslan, MacWattie or Risk.
✍ Secretary: 18 Iddlesleigh Avenue
Milngavie.
G62 8WT

CAMBUSLANG MARY CAMPBELL BURNS CLUB

Founded: 1965.
Aims & Activities: To promote knowl-

edge of the works of Burns. Annual dinner. Social.
Affiliations: The Burns Federation, No. 387.
✍ President: Mrs M. Rennie
50 Loren Terrace, Whitlawburn, Cambuslang, Glasgow.

CLAN FERGUSON SOCIETY

Aims & Activities: To promote awareness of the history and traditions of the clan and its septs. To strengthen overseas links. Genealogical.
Membership: Open to anyone with the name Ferguson, or variants of it.
✍ Secretary: Pendle Cottage
Dumgoyne, Glasgow.

CLAN MACKINNON SOCIETY

Aims & Activities: To promote awareness of the clan and family history and background. To collect and preseve material on the clan. To strengthen overseas links. Social.
Membership: Open to all connected with the clan or its septs by descent or marriage.
✍ Secretary: 222 Darnley Street
Glasgow.

CLAN MACLEAN SOCIETY

Aims & Activities: To maintain the traditions and encourage study of the history of the clan. To strengthen overseas links.
Membership: Open to all bearing the name (in its various spellings).
✍ Secretary: 12 Ellie Street
Glasgow.
G11 5HJ

CLAN MACNACHTEN

Aims & Activities: To maintain the traditions and encourage study of the history of the clan. To strengthen overseas links.

Membership: Open to all bearing the clan name or variants of it.
✍ Secretary: Miss A. Lawson
74 Beechlands Drive, Clarkston, Glasgow.
G76 7UX

CLAN URQUHART ASSOCIATION

Aims & Activities: To promote awareness of the clan history. To encourage genealogical interest. To strengthen overseas links.
Membership: Open to those of that name and their descendants or any connections of the Urquhart clan and its septs.
✍ Secretary: Faliskeour
Balfron Station, Glasgow.
G63 0QY

COLLEGE OF PIPING

Aims & Activities: To promote and teach bagpipe music and to preserve the traditions of the same.
Publications: The Piping Times.
✍ Apply to: 20 Otago Street
Glasgow.
G12
☎ 0141 334 3587

GLASGOW AND DISTRICT BURNS ASSOCIATION

Founded: 1907.
Aims & Activities: To promote co-operation amongst member clubs. To maintain the Jean Armour Burns Houses at Mauchline, Ayrshire. To encourage interest in the works of Robert Burns. Annual gathering. Overseas links. Charitable. Social.
Affiliations: The Burns Federation, No. 169.
✍ Secretary: Mr David L. Stevenson
Biggart, Baillie and Gifford, Dalmore House, 310 Vincent Street, Glasgow.
G2 5QR

GLASGOW BRANCH OF THE ROYAL SCOTTISH COUNTRY DANCE SOCIETY

Aims & Activities: See the RSCDS on page 47.
Membership: 485.
✍ Secretary: Christine Traynor
47 Castlehill Crescent,
Kilmalcolm.
PA13 4HY
☎ 01505 873409 (home)
☎ 01505 328261 (business)

GLASGOW HAGGIS CLUB

Founded: 1872.
Aims & Activities: Social. Annual gathering and dinner.
Affiliations: The Burns Federation, No. 33.
✍ Secretary: Mr D. R. Anderson
Gillespie & Anderson, Chartered Accountants, 147 Bath Street, Glasgow.
G2 4SN

GLASGOW MASONIC BURNS CLUB

Founded: 1919.
Aims & Activities: To encourage interest in the works of Robert Burns. Social.
Affiliations: The Burns Federation, No. 263.
Membership: Open to members of the Masonic fraternity.
✍ Secretary: Mr James Muir
15 Falkland Park, East Kilbride.
G74 1JD

GLASGOW SAINT ANDREW SOCIETY

Aims & Activities: Social. Annual dinner.
✍ Secretary: Jack Lindsay
c/o Elder, Mackenzie & Co,
98 West George St, Glasgow.
G2 2PJ
☎ 0141 333 1674 (business)

GLASGOW UNIVERSITY SCOTTISH COUNTRY DANCE CLUB

Aims & Activities: See the RSCDS on page 47.
✍ Secretary: Miss F. Chinn
Flat 2/1, 1040 Maryhill Road,
Glasgow.
G20 9TE
☎ 0141 945 5347

GRAND ANTIQUITY SOCIETY OF GLASGOW

Founded: 1756 and incorporated by Royal Charters in 1899 and 1969.
Aims & Activities: The work of the Society is principally for the relief of indigent members and their families. Charitable and social, including visitation of the needy elderly having connections with the Society.
Publications: Annual Accounts.
Membership: Membership of the Society is open to those holding tickets of free burgess-ship of Glasgow, at least one of whose parents (or of whose spouse's parents) and one of that parent's parents, or parents-in-law, have also been burgesses and free citizens of Glasgow.
✍ Clerk: Gordon M. Wyllie WS
310 St Vincent St, Glasgow.
G2 5QR
☎ 0141 228 8000
℃ 0141 228 8310

GRIFFIN BURNS CLUB, GARTCOSH

Founded: 1975.
Aims & Activities: Social. Annual dinner.
Affiliations: The Burns Federation, No. 939.
✍ Secretary: James L. Chalmers
JP, 39 Cardowan Drive, Stepps, Glasgow.
G33 6HQ

MACLENNAN SOCIETY

Founded: 1971.
Aims & Activities: To promote awareness of the clan history. To strengthen overseas links. Social.
Membership: Open to anyone with the name MacLennan, in its various spellings, their descendants, or those connected by marriage, and to the various septs.
✍ Gen. Secretary: Mrs E. McLennan
   31 Ascaig Crescent, Glasgow.
   G52 1BN

MILNGAVIE SCOTTISH COUNTRY DANCE CLUB

Aims & Activities: See the RSCDS on page 47.
✍ Secretary: Mrs H. M. Murray
   40 Lynn Drive, Milngavie, Glasgow.
   G62 8HN
☎ 0141 956 2698

NATIONAL BURNS MEMORIAL AND COTTAGE HOMES, MAUCHLINE

Founded: 1881.
Aims & Activities: To maintain 20 cottages for needy old folk and a Burns tower museum of the life and times of Robert Burns. To encourage interest in the life and works of Robert Burns. Charitable. Historical.
Affiliations: The Burns Federation, The Glasgow Mauchline Society.
✍ Secretary: Mr Alistair J. Campbell
   c/o Mitchell Robertson, George House, 36 North Hanover Street, Glasgow.
   G1 2AD

NETHERLEE SCOTTISH COUNTRY DANCE CLUB

Aims & Activities: See the RSCDS on page 47.
✍ Secretary: Mrs H. Blair
   8 Melford Avenue, Giffnock.

G46 6NA
☎ 0141 638 6589

NEWTON JEAN ARMOUR BURNS CLUB

Founded: 1924.
Aims & Activities: Social. Annual dinner. To encourage interest in Robert Burns.
Affiliations: The Burns Federation, No. 348.
✍ Secretary: Mrs S. Kean
   14 Woodland Crescent, Cambuslang, Glasgow.
   G72 8RB

OUPLAYMUIR BURNS CLUB

Founded: 1936.
Aims & Activities: Social. Annual gathering and dinner.
Affiliations: The Burns Federation, No. 748.
✍ Secretary: D. Carslaw
   Grianan, Pollick Avenue, Uplawmoor, Glasgow.
   G79 4AE

PARTICK BURNS CLUB

Founded: 1885.
Aims & Activities: Social. Charitable. Educational. To promote interest in the works of Robert Burns. Annual Gathering.
Affiliations: The Burns Federation, No. 72.
✍ Secretary: Mr G. Davidson
   c/o R & J. M. Hill Brown & Co., 3 Newton Place, Glasgow.
   G3 7PU

PIPING CENTRE

Founded: 1996
Aims & Activities: To promote, teach and encourage the study of the bagpipes. Facilities and services include auditorium, banquetting facilities, concerts, conferences, museum, refer-

ence library, rehearsal rooms, hotel suite, restaurant and shop.
Affiliations: The Royal Scottish Academy of Music and Drama.
✍ Director of Administration: John Drysdale
30-34 McPhater Street, Glasgow. G4 0HW
☎ 0141 353 0220
✆ 0141 353 1570
✍ Director of Piping: Roddy MacLeod

QUEENS PARK BOWLING CLUB CLARINDA BURNS CLUB

Founded: 1930.
Aims & Activities: Social. To encourage knowledge of the works of Burns.
Affiliations: The Burns Federation, No. 585.
✍ Secretary: J. Watson
42 Brownlie Street,
Mount Florida, Glasgow.
G42 9BT

ROYAL SCOTTISH PIPE BAND ASSOCIATION

Founded: 1930
Aims & Activities: To promote and encourage the culture and advancement of pipe band music internationally and to sponsor a pipe band college. To create and maintain a bond of fellowship with all pipe band personnel throughout the world. To devise and operate a proper system of pipe band contest rules. To organise the World, European, British, Scottish and all major championships held within the UK.
Publications: Bi-monthly magazine, The Pipe Band, and free tuitional text books in a structured learning series.
Membership: Open to pipe bands in the UK.
✍ Mitchell Hutchinson
RSPBA, 45 Washington Street, Glasgow.
G3 8AZ

☎ 0141 221 5414
✆ 0141 221 1561

ROYALTY BURNS CLUB

Founded: 1882.
Aims & Activities: To promote knowledge of the life and works of Robert Burns. Educational. Charitable. Social. Historical.
Affiliations: The Burns Federation, No. 9.
✍ Secretary: Mr Malcolm A. Clark
37 Burnhead Road, Newlands, Glasgow.

RUTHERGLEN BURNS CLUB

Founded: 1975.
Aims & Activities: Social. Annual Dinner.
Affiliations: The Burns Federation, No. 642.
✍ Secretary: Mrs Alison Brown
12 Melrose Court, Rutherglen, Glasgow.
G73 2DB

SANDYFORD BURNS CLUB

Founded: 1893.
Aims & Activities: Social. Charitable. Historical and Educational. Annual Dinner.
Affiliations: The Burns Federation, No. 68.
✍ Secretary: Mr C. Gore
9 Forest View, Cumbernauld.
G67 2DB

THISTLE BURNS CLUB

Founded: 1882.
Aims & Activities: Social. Charitable. Historical. Educational. To foster knowledge of the works of Robert Burns. Annual Gathering.
Affiliations: The Burns Federation, No. 7.
✍ Secretary: Mr Wm Falconer
c/o Wellcroft Bowling Club, 163

Queens Drive, Crosshill, Glasgow.
G42 8QR

TRADES HOUSE OF GLASGOW

Founded: 1605.
Aims & Activities: Charitable activities
in the Glasgow area, including work
for the elderly and disadvantaged, and
public purposes of a non-political
nature. Administration of charitable
funds and promotion of charitable
events within the purposes of the
House organised by its members.
Examples include the annual
Glasgow Schools Craft Competition,
the Glasgow Colleges Craft
Competition and Exhibition, the
Contact the Elderly group, visitation
of the needy elderly, and the support
of projects benefiting the City of
Glasgow and her people, including
the members' organisation of the
annual Glasgow Greets Vienna New
Year's Day Concert for Action
Research.
Publications: The Craftsman (newslet-
ter); Annual Accounts; The Trades
House of Glasgow — Past, Present
and Future; other ad hoc publica-
tions.
Membership: Sixty-four members
elected under the Glasgow Trades
House Order Confirmation Act 1920
from the 14 incorporated trades of
Glasgow, each of which forms a separate constituency. Full membership
of one of these confers entitlement to
election. The Glasgow crafts comprise
Hammermen, Tailors, Cordiners,
Maltmen, Weavers, Bakers, Skinners,
Wrights, Coopers, Fleshers, Masons,
Gardeners, Barbers, Bonnetmakers
and Dyers.
✍ Clerk: Gordon M. Wyllie WS
  310 St Vincent St, Glasgow.
  G2 5QR
☎ 0141 228 8000
✆ 0141 228 8310

WALLACE CLAN TRUST

Founded: 1986.
Aims & Activities: The Trust has an
open door policy for kith and kin and
any other interested party. To assist in
historical film productions set in
Scotland. To research Scottish history.
To acquire land for an international
clan settlement.
Membership: Open to all. Apply to 1
Shearer Street, Kingston, Glasgow, G5
8TA.
✍ CE: Seoras Wallace. Treasurer:
  Pamela Tucker. Secretaries: Tam
  McDermott
  Helen Craig.
☎ 0141 429 6915
✆ 0141 429 6968

WHIFFLET BURNS CLUB

Founded: 1920.
Aims & Activities: Social and to
encourage study of Burns and his
works.
Affiliations: The Burns Federation,
No. 392.
✍ Secretary: E. Bruce Wilkie
  34 Cromarty Road, Cairnhill,
  Airdrie.
  ML6 9RN

HIGHLAND

ABERNETHY HIGHLAND GAMES ASSOCIATION

Aims & Activities: To organise annual
amateur Highland Games and sports
in the area of Nethy Bridge. The Clan
Grant Rally is held at the same time
usually on the Saturday before the
12th of August at Nethy Bridge, a
small village five miles south-west of
Grantown-on-Spey.
✍ Secretary: James Rogerson
  Gowanlea, Nethybridge.
  PH25 3DR

ASSYNT GATHERING

Aims & Activities: To organise annual professional Highland Games and sports in the area of Lochinver.
Affiliations: The Scottish Games Association, (page 74).
✍ Secretary: Wilma Mackay
  10 Inverkirkaig, Lochinver.
  IV27 4LF
☎ 01571 844254

CAITHNESS HIGHLAND GAMES (HALKIRK)

Aims & Activities: To organise annual professional Highland Games and sports in the area of Caithness. Only six miles south of Thurso, this small agricultural and slate-quarrying village holds an annual Caithness Games, which are very much older than those held at Thurso (see below) which also call themselves the Caithness Games. The Halkirk Caithness Games are generally held at the end of July in the Recreation Park.
Affiliations: The Scottish Games Association, (page 74).
✍ Secretary: A. S. Budge
  Milton, Halkirk.
  KW12 6XQ
☎ 01847 831666

CAITHNESS HIGHLAND GAMES (THURSO)

Aims & Activities: To organise annual professional Highland Games and sports in the area of Caithness. These Games are held in Thurso, the northernmost town in Caithness, 18 miles north of Wick. These Games were started in the 1970 under the auspices of Lord Thurso and are currently held in early July in the Millbank Park. Like the Games held in Halkirk they call themselves the Caithness Highland Games.
Affiliations: The Scottish Games Association, (page 74).

✍ Chieftain: Lord Thurso
✍ Secretary: Mrs P. Bain, 2 Dale Cottage
  Dale Farm, Halkirk.
  KW12 6UW
☎ 01847 841268

CAMANACHD ASSOCIATION

Founded: 1893.
Aims & Activities: The controlling body in Scotland for the sport of Shinty. To oversee League competitions. To adjudicate on the Rules.
✍ Secretary: Alistair MacIntyre
  Algarve, Badabrie, Banavie,
  Fort William.
  PH33 7LX
☎ 01397 772461

CANNICH SCOTTISH COUNTRY DANCE CLASS

Aims & Activities: See the RSCDS on page 47.
✍ Secretary: Mr E. Geddes
  Burgan, Cannich, by Beauly.
☎ 01456 479435

CLAN FRASER SOCIETY

Aims & Activities: To promote the clan spirit worldwide. To collect and preserve all records concerning the clan history or genealogy. To strengthen overseas links. Social. Annual Gathering.
Membership: Open to those bearing the name Fraser and to members of the septs and those connected by descent, or marriage.
✍ Secretary: Balblair House
  Beauly.
  IV4 7AZ

CLAN MACDONALD

Aims & Activities: To foster clan sentiment. To collect and preserve clan records. To improve overseas links. Historical. Social.

Membership: Open to all bearing the name, or that of one of the septs, or connected with the clan by descent or marriage.

✍ Secretary: Rob Parker
Clan Donald Centre, Armadale, Isle of Skye.
IV45

CLAN MACDONELL OF GLENGARRY

Aims & Activities: To promote the clan spirit internationally. To collect and preserve clan records of historical or genealogical nature. Overseas links. Annual Gathering.

Membership: Open to all bearing the name MacDonell (in its various spellings) originating from the area of Glengarry, or those associated by descent or marriage.

✍ Secretary: Elonbank
Castle Street, Fortrose.

CLAN MACKINTOSH

Aims & Activities: To collect and collate clan genealogical and historical records. To enhance overseas links. Social. Clan Gathering.

Membership: Open to all those bearing the name, or that of one of the septs, or connected with the clan by descent or marriage.

✍ The Chieftain: The Mackintosh of Mackintosh
Moy Hall, Moy IV13 7YQ

CLAN MACLELLAN SOCIETY

Aims & Activities: To promote awareness of the clan history. To collate and preserve records of genealogical or clan interest. To strengthen overseas links.

Membership: Open to anyone bearing the MacLellan name, or those related by marriage or descent.

✍ Secretary: 3 Strath Gardens
Dores IV1 2TT

CLAN MACNICOL

Aims & Activities: To foster the clan spirit around the world. Genealogical. Historical. Overseas links.

Affiliations: Affiliated Societies: Clan MacNicol, NSW, Queensland, Australia. New Zealand.

Membership: Open to anyone of the MacNicol name, or its variants, and those connected by marriage, or descent.

✍ Secretary: Malcolm Nicolson
4 Heatherfield, Penifiler, Portree, Isle of Skye.
IVS1 9NE
☎ 01478 822235

CLAN MUNRO SOCIETY

Founded: 1937.

Aims & Activities: To encourage the clan spirit at home and abroad. To collect and preserve the history and traditions of the clan and its homeland. To preserve the wildlife and foster the culture of the Scottish Highlands. To strengthen overseas links. Charitable.

Publications: Clan Munro Newsletter (annual).

Membership: Open to all bearing the name or connected with it by descent or marriage.

✍ Secretary: Foulis Castle
Evanton.
IV16 9UX

CLAN ROSE

Aims & Activities: To encourage the clan spirit internationally. Overseas links. Genealogical. Historical.

Membership: Open to those with the name Rose, their descendants and those related by marriage.

✍ Officers: Secretary: Miss E. Rose
Kilravock Castle, Croy.
IV1 2PJ

CLAN SHAW SOCIETY

Aims & Activities: To collect and preserve clan records. To encourage overseas links. Historical. Genealogical.
Membership: Open to anyone with the name Shaw, and to those related by descent or marriage.
✍ Secretary: Tordarroch House
  Toredarroch, Farr.
  IV1 2XF

CLAN SUTHERLAND SOCIETY

Aims & Activities: To promote the clan spirit. To strengthen overseas links. Genealogical. Historical. Social. Annual Gathering.
Membership: Open to those with the name Sutherland, or those claiming links by descent or marriage, or closely associated with the area.
✍ Secretary: Dunrobin Castle
  Golspie.
  KW10

DINGWALL COUNTRY DANCE GROUP

Aims & Activities: See the RSCDS on page 47.
✍ Secretary: Mrs G. Simpson
  Tianavaig, 4 Wyndhill Park,
  Beauly.
  IV4 7AR
☎ 01463 782043

DINGWALL HIGHLAND GAMES

Aims & Activities: To organise annual professional Highland Games and sports in the area of Dingwall the capital of Ross and Cromarty, an attractive small Highland town at the foot of the Cromarty Firth. The Games are usually held in mid-July in the Jubilee Park.
Affiliations: The Scottish Games Association, (page 74).
✍ Secretary: A. W. Miller
  15 Old Evanton Road,
  Dingwall.
  IV15 9RA
☎ 01349 862024

DORNOCH HIGHLAND GAMES

Aims & Activities: To organise annual professional Highland Games and sports in the area of Dornoch, the county capital of Sutherland on the north shore of the Dornoch Firth. The Games are usually held before the 12th of August in the Meadows Park.
Affiliations: The Scottish Games Association, (page 74).
✍ Secretary: W. Grant
  Links House, Dornoch.
  IV25 3SD
☎ 01862 810806

DUNBEATH HIGHLAND GAMES

Founded: 1850.
Aims & Activities: To organise annual professional Highland Games and sports in the area of Dunbeath, a small coastal village half-way between Lybster and Helmsdale. This was one of the coastal villages founded by the Duke of Sutherland following the notorious 'Clearances' of the thriving inland townships of Kildonan and Strathnaver. The Games were established in mid-19th century but still maintain a high standard despite the smallness of the community.
Affiliations: The Scottish Games Association, (page 74).
✍ Secretary: Angus Wares
  4 Mey Terrace, Thurso, Caithness.
  KW14 7PE
☎ 01847 893161

DURNESS HIGHLAND GAMES

Aims & Activities: To organise annual professional Highland Games and sports in the area of Durness, a small village in the north-west corner of Sutherland, close to Cape Wrath.

Revived in 1960 the Games are usually held near the end of July in the Shore Park with impressive views of craggy cliffs.

Affiliations: The Scottish Games Association, (page 74).

✍ Secretary: Mrs J. Cordiner
2 Bard Terrace, Durness, Lairg.
IV27 4PS
☎ 01971 511358

GLENURQUHART HIGHLAND GAMES

Aims & Activities: To organise annual amateur Highland Games in the area of Drumnadrochit close to Loch Ness near the spectacular ruins of Glenurquhart Castle. Usually held towards the end of August and include a road race from Inverness.

✍ Secretary: Robert T. MacDonald
Westfeld, Lewiston,
Drumnadrochit.

GRANTOWN-ON-SPEY HIGHLAND GAMES

Aims & Activities: To organise annual professional Highland Games and sports in the area of Grantown-on-Spey, a small, but thriving, market town and agricultural centre, also geared to tourism, 12 miles north of the well-known tourist and ski-centre of Aviemore.

Affiliations: The Scottish Games Association, (page 74).

✍ Secretary: Mrs E. Watt
32 Kylintra Crescent,
Grantown-on-Spey.
PH26 3ES
☎ 01479 873237

HELMSDALE AND DISTRICT HIGHLAND GAMES

Aims & Activities: To organise annual professional Highland Games and sports in the area of Helmsdale, a small village at the mouth of the Helmsdale river, noted for its salmon fishing. This is another of the coastal villages created by the Duke of Sutherland after the notorious Clearances in the early 19th century. Now geared to tourism the Games are held in the latter part of August in the Couper Park.

Affiliations: The Scottish Games Association, (page 74).

✍ Secretary: Mrs F. Sutherland
Fhearnan, Old Caithness Road,
Helmsdale KW8 6JW
☎ 01431 821272

INVERCHARRON HIGHLAND GAMES

Aims & Activities: To organise annual professional Highland Games and sports in the area of Invercharron, situated between Bonar Bridge and Ardgay. Generally held in mid to late September and usually the last of the Highland Games in a truly Highland setting.

Affiliations: The Scottish Games Association, (page 74).

✍ Secretary: Morag Chalmers
Migdale Mill, Bonar Bridge.
IV24 3AR
☎ 01863 766521

INVERGORDON HIGHLAND GAMES

Aims & Activities: To organise annual professional Highland Games and sports in the area of Invergordon a seaside town on the west side of the Cromarty Firth, equidistant from Tain in the north and Dingwall in the south, now well known for its distillery complex. The Games are generally held towards the end of August in the castle grounds.

Affiliations: The Scottish Games Association, (page 74).

✍ Secretary: Mrs Alison Stewart
20 Moss Road, Tain IV19 1NN
☎ 01862 893952

INVERNESS AND DISTRICT BRANCH OF THE ROYAL SCOTTISH COUNTRY DANCE SOCIETY

Aims & Activities: See the RSCDS on page 47.
Membership: 127.
✍ Secretary: Miss I. Whyte
68 Drumossie Avenue, Inverness.
☎ 01463 235384 (home)
☎ 01463 703055 (business)

INVERNESS BURNS CLUB

Founded: 1949.
Aims & Activities: Social. Annual Gathering. To perpetuate the memory of Burns.
Affiliations: The Burns Federation, No. 691.
✍ Secretary: C. D. J. Silver
Inveraray, School Road, Conon Bridge, Dingwall.
IV7 8AE

INVERNESS HIGHLAND GAMES

Aims & Activities: To organise annual amateur Highland Games and sports in the area of Inverness and Beauly. Generally held in the Bucht Park in mid-July.
✍ Secretary: Joan West
10 Priory Court, Beauly.
IV4 7BL
☎ 01463 763040

ISLE OF SKYE BRANCH OF THE ROYAL SCOTTISH COUNTRY DANCE SOCIETY

Aims & Activities: See the RSCDS on page 47.
Membership: 52.
✍ Secretary: Mrs A. Prior
Yign-na-Coille, Duisdale, Isle Ornsay, Isle of Skye.
IV43 8QX

KILMALLIE SCOTTISH COUNTRY DANCE CLUB

Aims & Activities: See the RSCDS on page 47.
✍ Secretary: Mrs J. Cormack
Stroma, Corpach, Fort William.
PH33 7JS
☎ 01397 772286

KILMORACK SCOTTISH COUNTRY DANCE CLASS

Aims & Activities: See the RSCDS on page 47.
✍ Secretary: Mrs J. A. Masheter
Mains of Algas, Beauly.
IV4 7AD
☎ 01453 782423

KINGUSSIE SCOTTISH COUNTRY DANCE CLUB

Aims & Activities: See the RSCDS on page 47.
✍ Secretary: Miss J. Renton
6 Ruthven Court, Kingussie.
PH21 1JD

LOCHABER BRANCH OF THE ROYAL SCOTTISH COUNTRY DANCE SOCIETY

Aims & Activities: See the RSCDS on page 47.
Membership: 24.
✍ Secretary: Mrs S. Mainland
Hill House, Corpach, Fort William.
PH33
☎ 01397 772348

LOCHABER HIGHLAND GAMES

Aims & Activities: To organise annual amateur Highland Games in the area of Lochaber.
✍ Secretary: Ian R. Skinner
4 Pobs Drive, Corpach, Fort William.
PH33 7JP

LOCHCARRON HIGHLAND GAMES

Aims & Activities: To organise annual professional Highland Games and sports in the area of Lochcarron.
Affiliations: The Scottish Games Association, (page 74).
✍ Secretary: Mrs Maureen Brown
15 Sage Terrace, Lochcarron.
IV54 8XQ
☎ 01520 722554

NAIRN HIGHLAND GAMES

Aims & Activities: To organise annual amateur Highland Games in the area of Nairn the attractive small county town and municipal burgh sited on the Moray Firth, 15 miles east of Inverness. Generally held in mid-August.
✍ Secretary: Mrs Eleanor Somerville
4a Grant Street, Nairn.
IV12 4NN

NEWTONMORE HIGHLAND GAMES

Aims & Activities: To organise annual amateur Highland Games in the area of Newtonmore in the Spey Valley beneath the Cairngorms. The Games are usually held in early August at the same time as the Clan Macpherson Gathering.
✍ Secretary: Margaret Geddes
Inistrynich, Newtonmore.
PH20 1AR

SABHAL MOR OSTAIG

Aims & Activities: To teach, promote and help preserve Gaelic language and culture. Residential and short courses in Gaelic are available as well as courses in fiddle, clarsach, whistle/flute, accordion, piping, stepdance, Gaelic song and guitar/piano accompaniment.
Membership: Open to all.
✍ Short courses administrator:

Gavin Parsons
Sabhal Mor Ostaig, by Armadale, Sleat, Skye.
IV44 8RQ
☎ 01471 844373
✆ 01471 844383

SKYE HIGHLAND GAMES

Aims & Activities: To organise annual professional Highland Games and sports in the area of Skye, one of the best known and largest islands of the Inner Hebrides. The Games are usually held in Portree towards the end of August.
Affiliations: The Scottish Games Association, (page 74).
✍ Secretary: A. Stewart
Campbell, Stewart & MacLennan, Wentworth Street, Isle of Skye.
IV51
☎ 01478 612316

STRATHPEFFER BURNS CLUB

Founded: 1920.
Aims & Activities: Social. To promote interest in the works of Robert Burns. Annual Gathering.
Affiliations: The Burns Federation, No. 723.
✍ Secretary: Jock Watt
Burnhill, Strathpeffer.
IV14 9DH

STRATHPEFFER HIGHLAND GAMES

Founded: 1881.
Aims & Activities: To organise annual professional Highland Games and sports in the area of Strathpeffer, a Victorian Spa still geared to tourism amongst magnificent Highland scenery five miles west of Dingwall. The Games are held in the grounds of Leod Castle prior to the 12th of August to aviod a clash of interests with the opening of the shooting season.

Affiliations: The Scottish Games Association, (page 74).
✍ Secretary: George R. Spark
Glenesk, Strathpeffer.
IV14 9AT
☎ 01997 421348

TAIN HIGHLAND GAMES

Aims & Activities: To organise annual professional Highland Games and sports in the area of Tain.
Affiliations: The Scottish Games Association, (page 74).
✍ Secretary: Fiona Thomson
1a Stafford Street, Tain.
TV19 1LZ
☎ 01862 503067

INVERCLYDE

GOUROCK BURNS CLUB

Founded: 1887.
Aims & Activities: Social. To promote the study of Scots literature and the works of Robert Burns.
Affiliations: The Burns Federation, No. 430.
✍ Secretary: James M. Fisher
1, Park Avenue, Greenock.
PA16 7QX

GOUROCK JOLLY BEGGARS BURNS CLUB

Founded: 1893.
Aims & Activities: Social. Educational. Charitable. Annual gathering.
Affiliations: The Burns Federation, No. 59.
✍ President: Mr John S. Bruce
71 Albert Road. Gourock.
PA19 1NJ

GREENOCK BURNS CLUB

Founded: 1801.
Aims & Activities: Social. To foster

interest in the work of Robert Burns. Annual Gathering.
Affiliations: The Burns Federation, No. 21.
✍ Secretary: Mr D. Salmon
27 Ardgowan Square, Greenock.
PA16 8NJ

KILBARCHAN U. C. BURNS CLUB

Founded: 1958.
Aims & Activities: Social. Annual Gathering.
Affiliations: The Burns Federation, No. 1034.
✍ Secretary: Ian M. Campbell
18 Park View, Kilbarchan.
PA10 2LW

LANARKSHIRE, NORTH

AIRDRIE BURNS CLUB

Founded: 1884.
Aims & Activities: To foster interest in Robert Burns and Scottish literature. Annual gathering. Social.
Affiliations: The Burns Federation, No. 20.
✍ Secretary: Mr Alex J. Christie
18 Lingley Avenue, Airdrie.
ML6 9JR

ALLANTON JOLLY BEGGARS BURNS CLUB

Founded: 1957.
Aims & Activities: Social. Annual Gathering.
Affiliations: The Burns Federation, No. 809.
✍ Secretary: Mrs Helen Waddell
56 Allershaw Tower, Wishaw.
ML2 0LP

CUMBERNAULD AND DISTRICT BURNS CLUB

Founded: 1943.
Aims & Activities: Social. To perpetuate the memory of Robert Burns.
Affiliations: The Burns Federation, No. 581.
✍ Secretary: Chic Scott
159 Birch Road, Abronhill,
Cumbernauld.
G67 3PF

LANARKSHIRE ASSOCIATION OF BURNS CLUBS

Founded: 1924.
Aims & Activities: Co-ordination of activities.
Affiliations: The Burns Federation, No. 578.
✍ Secretary: Mrs Anne Pickering
9 Dyfrigg Street, Dykehead,
Shotts.
ML7 4DO

MONKLANDS BRANCH OF THE ROYAL SCOTTISH COUNTRY DANCE SOCIETY

Aims & Activities: See the RSCDS on page 47.
✍ Secretary: Mrs J. Gardner
2 Redwood Road, Holytown,
Motherwell, M.
ML1 4PG
☎ 01698 832449 (home)
☎ 01698 860603 (business)

MOTHERWELL UNITED SERVICES BURNS CLUB

Founded: 1934.
Aims & Activities: Social. Annual Gathering. To promote interest in the work of Robert Burns.
Affiliations: The Burns Federation, No. 494.
✍ Secretary: Archie Cowie
21 Mill Road, Hamilton.
ML3 8AA

RAVENSCRAIG BURNS CLUB

Aims & Activities: Social. Annual Gathering.
Affiliations: The Burns Federation, No. 1081.
✍ Secretary: Thomas Brennan
14 Hillside Place, Newarthill,
Motherwell.
ML1 5DH

SALSBURGH BURNS CLUB

Founded: 1967.
Aims & Activities: Social. Annual Gathering.
Affiliations: The Burns Federation, No. 973.
✍ Secretary: Mrs M. McDonald
147a Main Street, Salsburgh,
Shotts.
ML7 4LR

SHOTTS HIGHLAND GAMES

Aims & Activities: To organise annual amateur Highland Games in the area of Shotts six miles north of Wishaw. Generally held in early June.
✍ Secretary: Iain J. Close
3 Parkside Road, Dykehead,
Shotts.
ML7 4AT

THIRTY-SEVEN BURNS CLUB

Founded: 1957.
Aims & Activities: Social. Annual Gathering. To commemorate the work of Robert Burns.
Affiliations: The Burns Federation, No. 810.
✍ Secretary: Jack Gardner
12 Clyde Drive, Torbothie, Shotts.
ML7 5LY

LANARKSHIRE, SOUTH

A' THE AIRTS BURNS CLUB

Aims & Activities: Social. Annual dinner.
Affiliations: The Burns Federation, No. 907.
✍ Secretary: Mr D. Gibb
157 Strathaven Road,
Stonehouse.

CAMERON CLAN

Aims & Activities: To collect and preserve clan records, both historical and genealogical, and to build up the clan archives. To encourage overseas.
Membership: Open to members of the Cameron clan and its various septs, also to those connected by descent or marriage.
✍ Secretary: Mrs M. S. Cameron
5 Winbourne Crescent, Hamilton.
ML3 9BD

CLAN CARMICHAEL SOCIETY

Aims & Activities: To encourage interest in the clan records, both genealogical and historical.
Membership: Open to those bearing the name Carmichael, or variants of it, and those related by marriage or descent.
✍ The Clan Secretary:
Carmichael House
Biggar ML12

CLAN CRANSTOUN

Aims & Activities: To encourage overseas links. To collect clan records. Social.
Membership: Open to those of the name Cranstoun and its derivatives, or those connected with the clan.
✍ Secretary: D. A. S. Cranstoun
Corehouse, Lanark.
ML11 9TQ

CLAN LOCKHART SOCIETY

Aims & Activities: To collect and preserve clan historical and genealogical records. To strengthen overseas links.
Membership: Open to those with the name Lockhart, or those connected by marriage or descent.
✍ The Secretary: The Estates Office
Carnwath.
ML11 8JY

HAMILTON AND CLYDESDALE BRANCH OF THE ROYAL SCOTTISH COUNTRY DANCE SOCIETY

Aims & Activities: See the RSCDS on page 47.
Membership: 98.
✍ Secretary: Marie Husbands
51 Hamilton Road, Strathaven.
ML10 6JA
☎ 01357 20580

HAMILTON BURNS CLUB

Founded: 1877.
Aims & Activities: Social. Educational. Charitable. To encourage interest in the work of Robert Burns.
Affiliations: The Burns Federation, No. 152.
✍ Secretary: Dr S. S. I Parker
25 Burnside Place, Larkhall.
ML9 8EQ

LANARK BRANCH OF THE ROYAL SCOTTISH COUNTRY DANCE SOCIETY

Aims & Activities: See the RSCDS on page 47.
Membership: 61.
✍ Secretary: Mrs M. Longair
Cawnpore, Bowling Green Road,
Waterloo Road, Lanark.
ML11 7QJ
☎ 01555 664543

LARKHALL BURNS CLUB

Founded: 1963.

Aims & Activities: Social. Annual Gathering. To perpetuate the memory of Burns.

Affiliations: The Burns Federation, No. 961.

✍ Secretary: Mrs Irene Kerr
16 John Street, Larkhall.

M|DLOTHIAN

BALERNO BURNS CLUB

Founded: 1881.

Aims & Activities: To promote the works of Robert Burns.

Affiliations: The Burns Federation, No. 340.

✍ Secretary: Mr Ian P. Campbell
18 Crosswood Crescent, Balerno.
EH14 7HG

CLAN BORTHWICK

Aims & Activities: To collect genealogical information and promote overseas links.

Affiliations: Clan Borthwick Association, Maine, USA.

Membership: Open to members of the Borthwick clan and those bearing that name, or variants of it.

✍ Chieftain: The Lord Borthwick
Crookston, Heriot EH38 5YE

NEWTON LADS BURNS CLUB, MIDLOTHIAN

Founded: 1968.

Aims & Activities: Social and to encourage an interest in the works of Robert Burns.

Affiliations: The Burns Federation, No. 1025.

✍ Secretary: James Oswald Jr.
32 Clarinda Terrace, Kirk Brae, Liberton, Edinburgh.
EH16 6XW

PENICUIK SCOTTISH COUNTRY DANCE CLUB

Aims & Activities: See the RSCDS on page 47

✍ Secretary: Mrs S. Young
Dellburn, 15 Broomhill Road, Penicuik.
EH25 9EE

MORAY

CLAN BRODIE SOCIETY

Aims & Activities: To encourage overseas links. To collect and preserve clan records, both historical and genealogical in the clan archives. To improve overseas links. Annual Gathering.

Affiliations: Associated Societies: Clan Brodie, Texas.

Membership: Open to those with the name Brodie and its variants, also to those related by marriage or descent.

✍ Secretary: Brodie Castle
Forres.
IV36 0TE

DUFFTOWN HIGHLAND GAMES

Aims & Activities: To organise annual professional Highland Games and sports in the area of Dufftown, 'the Whisky Capital of the Highlands'. The Games are usually held in late July.

Affiliations: The Scottish Games Association, (page 74).

✍ Secretary: Arthur Brown
Ashville, Church Street, Dufftown.
AB55 4AR
☎ 01340 820342

ELGIN BURNS CLUB

Founded: 1901.

Aims & Activities: Social and to stimulate interest in Robert Burns and his works.

Affiliations: The Burns Federation, No. 149.

✍ Secretary: Mr W. A. D. Macphail C. A., Commerce House, South St, Elgin. IV30 1JE

FOCHABERS BURNS CLUB

Aims & Activities: Annual Gathering. *Affiliations:* The Burns Federation, No. 1066.

✍ Secretary: William K. Barclay Tor-Na-Bar, Spey Bay Road, Fochabers, IV. 32 7PQ

FORRES BRANCH OF THE ROYAL SCOTTISH COUNTRY DANCE SOCIETY

Aims & Activities: See the RSCDS on page 47. *Membership:* 81.

✍ Secretary: Mrs C. Grant 15 St Leonard's Drive, Forres. IV36 0GD

☎ 01309 675187

FORRES HIGHLAND GAMES

Aims & Activities: To organise annual amateur Highland Games in the area of Forres. Generally held in early July.

✍ Secretary: Michael W. Scott 7 Fleurs Road, Forres. IV36 0LY

HOUSE OF ALTYRE

Aims & Activities: To encourage overseas links. To collect and preserve clan records of historical and genealogical interest. Annual Gathering. *Membership:* Open to those bearing the name Altyre, in its various spellings, and those connected by descent or marriage.

✍ Secretary: House of Altyre Forres. IV36 0SH

ST GILES BURNS CLUB, ELGIN

Founded: 1924.

Aims & Activities: To encourage interest in the works of Robert Burns. Social.

Affiliations: The Burns Federation, No. 470.

✍ Secretary: George S. Peterkin 24 Pansport Road, Elgin. IV30 1HD

PERTH AND KINROSS

ATHOLL AND BREADALBANE HIGHLAND GAMES

Aims & Activities: To organise annual professional Highland Games and athletic sports in the area of Aberfeldy and district.

Affiliations: The Scottish Games Association, (page 74).

✍ Secretary: G. Grant Bank of Scotland, Bank Street, Aberfeldy.

☎ 01887 820321

BALQUHIDDER, LOCHEARNHEAD AND STRATHYRE HIGHLAND GAMES

Aims & Activities: To organise annual professional Highland Games and sports in the area of Lochearnhead.

Affiliations: The Scottish Games Association, (page 74).

✍ Secretary: Mrs C. McNally 2 Strathearn View, Millar Street, Crieff. PH7 3AJ

☎ 01764 654519

BIRNAM HIGHLAND GAMES

Founded: 1865.

Aims & Activities: To organise annual professional Highland Games and sports in the area of Birnam and Dunkeld, usually in late August.

Affiliations: The Scottish Games Association, (page 74).
✍ Secretary: Martin Brown
  25 Stell Park Road, Birnam,
  Dunkeld.
  PH8 0QA
☎ 01350 727768

BLACKFORD HIGHLAND GAMES

Aims & Activities: To organise annual professional Highland Games and sports in the area of Blackford, about nine miles east of Dunblane.
Affiliations: The Scottish Games Association, (page 74).
✍ Secretary: Peter Dobbie
  Rattray House, Blackford.
  PH4 1QA
☎ 01764 692502

BLAIRGOWRIE HIGHLAND GAMES

Aims & Activities: To organise annual professional Highland Games and sports in the area of Blairgowrie. Generally held on the first Sunday after the Braemar Gathering.
Affiliations: The Scottish Games Association, (page 74).
✍ Secretary: Mrs A. D. Mitchell
  Kingseat, Bridge of Cally,
  Blairgowrie.
  PH10 7JW

CLAN CRICHTON

Aims & Activities: To improve overseas links. To collect and preserve genealogical and historical records. Social.
Membership: Open to anyone named Crichton, and those related by descent or marriage.
✍ Secretary: Charles Crichton
  Monzie, Perth.

CLAN DRUMMOND

Aims & Activities: To encourage the clan spirit. To record the clan history. Genealogical. Overseas links.
Membership: Membership is open to anyone bearing the name Drummond and to those connected by marriage or descent and interested in the aims.
✍ Chieftain: The Earl of Perth
  Stobhall, Perth.

CLAN DUNBAR

Aims & Activities: To encourage the clan spirit worldwide. To collect and collate the clan records, both genealogical and historical. To promote overseas links.
Affiliations: Clan Dunbar Society of Nova Scotia.
Membership: Open to those with the name Dunbar, or related by marriage or descent.
✍ Secretary: A. Dunbar
  Pitgaveny, Elgin, Moray.

CLAN HALDANE

Aims & Activities: To preserve the clan records, both historical and genealogical. To encourage overseas links.
Membership: Open to those named Haldane, in variant spellings, and to those related by marriage and descent.
✍ Secretary: A. N. C. Haldane of
  Gleneagles
  Auchterarder.
  PH3

CLAN HAY SOCIETY

Founded: 1951.
Aims & Activities: To promote clan spirit worldwide. To foster interest in Scotland, its history and its prosperity. To research and preserve the clan history and genealogy and to publish material on these subjects. To acquire former Hay lands. To strengthen overseas links.

Membership: Open to all connected with the clan or its septs by descent or marriage.

✍ Chief: The Earl of Errol; Patron: The Marquis of Tweeddale.

✍ Commissioner: Falcon Stone
7 Orchard Park, Crieff.
PH7 3ES

CLAN MACNAB

Founded: 1903.

Aims & Activities: To collect and preserve material on the history of the clan. To foster clan sentiments. To cooperate with organisations with similar aims. To encourage overseas links. To hold an annual Gathering.

Affiliations: Clan MacNab Society of California.

Publications: Annual newsletter.

Membership: Open to all of the name (in any of its spellings) or connected with the clan or its septs (Abbot, Abbotson, Dewar, Gilfillan, Macandeoir) by descent or marriage.

✍ Information officer
The Tourist Information Centre,
Main Street, Killin.
FK21

CLAN MONCRIEFFE SOCIETY

Aims & Activities: To collect and preserve records of the clan history and genealogy. To strengthen overseas links.

Membership: Open to those named Moncrieffe (in its varied spellings) and those related by descent or marriage.

✍ Secretary: Easter Moncrieffe
Perth and Kinross.

CLAN RATTRAY SOCIETY

Aims & Activities: Social. Historical. Genealogical. Overseas links.

Membership: Open to those with the name Rattray and close connections by marriage or descent, or with strong connections to the area.

✍ Secretary: Craighall Castle
Rattray, Blairgowrie.
PH10 7JB

CRIEFF HIGHLAND GAMES

Aims & Activities: To organise annual professional Highland Games and sports in the area of Crieff.

Affiliations: The Scottish Games Association, (page 74).

✍ Secretary: Andrew Rettie
24 Florence Place, Perth.
PH1 5BH
☎ 01738 627782

GREENLOANING BURNS CLUB

Founded: 1889.

Aims & Activities: To foster knowledge and understanding of Robert Burns, his life and poetry. Social. Annual gathering.

Affiliations: The Burns Federation, No. 116.

✍ Secretary: Mr R. L. Muir
9 Gentle Croft, Braco, Dunblane.
FK15 9PN

KENMORE HIGHLAND GAMES

Aims & Activities: To organise annual professional Highland Games and sports in the area of Kenmore at the eastern end of Loch Tay. These small Highland Games in a delightful setting are usually held in the evening.

Affiliations: The Scottish Games Association, (page 74).

✍ Secretary: Mrs A. Garnett
MacBeth's Cottage, Fortingall,
Aberfeldy.
PH15 2LL
☎ 01887 830486

KINROSS JOLLY BEGGARS CLUB

Founded: 1889.

Aims & Activities: Annual Gathering.

Social. Educational. Charitable. To perpetuate the memory of Robert Burns.
Affiliations: The Burns Federation, No. 627.
✍ Secretary: Gordon Y. George 'Ythan', 14 Muirpark Road, Kinross.
KY13 7AT

PERTH AND PERTHSHIRE BRANCH OF THE ROYAL SCOTTISH COUNTRY DANCE SOCIETY

Aims & Activities: See the RSCDS on page 47.
Membership: 217.
✍ Secretary: Mrs C. Munro 9 Unity Crescent, Perth.
PH1 2BI
☎ 01738 628349 (home)
☎ 01738 620071 (business)

PERTH BURNS CLUB

Founded: 1873.
Aims & Activities: Social. Annual Gathering. To encourage appreciation of the life and poetry of Robert Burns.
Affiliations: The Burns Federation, No. 26.
✍ Secretary: Mr Donald M. Paton 75 Needless Road, Perth.
PH2 0LD

PERTH HIGHLAND GAMES

Aims & Activities: To organise annual professional Highland Games and sports in the area of Perth. These Games are customarily held on the South Inch around mid-August.
Affiliations: The Scottish Games Association, (page 74).
✍ Secretary: Andrew Rettie 24 Florence Place, Perth.
PH1 5BH

PITLOCHRY HIGHLAND GAMES

Aims & Activities: To organise annual professional Highland Games and sports in the area of Pitlochry and usually in September amongst the last of the Games.
Affiliations: The Scottish Games Association, (page 74).
✍ Secretary: F. Shepherd 16 Braeside Road, Ballinluig.
☎ 01796 482427

SCOTS LANGUAGE RESOURCE CENTRE

Aims & Activities: To further study of the Scots language.
Affiliations: The Burns Federation, No. 1118.
✍ Secretary: John M. Law Blackford House, Blackford.
PH4 1QP

SCOTTISH GAMES ASSOCIATION

Aims & Activities: The official body organising over 70 professional Highland Games and Border Common Ridings and Festivals, also sports meetings in Scotland and over the Border in Northumberland and Cumbria, to which many overseas Highland Games are also affiliated.
✍ President: A Webster 5 Jeanfield Crescent, Forfar, DD8 1JR; Secretary: Andrew Rettie, 24 Florence Place, Perth.
PH1 5BH
✍ Treasurer: Margaret Gallagher 7 Aitchison Drive, Larbert.
FK5 4PB
☎ 01324 558519

SCOTTISH TARTANS AUTHORITY

Founded: 1996.
Aims & Activities: To study, record, stimulate research and educate the public about the origins, hstory and devlopment of the Scottish tartans. To develop and manage interpretative

museums, exhibitions, libraries, lectures and encourage publications, etc. To encourage a spirit of commitment in others towards these objects.

✍ J & H Mitchell
W. S., Secretaries to The Scottish Tartans Authority, Dept. STA, 51 Atholl Road, Pitlochry.
PH16 5BU

SCOTTISH TARTANS SOCIETY

Founded: 1963.

Aims & Activities: To maintain a worldwide membership with a Scottish tartan museum. To create and run the register of all publicly known tartans and encourage research into Highland dress and tartans. Authentication and accreditation of tartans. Design and research. Clan history certificates. Academic research. Heritage fellowship award.

Membership: Individual and corporate membership available.

✍ Executive Chairman: Dr Gordon Teall of Teallach
✍ Tartan administrators: Keith and Elizabeth Lumsden
Hall of Records, Port-na-Craig Road, Pitlochry.
PH16 5ND
☎ 01796 474079 or 01350 728849

STRATHEARN BURNS CLUB

Founded: 1889.

Aims & Activities: To foster study and appreciation of the literature and poetry of Robert Burns. Social. Annual Gathering.

Affiliations: The Burns Federation, No. 42.

✍ Secretary: Mr Michael Kidd
Brae Cottage, Ardvreck, Crieff.
PH7 4EX

RENFREWSHIRE

ALAMO BURNS CLUB

Founded: 1973.

Aims & Activities: Social. Annual Gathering. To perpetuate the memory of Robert Burns.

Affiliations: The Burns Federation, No. 944.

✍ Secretary: James Fisher
Flat 1/1, 9 Inchinnan Road, Paisley.

CLAN LINDSAY SOCIETY

Founded: 1897.

Aims & Activities: To promote overseas links. Annual Gathering. Social.

Publications: News bulletin (occasional).

Membership: Open to all bearing the name or connected with it by descent or marriage. To collect and preserve records of the Lindsays.

✍ President: Earl of Crawford & Balcarres; Secretary: 112 Corsebar Road
Paisley PA2 9PY

CLAN MACKAY SOCIETY

Founded: 1806.

Aims & Activities: Overseas links. Historical. Social.

Affiliations: Clan Mackay Association of Canada.

Membership: Open to members of the clan and its septs, also to those connected by marriage or descent.

✍ Secretary: Norman MacKay
62 Kings Park Ave, Glasgow G4

CLAN MACMILLAN CENTRE DANCE GROUP

Aims & Activities: See the RSCDS on page 47.

✍ Secretary: Mr Peter MacMillan
Finlaystone, Langbank.
PA14 6TJ

FORT MATILDA BURNS CLUB

Founded: 1934.
Aims & Activities: Social. Annual gathering. To perpetuate the memory of Robert Burns.
Affiliations: The Burns Federation, No. 576.
✍ Secretary: S. Austin
46 Newark Street, Greenock.
PA16 7UN

PAISLEY BURNS CLUB

Founded: 1805.
Aims & Activities: To foster study of the works of Robert Burns. Educational. Historical. Social.
Affiliations: The Burns Federation, No. 48.
✍ Secretary: Mr Alan M. L. Mill
Flat 12, Park View, Park Road, Paisley.
PA2 6EQ

PAISLEY MONDAY CLASS

Aims & Activities: See the RSCDS on page 47.
✍ Secretary: Mr G. Lawson
17 Golf Drive, Paisley.
PA1 3LA
☎ 0141 889 9860

RENFREWSHIRE ASSOCIATION OF BURNS CLUBS

Founded: 1929.
Affiliations: The Burns Federation, No. 472.
✍ Secretary: Andrew McKee
27 Balfron Road, Paisley.

RENFREWSHIRE WEST BRANCH OF THE ROYAL SCOTTISH COUNTRY DANCE SOCIETY

Aims & Activities: See the RSCDS on page 47.
Membership: 134.
✍ Secretary: Mrs S. Miller

35 Wallace Avenue, Bishopton.
PA7 5ER
☎ 01505 863685

TRUSTY FIERES, ERSKINE

Founded: 1968.
Aims & Activities: Social. Annual Gathering.
Affiliations: The Burns Federation, No. 1065.
✍ Secretary: Mrs J. W. Richardson
33 Churchill Drive, Bishopton.
PA7 5HF

SCOTTISH BORDERS

BERWICK-UPON-TWEED BRANCH OF THE ROYAL SCOTTISH COUNTRY DANCE SOCIETY

Aims & Activities: See the RSCDS on page 47.
Membership: 42.
✍ Secretary: Miss J. Gray
35 Union Park Road, Tweedmouth, Berwick-upon-Tweed.
TD15 2HY

CHIRNSIDE GAMES

Aims & Activities: To organise annual professional Games and sports in the area of Chirnside in Berwickshire.
Affiliations: The Scottish Games Association, (page 74).
✍ Secretary: Henry Gray
Westerlea, Chirnside.
TD11 3UQ
☎ 01890 818204

CLAN ELLIOTT SOCIETY

Aims & Activities: To promote the clan spirit worldwide. To gather together and to preserve clan records. Genealogical. Historical. To strengthen overseas links. Annual Gathering.

Membership: Open to any bearing the name Elliott, or connected by descent or marriage.

✍ Secretary: Redheugh
Newcastleton.
TD9 0SB

CLAN KERR

Aims & Activities: To collect and preserve historical and genealogical clan records. To promote the clan spirit and foster overseas links. Social.

Membership: Open to those bearing the name Kerr (or variants of it) and those related by marriage or descent.

✍ Chieftain: The Marquis of
Lothian
Ferniehirst Castle, Jedburgh.
TD8

CLAN MAR

Aims & Activities: To preserve historical and genealogical records of the clan. To improve overseas links.

Membership: Open to those bearing the name Mar, or variants of it, and those connected by marriage or descent.

✍ Secretary: David Lumsden of
Cushie
Leithen Lodge, Innerleithen.
EH44 6NW

CLAN SCOTT

Aims & Activities: To promote the clan spirit worldwide and foster overseas ties. To preserve and collate the clan genealogical and historical records. Social. Annual gathering.

Membership: Open to all bearing the name or connected by marriage or descent.

✍ Chieftain: The Duke of
Buccleuch
Bowhill, Selkirk.
TD7 5ET

COLDSTREAM BURNS CLUB

Aims & Activities: Social and to perpetuate the memory of Burns. Annual Dinner.

Affiliations: The Burns Federation, No. 839.

✍ John A. Fulton
B. Ed., 28 High Street,
Coldstream.
TD12 4AG

DUNS AND DISTRICT BRANCH OF THE ROYAL SCOTTISH COUNTRY DANCE SOCIETY

Aims & Activities: See the RSCDS on page 47.

Membership: 121.

✍ Secretary: Mrs S. Sergeant
Holmford, Victoria Road,
Eyemouth.
TD14 5JD
☎ 01890 751217

DUNS BURNS CLUB

Founded: 1952.

Aims & Activities: Social. To encourage a greater knowledge and appreciation of Robert Burns and his work.

Affiliations: The Burns Federation, No. 1026.

✍ Secretary: Murray J. Henderson
16 Gourlay's Wynd, Duns.
TD11 3DZ

EYEMOUTH CLACHAN BURNS CLUB

Founded: 1948.

Aims & Activities: Social. Annual meeting. To promote greater knowledge of the poetry of Robert Burns.

Affiliations: The Burns Federation, No. 998.

✍ Secretary: Thomas Wilson
5A Paxton Terrace, Eyemouth.

GALASHIELS BURNS CLUB

Founded: 1908.
Aims & Activities: Social. To perpetuate the memory of Robert Burns.
Affiliations: The Burns Federation, No. 187.
✍ Secretary: Mr Alexander E. Hogg
Redcroft, 7 Glenfield Road East, Galashiels.
TD1 2AW

HAIG FAMILY

Aims & Activities: To promote family links around the world. To collect and preserve genealogical and historical records. Social.
Membership: Open to all those with the name Haig, or connected by descent or marriage.
✍ Earl Haig
Bemersyde, Melrose.
TD6 9DF

HAWICK BURNS CLUB

Founded: 1878.
Aims & Activities: Social. Educational. To promote interest in the work of Robert Burns.
Affiliations: The Burns Federation, No. 239.
✍ Secretary: Mr M. T. Hogg
Albert Bridge, Hawick.

HAWICK COMMON RIDING

Aims & Activities: To organise an annual riding of the Marches and beating of the town boundaries to commemorate a famous victory over the English shortly after Flodden, when the young men of the town routed a much superior English force led by the Bishop of Durham. Like most of the Border Common Ridings, this attracts numerous spectators and overseas visitors with connections to the area. The festivities include professional athletics.

Affiliations: The Scottish Games Association, (page 74).
✍ Secretary: Alan Scott
6 Mansfield Crescent, Hawick.
TD9 8AQ

JEDBURGH BURNS CLUB

Founded: 1853.
Aims & Activities: Social. Educational. To foster interest in the literature of Robert Burns. Annual gathering.
Affiliations: The Burns Federation, No. 96.
✍ Secretary: Mr George Jeffrey
18 Hatrigge Road, Jedburgh.
TD8 6JF

JEDBURGH COMMON RIDING

Aims & Activities: The town is virtually closed and all shops boarded up while the annual 'Uppies and Doonies' ball game takes place with one half of town playing against the other. This commemorates the freeing of the town from English occupation when the heads of Englishmen were used as footballs. The Riding of the Marches and professional athletics accompany these annual celebrations which attract numerous overseas visitors with Border connections.
Affiliations: The Scottish Games Association, (page 74).
✍ Secretary: Allan Ferguson
14 Athol Court, Jedburgh.
TD8 6BQ
☎ 01835 863677

KELSO BURNS CLUB

Founded: 1872.
Aims & Activities: Social. To foster interest in Scottish literature and the poetry of Robert Burns.
Affiliations: The Burns Federation, No. 784.
✍ Secretary: Robert Donaldson
17 Dyers Court, Kelso.
TD5 7NQ

MOREBATTLE GAMES

Aims & Activities: To organise annual professional Games and sports in the area of Morebattle.

Affiliations: The Scottish Games Association, (page 74).

✍ Secretary: E. B. Young
30 Mainsfield Avenue, Morebattle, Kelso.
TD5 8QP

☎ 01573 440346

OXTON GAMES

Aims & Activities: To organise annual professional Games and sports in the area of Oxton.

Affiliations: The Scottish Games Association, (page 74).

✍ Secretary: Marion Young
Rosebank, Oxton, Lauder.
TD2 6PP

☎ 01578 750301

OXTON SCOTTISH COUNTRY DANCERS

Aims & Activities: See the RSCDS on page 47.

✍ Secretary: Mrs Irene Gilchrist
Helmsdale, Oxton, Lauder.
TD2 6PH

ROXBURGH, SELKIRK AND PEEBLES BRANCH OF THE ROYAL SCOTTISH COUNTRY DANCE SOCIETY

Aims & Activities: See the RSCDS on page 47.

Membership: 132.

✍ Secretary: Mrs A. Mitchinson
28 Kilncroft, Selkirk.
TD7 5AQ

☎ 01750 20598 (home)

☎ 01896 754333, ext: 1016 (business)

ROYAL BURGH OF PEEBLES HIGHLAND GAMES ASSOCIATION

Aims & Activities: To organise annual amateur Highland Games and sports in the area of Peebles.

✍ Secretary: W. Williamson
3 Caledonian Cottages, Peebles.
EH45 9DW

SELKIRK GAMES

Aims & Activities: To organise annual professional Games and sports in the area of Selkirk, combined with the annual Common Riding of the Marches.

Affiliations: The Scottish Games Association, (page 74).

✍ Secretary: A Douglas
34 Roberts Avenue, Selkirk.

ST RONAN'S GAMES

Aims & Activities: To organise annual professional Games and sports in the area of Innerleithen.

Affiliations: The Scottish Games Association, (page 74).

✍ Secretary: J. D. Patterson
10 Princes Street, Innerleithen.
EH44 6JT

☎ 01896 830197

WALKERBURN GAMES

Aims & Activities: To organise annual professional Games and sports in the area of Walkerburn.

Affiliations: The Scottish Games Association, (page 74).

✍ Secretary: Colin Kerr
75 Tweedholm Avenue,
Walkerburn.
EH43 6AP

☎ 01896 870670

WHITEADDER BURNS CLUB

Founded: 1967.

Aims & Activities: Social. Annual din-

79

ner. To promote a greater knowledge of the work of Robert Burns.
Affiliations: The Burns Federation, No. 1003.
✍ Secretary: J. C. Gardiner
26 The Meadows,
Berwick-upon-Tweed.
TD15 1NY

STIRLING

ABBEY CRAIG BURNS CLUB

Founded: 1935.
Aims & Activities: Social. Annual Gathering. To promote the study of the works of Burns.
Affiliations: The Burns Federation, No. 543.
✍ Secretary: I. B. Kennedy
53 Castle Road, Stirling.
FK9 4JE

BLANE VALLEY BURNS CLUB

Aims & Activities: Annual dinner. Social.
Affiliations: The Burns Federation, No. 1022.
✍ Secretary: Mr B. S. Crofts
43 Southview Drive, Bearsden,
Glasgow.
G61 4HG

CALLANDER BURNS CLUB

Founded: 1887.
Aims & Activities: Social. Educational. To encourage study of Scottish literature and the work of Robert Burns.
Affiliations: The Burns Federation, No. 4.
✍ Secretary: Mr Ron Buchanan
Riverside Inn, Leny Road,
Callander.
FK17 8BA

CLAN GALBRAITH SOCIETY

Aims & Activities: To further the clan spirit. To collect and preserve clan records. Genealogical. Historical. Overseas links.
Membership: Open to those with the name Galbraith, or connected by descent or marriage.
✍ Secretary: Culcreuch Castle
Fintry.
G63 0LW

CLAN LEASK SOCIETY

Aims & Activities: Historical. Genealogical. To strengthen overseas links.
Membership: Open to those of the name Leask or its variants and those related by marriage or descent.
✍ Secretary: 9 Abercromby Place,
Stirling.
FK8 1XG

DUNBLANE BURNS CLUB

Founded: 1923.
Aims & Activities: Social. Annual Gathering. To perpetuate the memory of Robert Burns.
Affiliations: The Burns Federation, No. 503.
✍ Secretary: Mrs Mary Betts
48 Strathmore Avenue, Dunblane.
FK15 9HX

OLD MANOR BURNS CLUB

Aims & Activities: Social. To erncourage interest in the works of Burns. Annual Dinner.
Affiliations: The Burns Federation, No. 923.
✍ Secretary: John W. Morgan
Prospect Place, 21 Claremont Drive, Bridge of Allan.
FK9 4EE

SCOTTISH OFFICIAL HIGHLAND DANCING ASSOCIATION

Founded: 1947.

Aims & Activities: To organise and approve Highland Dancing Competitions.

Affiliations: Victoria Scottish Union, Australia; Stockholm Caledonian Dance Circle, Sweden; Highland & National Dancers of Australia, Victoria, Australia.

✍ President: Alex McGuire
240 Braes View, Denny.
FK6 5NF
☎ 01324 824360
✍ Secretary: Shirley-Ann Mitchell
18 Findowrie Place, Dundee.
☎ 01382 508969

ST RINGANS BURNS CLUB

Aims & Activities: Educational. To promote interest in the works of Robert Burns. Social. Annual Gathering.

Affiliations: The Burns Federation, No. 399.

✍ Secretary: F. Agnew
2 Murrayshall Road, St Ninians, Stirling.

STIRLING BURNS CLUB

Founded: 1886.

Aims & Activities: Educational. Charitable. To foster interest in the literature of Robert Burns. Annual gathering.

Affiliations: The Burns Federation, No. 50.

✍ Secretary: Mr Alexander C. Tennant
Hill & Robb, Solicitors, 3 Pitt Terrace, Stirling.
FK8 8EY

STIRLING CASTLE SCOTTISH COUNTRY DANCE GROUP

Aims & Activities: See the RSCDS on page 47.

✍ Secretary: Mrs A. M. Taylor

11 Dalmorglen Park, Stirling.
FK7 9JL
☎ 01786 475329

STIRLING, CLACKMANNAN AND WEST PERTHSHIRE BURNS CLUB

Aims & Activities: Annual Dinner. To promote interest in the works of Burns.

Affiliations: The Burns Federation, No. 824.

✍ Secretary: Brian S. Crofts
43 Southview Drive, Bearsden, Glasgow.
G61 4HG

STIRLING HIGHLAND GAMES

Aims & Activities: To organise annual professional Highland Games and sports in the area of Stirling.

Affiliations: The Scottish Games Association, (page 74).

✍ Secretary: M. Kaney
1 Sheriffmuirlands Road, Causewayhead, Stirling.
FK9 5EF
☎ 01786 464880

STIRLINGSHIRE BRANCH OF THE ROYAL SCOTTISH COUNTRY DANCE SOCIETY.

Aims & Activities: See the RSCDS on page 47.

Membership: 130.

✍ Secretary: Mr J. Walker
12 Avonlea Drive, Polmont, Falkirk.
☎ 01324 711466

STIRLINGSHIRE EAST BRANCH OF THE ROYAL SCOTTISH COUNTRY DANCE SOCIETY

Aims & Activities: See the RSCDS on page 47.

Membership: 276.

✍ Secretary: Miss F. Martin
20 Gartcows Road, Falkirk.

TARTAN WEAVERS BURNS CLUB

Aims & Activities: Social. To perpetu-
ate the memory of Robert Burns.
Affiliations: The Burns Federation,
No. 1085.
✍ Secretary: T. Gow
15 St Annes Crescent,
Bannockburn.
FK7 8JL

TORBEX INN BURNS CLUB

Founded: 1975.
Aims & Activities: Social. Annual
Gathering. To commemorate the
works of Robert Burns.
Affiliations: The Burns Federation,
No. 935.
✍ Secretary: David C Grindlay
36 Kenningknowes Road,
Stirling.
FK7 9JG

WEST LOTHIAN

BATHGATE AND WEST LOTHIAN HIGHLAND GAMES

Aims & Activities: To organise annual
amateur Highland Games and sports
in the area of Bathgate, generally
towards the end of May.
✍ Secretary: Mrs M. Ross
198 Elizabeth Drive, Bathgate.

BATHGATE 'JOLLY BEGGARS' BURNS CLUB

Founded: 1974.
Aims & Activities: Social. Annual
Gathering. To perpetuate the name of
Robert Burns.
Affiliations: The Burns Federation,
No. 929.
✍ Secretary: A. Mackie
54 Mid Street, Bathgate.
EH48 1PT

BENIDORM BURNS CLUB

Aims & Activities: Social. Annual
Gathering.
Affiliations: The Burns Federation,
No. 1084.
✍ Secretary: E. McCue
5 Deanburn Park, Linlithgow.
EH49 6EZ

FAULDHOUSE AND CROFTHEAD BURNS CLUB

Aims & Activities: Social.
Affiliations: The Burns Federation,
No. 1117.
✍ Secretary: J. B. Gilmour
1 Kirk Brae, Longridge.
EH47 8AH

LINLITHGOW SCOTTISH COUNTRY DANCE CLUB

Aims & Activities: See the RSCDS on
page 47.
✍ Secretary: Janette Scott
35 Springfield Road, Linlithgow.
EH49 7JH
☎ 01506 842602

QUEENSFERRY SCOTTISH COUNTRY DANCE CLUB

Aims & Activities: See the RSCDS on
page 47.
✍ Secretary: Mrs H. Knox
6 Ashley Hall Gardens,
Linlithgow EH49 7DN
☎ 01506 847862

WEST LOTHIAN BRANCH OF THE ROYAL SCOTTISH COUNTRY DANCE SOCIETY

Aims & Activities: See the RSCDS on
page 47.
Membership: 179.
✍ Secretary: Mrs A. D. MacMichael
8 Fergusson Road, Broxburn.
EH52 5BL
☎ 01506 857494 (home)
☎ 01506 871561 (business)

WESTERN ISLES

CLAN MORRISON SOCIETY

Aims & Activities: To preserve the clan records. To promote overseas links. Genealogical. Historical.
Membership: Open to those with the name Morrison and those connected by descent or marriage.
✍ Secretary: Morrison Clan Society
Ruchdie, Lochmaddy,
North Uist.
PA82

STORNOWAY SCOTTISH COUNTRY DANCE CLUB

Aims & Activities: See the RSCDS on page 47.
✍ Officers: Secretary: Mr K. N.
MacDonald
56 Bayhead, Stornoway,
Isle of Lewis.
PA87 2DZ
☎ 01851 705142

ENGLAND

AVON

BATH BRANCH OF THE ROYAL SCOTTISH COUNTRY DANCE SOCIETY

Aims & Activities: See the RSCDS on page 47.
Membership: 79.
✍ Secretary: Mrs J. Hammond
73 Church Road, Combe Down, Bath.
BA2 5JQ
☎ 01225 833411

BIRNBECK BURNS CLUB

Founded: 1976.
Aims & Activities: To encourage the study of Burns. Educational. Social. Annual gathering.
Affiliations: The Burns Federation, No. 951.
Membership: Open to all interested in the aims of the club.
✍ Secretary: Mrs Jean Kemlo
21 Chestnut Grove, Clevedon.
BS21 7LA

BRISTOL BRANCH OF THE ROYAL SCOTTISH COUNTRY DANCE SOCIETY

Aims & Activities: See the RSCDS on page 47.
Membership: 65.
✍ Secretary: Mrs C. Dunn
18 Edgecumbe Road, Redland, Bristol.
BS6 7A
☎ 0117 9249226

BRISTOL CALEDONIAN SOCIETY

Founded: 1820.
Aims & Activities: Open to all Scots or those of Scots descent, or those married to Scots. Social. Annual Gathering.
Affiliations: The Burns Federation, No. 120.
✍ Secretary: Mrs Joan Phelps
43 Cleeve Hill, Downend, Bristol.
BS16 6ET

CLAN GRANT SOCIETY

Aims & Activities: Open to anyone of that name, or of the various septs, or related by descent or marriage. To promote the clan spirit worldwide. To collect and preserve all records relating to the clan history or genealogy. To strengthen overseas links. Annual Gathering.
✍ Secretary: 20 Laurie Crescent
Bristol.
BS9 4TA

WESTBURY SCOTTISH CLUB

Aims & Activities: See the RSCDS on page 47.
✍ Secretary: Mr J. Hindley
Gages Mead, Butcombe, Bristol.
BS18 6SF
☎ 01761 462089

BEDFORDSHIRE

BEDFORDSHIRE BRANCH OF THE ROYAL SCOTTISH COUNTRY DANCE SOCIETY

Aims & Activities: See the RSCDS on page 47.
Membership: 43.
✍ Secretary: Mr Butchart
28 Rowallan Drive, Bedford.
MK41 8AR

☎ 01234 351612 (home)
☎ 01234 272000 (business)

LONDON BURNS CLUB

Aims & Activities: Educational. Charitable. To foster interest in Scottish literature and the work of Robert Burns. Annual Gathering.
Affiliations: The Burns Federation, No. 1.
✍ Secretary: Mrs Mary M. Dunsmore
59 Beechwood Court, Dunstable. LU6 1QA

LUTON SCOTTISH REEL CLUB

Aims & Activities: See the RSCDS on page 47.
✍ Secretary: Mr M. J. Hale
Schiehallion, 54 Hill Rise, Sundon Park, Luton. LU3 3EE
☎ 01582 574831

ST NINIAN'S SCOTTISH COUNTRY DANCERS

Aims & Activities: See the RSCDS on page 47.
✍ Secretary: Mrs M. Garrett
204 Dunstable Road, Totternhoe, Dunstable. LU6 2AN
☎ 01582 665526

BERKSHIRE

ARGYLL SCOTTISH COUNTRY DANCE GROUP

Aims & Activities: See the RSCDS on page 47.
✍ Secretary: Mr T. Simpson
22 Grayswood Point, Norley Vale, Roehampton, London. SW15 4BT
☎ 0181 788 8042

BERKS/HANTS/SURREY BORDER BRANCH OF THE ROYAL SCOTTISH COUNTRY DANCE SOCIETY

Aims & Activities: See the RSCDS on page 47.
Membership: 180.
✍ Secretary: Sue Davis
2 Larkswood Drive, Crowthorne, Berkshire. RG11 6RL
☎ 01344 774344

BRACKNELL REEL CLUB

Aims & Activities: See the RSCDS on page 47.
✍ Secretary: Mrs P. M. Johnston
24 Starmead Drive, Wokingham. RG11 2HX
☎ 01734 788585

CLAN DARROCH

Aims & Activities: Open to those with the name Darroch, or variants of it, and those related by descent or marriage. To promote the clan spirit. To collect clan records. To enhance overseas links.
✍ Secretary: Capt. D. Darroch of Gourock
The Red House, Branksome Park Road, Camberley, Surrey.

CLAN DEWAR

Aims & Activities: Open to those of the name Dewar and those related by marriage or descent. To promote the clan spirit. To foster overseas links. Historical. Genealogical.
✍ Secretary: K. M. J. Dewar
The Dower House, Headley Road, Brayshott, Surrey. GU26 6DS

MAIDENHEAD SCOTTISH COUNTRY DANCING CLUB

Aims & Activities: See the RSCDS on page 47.

✍ Secretary: Mollie Cooper
73 Brunel Road, Maidenhead.
SL6 2RT

NEWBURY AND DISTRICT CALEDONIAN SOCIETY

Aims & Activities: See the RSCDS on page 47.

✍ Secretary: Mrs B. M. Hayward
25 Normay Rise, Newbury.
RG14 6RY

PURLEY SCOTTISH COUNTRY DANCING CLUB

Aims & Activities: See the RSCDS on page 47.

✍ Secretary: Mrs C. Woodward
36 Betchworth Avenue, Earley,
Reading.
RG7 5NW
☎ 01734 268757

SCOTS' SOCIETY OF ST ANDREW

Aims & Activities: See the RSCDS on page 47.

✍ Secretary: Mr S. Ward
13 Highfield Lane, Maidenhead.
SL6 3AN

ST ANDREW'S SCOTTISH COUNTRY DANCING SOCIETY

Aims & Activities: See the RSCDS on page 47.

✍ Secretary: Miss J. Healey
1 Privet Cottages, Church Road,
Seer Green, Beaconsfield.
HP9 2XZ
☎ 01494 673453

ST JOHN'S SCOTTISH COUNTRY DANCE CLUB

Aims & Activities: See the RSCDS on page 47.

✍ Secretary: Mrs E. Oxlade
26 Hamilton Road, Thame,
Oxfordshire.
OX9 3XZ
☎ 01844 213256

BUCKINGHAMSHIRE

CLAN MAITLAND

Aims & Activities: Open to those with the name Maitland, or to those related by marriage or descent. To promote the clan spirit. Overseas links. Historical. Genealogical.

✍ Secretary: A. Maitland
Hitchenden House, Hitchenden
Farm, Hughenden,
High Wycombe.
HP14 4LB

CLAN MOFFAT

Aims & Activities: Open to those bearing the name Moffat (in its varied spellings) and to those related by descent or marriage. To foster the clan spirit internationally. To collect and preserve clan records. Historical. Genealogical. Annual Gathering.

✍ Secretary: Madam Moffat
St Jasual, Bullocks Farm Lane,
Wheeler End Common,
High Wycombe.
HP14 3NH

GERRARDS CROSS SCOTTISH COUNTRY DANCE CLUB

Aims & Activities: See the RSCDS on page 47.

✍ Secretary: Mrs P. Smith
Plum Tree Cottage, Oxford
Road, Gerrards Cross.
SL9 7RH

MILTON KEYNES BRANCH OF THE ROYAL SCOTTISH COUNTRY DANCE SOCIETY

Aims & Activities: See the RSCDS on page 47.
Membership: 27.
✍ Secretary: Mrs D. Miller
15 The Green, Woughton on the Green, Milton Keynes.
MK6 3BE
☎ 01908 667901

CAMBRIDGESHIRE

CAMBRIDGE AND DISTRICT BRANCH OF THE ROYAL SCOTTISH COUNTRY DANCE SOCIETY

Aims & Activities: See the RSCDS on page 47.
Membership: 51.
✍ Secretary: Mrs V. Nedderman
56a Bill Rickaby Drive,
Newmarket, Suffolk.
CB8 0HQ
☎ 01638 561476 (home)
☎ 01954 210636 (business)

CAMBRIDGE SCOTTISH SOCIETY AND DANCE CIRCLE

Aims & Activities: See the RSCDS on page 47.
✍ Secretary: Mrs N. J. Howarth
2 Sudely Grove, Hardwick,
Cambridge.
CB3 7XS
☎ 01954 210020

CAMBRIDGE UNIVERSITY STRATHSPEY AND REEL CLUB

Aims & Activities: See the RSCDS on page 47.
✍ Secretary: Stacy Connolly
3 Ballard Close, Milton,
Cambridge.
CB4 6DW

HUNTINGDON AND DISTRICT CALEDONIAN SOCIETY

Aims & Activities: Social and to encourage interest in Scottish heritage.
Affiliations: The Royal Scottish Country Dance Society, (page 47).
✍ Reel Club Convener: Mrs P. E. Crowe
The Poplars, 18 Mill Common,
Huntingdon.
PE18 6AU
☎ 01480 453774

PETERBOROUGH AND DISTRICT BRANCH OF THE ROYAL SCOTTISH COUNTRY DANCE SOCIETY

Aims & Activities: See the RSCDS on page 47.
Membership: 45.
✍ Secretary: Mr M. Pagella
59 Horse Gate, Deeping St James,
Peterborough.
PE6 8EW
☎ 01778 380728 (home)
☎ 01778 345434 (business)

ROYSTON BURNS SOCIETY

Aims & Activities: Social and to promote the study of the works of Burns. Annual Gathering.
Affiliations: The Burns Federation, No. 1113.
✍ Secretary: W. C. Shaw
3 Butler Way, Haslingfield.
CB3 7JG

CHESHIRE

ALDERLEY AND DISTRICT CALEDONIAN SOCIETY

Aims & Activities: Social and to encourage interest in Scottish heritage.
Affiliations: The Royal Scottish Country Dance Society, (page 47).

✍ Secretary: Judith Holden
Tanglewood, Withinlee Road,
Mottram St Andrew.
SK10 4AU
☎ 01625 829898

BRAMHALL BRANCH OF THE ROYAL SCOTTISH COUNTRY DANCE SOCIETY

Aims & Activities: See the RSCDS on page 47.
Membership: 47.
✍ Secretary: Pauline Draycott
184 Cheadle Old Road, Edgeley,
Stockport.
SK3 9RH
☎ 0161 477 7497 (home)
☎ 0161 474 4875 (business)

CHESHIRE BRANCH OF THE ROYAL SCOTTISH COUNTRY DANCE SOCIETY

Aims & Activities: See the RSCDS on page 47.
Membership: 54.
✍ Secretary: Mr P. Marshall
9 Clowes Avenue, Alsagar,
Stoke-on-Trent, Staffordshire.
ST7 2RL
☎ 01270 877309 (home)
☎ 01782 794719 (business)

CHESTER CALEDONIAN ASSOCIATION

Founded: 1884.
Aims & Activities: Open to Scots by birth or descent. Literary (Burns). Scottish Country dancing (see Chester Caledonian Reel Club below). Highland dancing. Charitable. Social.
Affiliations: The Burns Federation, No. 572.
✍ Secretary: T. S. Lea
Kirkton House, Hunter Street,
Chester CH1 2AS

CHESTER CALEDONIAN REEL CLUB

Aims & Activities: See the RSCDS on page 47.
✍ Secretary: Mrs B Macaskill
69 Wepre Lane, Connah's Quay,
Deeside, Clwyd.
CH5 4JR
☎ 01244 818437

CHESTER ST ANDREW SOCIETY

Aims & Activities: Social and to encourage interest in Scottish heritage.
Affiliations: The Royal Scottish Country Dance Society, (page 47).
✍ Secretary: Mrs J. Johnson
47 Primrose Lane, Helsby,
Warrington.
WA6 0HH
☎ 01928 722182

DATEN SCOTTISH COUNTRY DANCE SOCIETY

Aims & Activities: See the RSCDS on page 47.
✍ Secretary: Mrs C. MacFarlane
10 Ribble Close, Culcheth,
Warrington.
WA3 5EA
☎ 01925 763789

FRODSHAM AND DISTRICT ST ANDREW'S SOCIETY

Aims & Activities: Social and to encourage interest in Scottish heritage.
Affiliations: The Royal Scottish Country Dance Society, (page 47).
✍ Secretary: Mrs M. Newman
122 Old Chester Road, Helsby,
Warrington.
WA3 5EA
☎ 01828 722321

HELSBY AND DISTRICT CALEDONIAN SOCIETY

Aims & Activities: Social and to encourage interest in Scottish heritage.
Affiliations: The Royal Scottish Country Dance Society, (page 47).
✍ Secretary: Mrs P. Sweetingham
38 Denehurst Parkway, Delamere Park, Cuddington.
CW8 2UD
☎ 01606 888667

KNUTSFORD SCOTTISH COUNTRY DANCE GROUP

Aims & Activities: See the RSCDS on page 47.
✍ Secretary: Mr J. A. Pleydell
5 Ladies' Mile, Knutsford.
WA16 0ND
☎ 01565 632493

LYMM SCOTTISH COUNTRY AND SEQUENCE DANCE CLUB

Aims & Activities: See the RSCDS on page 47.
✍ Secretary: Mrs R. Fleming
2 Greenwood Road, Lymm.
WA13 0LA
☎ 01925 755125

MACCLESFIELD SCOTTISH COUNTRY DANCE GROUP

Aims & Activities: See the RSCDS on page 47.
✍ Secretary: Mrs A. Sutcliffe
Lower Windy Way Farm, Walker Barn, Macclesfield SK11 0AW
☎ 01625 422093

MALPAS AND DISTRICT SCOTTISH SOCIETY

Aims & Activities: Social. See the RSCDS on page 47.
✍ Secretary: Mrs A. Greenough
5 Fismes Way, Wem, Shropshire.
SY4 5YD

MALPAS AND DISTRICT SCOTTISH SOCIETY

Aims & Activities: Social and to encourage interest in Scottish heritage. See the RSCDS on page 47.
✍ Secretary: Mrs M. Hewitt
Grindley Brook Hotel, Chester Road, Whitchurch.

NANTWICH AND DISTRICT SCOTTISH SOCIETY

Aims & Activities: Social and to encourage interest in Scottish heritage.
Affiliations: The Royal Scottish Country Dance Society, (page 47).
✍ Secretary: Mrs C. Jones
8 Carisbrooke Close, Wistaston, Crewe.
CW2 8JD

NORTHWICH AND DISTRICT SCOTS' SOCIETY

Aims & Activities: Social and to encourage interest in Scottish heritage.
Affiliations: The Royal Scottish Country Dance Society, (page 47).
✍ Secretary: Mr B. Notman
9 Windsor Close, Cuddington, Northwich.
CW8 2LQ
☎ 01606 888123

POYNTON SCOTTISH COUNTRY DANCE SOCIETY

Aims & Activities: See the RSCDS on page 47.
✍ Secretary: Mrs S. P. Davenport
Silverhill, Bollin Way, Prestbury, Macclesfield.
SK10 4BX
☎ 01625 829637

SANDBACH AND DISTRICT CALEDONIAN SOCIETY

Aims & Activities: Social and to

encourage an interest in Scottish heritage.

Affiliations: The Royal Scottish Country Dance Society, (page 47).

✍ Secretary: Mrs M. J. Forster
Roughwood Cottage,
Roughwood, Betchton,
Sandbach.
CW11 0XX

CLEVELAND

GUISBOROUGH SCOTTISH COUNTRY DANCE CLUB

Aims & Activities: See the RSCDS on page 47.

✍ Secretary: Mr I. Barbour
2 Langdale, Cleveland Park,
Guisborough.
☎ 01287 634448

HARTLEPOOL CALEDONIAN SOCIETY

Aims & Activities: Social and to encourage an interest in Scottish heritage. See the RSCDS on page 47.

✍ Secretary: Mrs J. J. White
152 Park Road, Hartlepool, T.
TS26 9HY
☎ 01429 279529

HARTLEPOOL SCOTTISH COUNTRY DANCE GROUP

Aims & Activities: See the RSCDS on page 47.

✍ Secretary: Mrs T. Rushmer
215 Park Road, Hartlepool.
TS26 9NG
☎ 01429 270187

TEESIDE BRANCH OF THE ROYAL SCOTTISH COUNTRY DANCE SOCIETY

Aims & Activities: See the RSCDS on page 47.

Membership: 121.

✍ Secretary: Mrs E. Kemp
16 Kipling Grove, Fairfield,
Stockton-on-Tees.
TS19 7QT
☎ 01642 583022

CORNWALL

CORNWALL BRANCH OF THE ROYAL SCOTTISH COUNTRY DANCE SOCIETY

Aims & Activities: See the RSCDS on page 47.

Membership: 48.

✍ Secretary: Miss P. Gay
44 Carn Bosavern, St Just,
Penzance.
TR19 7QX
☎ 01736 788893 (home)
☎ 01209 710158 (business)

FALMOUTH WHITE HEATHER CLUB

Aims & Activities: See the RSCDS on page 47.

✍ Secretary: Mrs P. Barton
Grass Vale, Penpoll, Feock, Truro.
TR3 6RU
☎ 01872 862425

LISKEARD SCOTTISH DANCE CLUB

Aims & Activities: See the RSCDS on page 47.

✍ Secretary: Mrs M. C. Oakley
Cleerview, 16 Pendean Avenue,
Liskeard.
PL14 6DA
☎ 01578 348224

LOOE SCOTTISH COUNTRY DANCE CLUB

Aims & Activities: See the RSCDS on page 47.

✍ Secretary: Mrs J. Wilson
Plovers, Cleveland Avenue, Plaidy,
Looe.
PL13 1JU
☎ 01503 265301

PENZANCE SCOTTISH COUNTRY DANCING CLUB

Aims & Activities: See the RSCDS on page 47.
✍ Secretary: Mrs E. R. Southwood
Red Lane Farm, Rosudgeon,
Penzance.
PR20 9PU

SALTASH SCOTTISH COUNTRY DANCE CLUB

Aims & Activities: See the RSCDS on page 47.
✍ Secretary: Mrs J. C. Carmichael
Okataina, Miner's Meadow,
Liskeard.
PL14 3ET
☎ 01579 344644

WEST CORNWALL SCOTTISH COUNTRY DANCERS

Aims & Activities: See the RSCDS on page 47.
✍ Secretary: Mrs D. Reid
Rockmount, Marazion.
TR17 0DF

CUMBRIA

AMBLESIDE GAMES

Aims & Activities: To organise annual professional Games and sports in the area of Ambleside.
Affiliations: The Scottish Games Association, (page 74).
✍ Secretary: Mrs C. Laidler
4 Oldfield Court, Windermere.
LA23 2HH
☎ 01539 445531

BARROW-IN-FURNESS SCOTTISH COUNTRY DANCE GROUP

Aims & Activities: See the RSCDS on page 47.
✍ Secretary: Mrs E. R. Cottam
168 Harrogate Street, Barrow-in-Furness.
LA14 5NA
☎ 01229 838575

BARROW-IN-FURNESS ST ANDREW SOCIETY

Aims & Activities: Social.
Membership: Open to all.
✍ Secretary: Ron Preston.

CALEDONIAN SOCIETY OF WEST CUMBERLAND

Founded: 1952.
Aims & Activities: Social. Open to Scots in the area and to those of Scots descent. To encourage interest in Scottish heritage.
Affiliations: The Burns Federation, No. 1008.
✍ Secretary: Mrs Joyce Goode
1 Meadow Grove, Cockermouth.
CA13 9PB

CARLISLE AND BORDER BRANCH OF THE ROYAL SCOTTISH COUNTRY DANCE SOCIETY

Aims & Activities: See the RSCDS on page 47.
Membership: 65.
✍ Secretary: Mrs M. Parker
41 Dunmail Drive, Carlisle.
CA2 6DF
☎ 01228 515991

DALLAM SCOTTISH COUNTRY DANCE CLASS

Aims & Activities: See the RSCDS on page 47.
✍ Secretary: Mrs P. Matthews
Conifers, 13 Nuns Avenue,
Carrbank,

Milnthorpe.
LA7 7JX
☎ 01524 761492

DERWENT SCOTTISH COUNTRY DANCE CLUB, COCKERMOUTH

Aims & Activities: See the RSCDS on page 47.
✍ Secretary: Mrs J. Cassells
Cornerstones, Papcastle,
Cockermouth.
CA13 0LB
☎ 01900 828046

FLOOKBURGH AND DISTRICT SCOTTISH COUNTRY DANCE CLUB

Aims & Activities: See the RSCDS on page 47.
✍ Secretary: Mr D. B. Wilkinson
19 Priory Crescent, Kents Bank,
Grange-over-Sands.
LA11 7BL
☎ 01539 534123

GRASMERE GAMES

Aims & Activities: To organise annual professional games and sports in the area of Grasmere.
Affiliations: The Scottish Games Association, (page 74).
✍ Secretary: Chris Lane
Slack Cottage, High Wray,
Ambleside.
LA22 0JQ
☎ 01539 432127

HAWKSHEAD SCOTTISH COUNTRY DANCERS

Aims & Activities: The Royal Scottish Country Dance Society.
✍ Secretary: Mrs A. Ball
The Honeypot, Hawkshead.
LA22 0NZ
☎ 01539 436267

KENDAL/HIGHGATE SCOTTISH COUNTRY DANCE CLUB

Aims & Activities: See the RSCDS on page 47.
✍ Secretary: Mrs E. D. Hatrick
10 Logmire Way, Morecambe,
Lancs.
LA4 4EN
☎ 01524 422038

KESWICK GAMES

Aims & Activities: To organise annual professional Games and sports in the area of Keswick.
Affiliations: The Scottish Games Association, (page 74).
✍ Secretary: R. Taylor
Carlside, Portinscale, Keswick.
CA12 5RW
☎ 01768 771337

SASRA SEASCALE SCOTTISH COUNTRY DANCE CLUB

Aims & Activities: See the RSCDS on page 47.
✍ Secretary: Mr J. W. Young
Aviemore, Drigg Road, Seascale.
CA20 1NX
☎ 01946 728155

ST ANDREW'S SCOTTISH COUNTRY DANCE SOCIETY, WORKINGTON

Aims & Activities: See the RSCDS on page 47.
✍ Secretary: Mrs L. Potter
Tall Trees, 15 Eldred Road,
Workington.
☎ 01900 615140

WALNEY JOLLY BEGGARS LADIES' CLUB

Founded: 1929.
Aims & Activities: Social. Annual Gathering. To promote interest in Scottish literature and the work of Robert Burns.

Affiliations: The Burns Federation, No. 436.
🖎 Secretary: Mrs Joyce Murray
34 Folkestone Avenue,
Barrow-in-Furness.
LA14 3BE

WHITEHAVEN BURNS CLUB

Founded: 1914.
Aims & Activities: Social. To promote interest in the work of Robert Burns.
Affiliations: The Burns Federation, No. 236.
🖎 Secretary: Mr M. Pringle
42 Coniston Avenue, Seascale.
CA20 1LU

WINDERMERE SCOTTISH COUNTRY DANCE GROUP

Aims & Activities: See the RSCDS on page 47.
🖎 Secretary: Mrs D. King
14 Michaelson Road, Kendal.
LA9 5JQ
☎ 01539 731223

DERBYSHIRE

BELPER SCOTTISH COUNTRY DANCE SOCIETY

Aims & Activities: See the RSCDS on page 47.
🖎 Secretary: Mrs J. J. Steel
Hy-Brasail, Riber Road,
Starkholmes, Matlock.
DE4 5JB

BUXTON AND DISTRICT SCOTTISH COUNTRY DANCE SOCIETY

Aims & Activities: See the RSCDS on page 47.
🖎 Secretary: Dr H. Phillips. 27
Errwood Avenue
Buxton SK17 9BD

CHESTERFIELD AND DISTRICT CALEDONIAN ASSOCIATION

Founded: 1886.
Aims & Activities: To perpetuate all things Scottish and the memory of Robert Burns. Social.
Affiliations: The Burns Federation, No. 11.
Membership: Open to all those of Scottish birth or descent.
🖎 Secretary: Mr James L. Bullions
Grey Gables, 27 Norbriggs Road,
Chesterfield.
S43 3BT

CHESTERFIELD CALEDONIAN COUNTRY DANCE CLASS

Aims & Activities: See the RSCDS on page 47.
🖎 Secretary: Mrs E. J. Andrews
5 Mill Stream Close, Walton,.
Chesterfield.
S40 3DS
☎ 01246 274480

DERBY SCOTTISH ASSOCIATION AND BURNS CLUB

Founded: 1890.
Aims & Activities: Social and to perpetuate Scottish culture and the memory of Robert Burns. Scottish country dancing. Bridge club.
Affiliations: The Royal Scottish Country Dance Society and the Burns Federation, No. 55.
Membership: Open to Scots by birth, marriage, or descent (to grandfather). Associate membership open to all interested in their aims.
🖎 Secretary: Mrs K. Dick
8 Greenside Court, Mickleover,
Derby.
DE3 5RG
☎ 01322 512785
🖎 Dr S. B. L. Wilson
22 Moorway Lane, Littleover,
Derby.
☎ 01332 767138

GLOSSOP SCOTTISH COUNTRY DANCERS

Aims & Activities: See the RSCDS on page 47.

✍ Secretary: Mrs B. A. Handley
5 Bexley Close, The Heath, Glossop SK13 9BG

☎ 01457 861570

DEVON

BIDEFORD AND DISTRICT SCOTTISH COUNTRY DANCE CLUB

Aims & Activities: See the RSCDS on page 47.

✍ Secretary: Mrs P. Gales
31 Shrubbery Close, Newport, Barnstaple.
EX32 9DG

EXETER BRANCH OF THE ROYAL SCOTTISH COUNTRY DANCE SOCIETY

Aims & Activities: See the RSCDS on page 47.
Membership: 111.

✍ Secretary: Mrs F. C. Quartly
54 Hoker Road, Exeter.
EX2 5HP

KINGSKERSWELL/NEWTON ABBOT/CARSWELLA SCOTTISH COUNTRY DANCERS

Aims & Activities: See the RSCDS on page 47.

✍ Secretary: Mr E. C. Hutchings
Shalom, 50 Barcombe Heights, Preston, Paignton.
TQ3 1PT

PLYMOUTH BURNS CLUB

Founded: 1947.

Aims & Activities: To strengthen the bonds of frendship among Scots in Plymouth and to sustain interest in Scottish culture. Burns Anniversary Dinner Dance. Scottish country dancing.

Affiliations: The Burns Federation, No. 721.

Membership: Open to Scots by birth, marriage, or descent. Associate membership open to others.

✍ Secretary: Joe Main
21 Ridge Park Road, Plympton.
PL7 3BG

SALCOMBE SCOTTISH COUNTRY DANCING CLUB

Aims & Activities: See the RSCDS on page 47.

✍ Secretary: Mrs G. P. Bentley
Old Longclose, Goveton, Kingsbridge TQ7 2DT

TRINITY UNITED REFORMED SCOTTISH COUNTRY DANCE CLASS

Aims & Activities: See the RSCDS on page 47.

✍ Secretary: Mrs S. Hosking
370 Taunton Avenue, Whitleigh, Plymouth PL5 4EL

YELVERTON SCOTTISH DANCERS

Aims & Activities: See the RSCDS on page 47.

✍ Secretary: Mrs E. Morgan
2 Meavy Villas, Yelverton.
PL20 6AQ

☎ 01822 853288

DORSET

BOURNEMOUTH BRANCH OF THE ROYAL SCOTTISH COUNTRY DANCE SOCIETY

Aims & Activities: See the RSCDS on page 47.

Membership: 100.
✍ Secretary: Mrs T. Green
  67 Pound Lane, Poole BH15
  3RR
☎ 01202 673067

BOURNEMOUTH CALEDONIAN SOCIETY

Aims & Activities: Social and to encourage an interest in Scottish heritage. Highland Dancing. Scottish Country Dancing. History. The works of Robert Burns. Annual Gathering.
Affiliations: The Royal Scottish Country Dance Society and The Burns Federation, No. 663.
✍ Secretary: Mr John Steed
  33 Leybourne Avenue,
  Bournemouth BH10 6ES
☎ 01202 514339

HINDON AND EAST KNOYLE SCOTTISH COUNTRY DANCERS

Aims & Activities: See the RSCDS on page 47.
✍ Secretary: Mr J. McNeile
  The Old Vicarage, Fisherton de la Mere, Warminster, Wilts.
  BA12 0PT
☎ 01985 624826

SOUTH DORSET CALEDONIAN SOCIETY

Aims & Activities: Social and to encourage an interest in Scottish heritage. See the RSCDS on page 47.
✍ Secretary: Mrs K. Allan
  16 Culliford Road, Dorchester.
  DT1 2AT
☎ 01305 262832

DURHAM

BARNARD CASTLE SCOTTISH COUNTRY DANCE GROUP

Aims & Activities: See the RSCDS on page 47.
✍ Secretary: Mrs A. Bell
  Midway, 10 Teesdale Road,
  Startforth, Barnard Castle.
  DL12 9AT
☎ 01833 638359

DARLINGTON GAELIC SOCIETY

Founded: 1968.
Aims & Activities: Social and to encourage the Gaelic tradition.
Affiliations: The Burns Federation, No. 1030.
✍ Secretary: R. M. Jones
  396 Coniscliffe Road, Darlington.
  DL3 8AJ

DARLINGTON SCOTTISH COUNTRY DANCE GROUP

Aims & Activities: See the RSCDS on page 47.
✍ Secretary: Mrs R. Tindale
  4 Elton Grove, Darlington.
  DL3 8HP
☎ 01325 466388

DARLINGTON THISTLE CLUB

Aims & Activities: See the RSCDS on page 47.
✍ Secretary: Mrs K. Stansbie
  135 Greenbank Road,
  Darlington.
  DL3 6EN
☎ 01325 354628

DURHAM AND DISTRICT CALEDOANIAN SOCIETY

Founded: 1950.
Aims & Activities: To foster Scottish traditions. Social. Charitable. Educational. Historical.

Affiliations: The Burns Federation, No. 744.

Membership: Open to all those of Scottish descent (to grandparents).

✍ Secretary: Mrs A. Nicol
   62 High Street, Willington.
   DL15 0PF

LANCHESTER SCOTTISH COUNTRY DANCING GROUP

Aims & Activities: See the RSCDS on page 47.

✍ Secretary: Jill Mair
   6 Percy Crescent, Lanchester.
   DH7 0EU

☎ 01207 520139

ESSEX

BARCLAY SOCIETY

Aims & Activities: Open to those with the name Barclay (in its varied spellings) and to those related by marriage or descent. To promote the clan and family spirit worldwide. Social. Historical. Genealogical.

✍ Secretary: Batemans
   Stratford St Mary, Colchester, Essex.

BASILDON CALEDONIAN SOCIETY

Aims & Activities: Social and to encourage an interest in Scottish heritage.

Affiliations: The Royal Scottish Country Dance Society, (page 47).

✍ Secretary: Mr E. Philpot
   184 Western Road, Billericay.
   CM12 9JP

☎ 01277 657247

CALEDONIAN SOCIETY OF COLCHESTER

Founded: 1968.

Aims & Activities: Social. To encourage interest in Scottish heritage, history and traditions. Annual Gathering.

Affiliations: The Burns Federation, No. 1047.

✍ Secretary: Mrs Anne Fairley
   Park Farm, Great Bromley, Colchester.
   CO7 7US

EPPING FOREST SCOTTISH ASSOCIATION

Aims & Activities: See the RSCDS on page 47. Social.

✍ Secretary: Mrs M. Hayter
   8 Buttercross Lane, Epping.
   CM16 5AA

☎ 01992 573860

GREYFRIARS SCOTTISH DANCERS, COLCHESTER

Aims & Activities: See the RSCDS on page 47.

✍ Secretary: Mr G. Rant
   Jennings Farm House, Ardleigh Road, Little Bromley, Manningtree.
   CO11 2QB

☎ 01206 392032

LEIGH-ON-SEA CALEDONIAN DANCERS

Aims & Activities: See the RSCDS on page 47.

✍ Secretary: Mrs K. Bacon
   3 Northville Drive, Westcliffe-on-Sea.
   SS0 0QA

☎ 01702 342903

LITTLE BADDOW SCOTTISH COUNTRY DANCE CLUB

Aims & Activities: See the RSCDS on page 47.

✍ Secretary: Mr K. G. Carter
33 Anchor Road, Tiptree.
CO5 0AP
☎ 01621 816459

SANDON SCOTTISH COUNTRY DANCE CLUB

Aims & Activities: See the RSCDS on page 47.
✍ Secretary: Mrs E. Hatwell
6 Sebastian Avenue, Shenfield.
CM15 8PW
☎ 01277 211488

SOUTH-EAST ESSEX SCOTTISH SOCIETY

Aims & Activities: Social and to encourage an interest in Scottish heritage.
Affiliations: The Royal Scottish Country Dance Society, (page 47).
✍ Secretary: Mr B. Carney
74 Grove Road, Benfleet, Essex.
SS7 1JJ
☎ 01268 752467

WITHAM AND DISTRICT CALEDONIAN SOCIETY

Aims & Activities: Social and to encourage an interest in Scottish heritage.
Affiliations: The Royal Scottish Country Dance Society, (page 47).
✍ Secretary: Ms B. R. Moody
81 Cedar Chase, Heybridge, Maldon.
CM9 7NR

GLOUCESTERSHIRE

CHELTENHAM BRANCH OF THE ROYAL SCOTTISH COUNTRY DANCE SOCIETY

Aims & Activities: See the RSCDS on page 47.

Membership: 134.
✍ Secretary: Mrs B. Adams
43 Ravensgate Road, Charlton Kings, Cheltenham.
GL53 8NS
☎ 01242 234571

CHELTENHAM SCOTTISH SOCIETY

Founded: 1929.
Aims & Activities: To encourage the study and appreciation of Scottish tradition and culture. Annual Gathering. Highland dancing. Charitable. Educational. Historical. Social.
Affiliations: The Royal Scottish Country Dance Society and the Burns Federation, No. 462.
Membership: Open to Scots by birth or descent. (to grandparents).
✍ Secretary: Mrs D. Steele
45 Dark Lane, Swindon Village, Cheltenham.
GL12 9RN
☎ 01242 528220

GLOUCESTER SCOTTISH SOCIETY

Aims & Activities: Social and to encourage an interest in Scottish heritage. Annual Gathering.
Affiliations: The Royal Scottish Country Dance Society and the Burns Federation, No. 774.
✍ Secretary: James. M. Laurie
Durisdeer, 5 Howard Place, Hucclecote.
GL3 3RZ
☎ 01452 618537

STOW-ON-THE-WOLD SCOTTISH COUNTRY DANCE GROUP

Aims & Activities: See the RSCDS on page 47.
✍ Secretary: Miss B. Parsons
Valley View, Maugersbury, Stow-on-the-Wold.
GL54 1HR

GREATER MANCHESTER

ALTRINCHAM SCOTTISH COUNTRY DANCE GROUP

Aims & Activities: See the RSCDS on page 47.
✍ Secretary: Mrs A. Thistlewaite
14 Paddock Lane, Dunham Massey, Altrincham.
WA14 5RP
☎ 0161 928 9127

ASHMERG SCOTTISH COUNTRY DANCE GROUP

Aims & Activities: See the RSCDS on page 47.
✍ Secretary: Mr J. Haworth
23 Winstanley Road, Sale.
M33 2AG
☎ 0161 969 1202

BOLTON BURNS CLUB

Founded: 1881.
Aims & Activities: Social. Annual Gathering. To foster interest in the work of Robert Burns.
Affiliations: The Burns Federation, No. 95.
✍ Secretary: Mrs W. G. Diggle
24 Gorses Mount, Darcy Lever, Bolton.
BL2 1PQ

BROOKDALE CLUB SCOTTISH COUNTRY DANCERS

Aims & Activities: See the RSCDS on page 47.
✍ Secretary: Mrs C. A. Taylor
Svedale, Sugar Lane, Adlington, nr Macclesfield, Cheshire.
SK10 5SQ
☎ 0625 572390

CLAN IRVINE OF DRUM

Aims & Activities: To promote the clan spirit. Overseas links. Genealogical. Historical.
Membership: Open to those of the name Irvine and those connected by descent and marriage.
✍ Secretary: David C. Irvine of Drum
20 Enville Road, Bowdon, Altrincham.
WA14 2PQ

GOYT VALLEY SCOTTISH COUNTRY DANCE CLUB

Aims & Activities: Social. See the RSCDS on page 47.
✍ Secretary: Miss Brenda Newport
Crantock, 3 Carrwood Avenue, Bramhall, Stockport.
SK7 2PX
☎ 0161 439 2864

MANCHESTER AND SALFORD CALEDONIAN ASSOCIATION

Founded: 1948.
Aims & Activities: Social. To foster friendly relations amongst Scots in the Manchester and Salford area. Annual Gathering. Highland dancing. Historical. To increase appreciation of the works of Burns.
Affiliations: The Burns Federation, No. 674.
✍ Secretaries: Mr & Mrs A. Williams, 47 South Drive Chorltonville, Manchester.
M21 2DZ

MANCHESTER BRANCH OF THE ROYAL SCOTTISH COUNTRY DANCE SOCIETY

Aims & Activities: See the RSCDS on page 47.
Membership: 216.
✍ Secretary: Mrs C. Mottram
136 Altrincham Road, Wilmslow, Cheshire.
SK9 5NQ
☎ 01625 531728

MANCHESTER SCOTTISH DANCE PARTY

Aims & Activities: See the RSCDS on page 47.

✍ Secretary: Mr J. R. E. Lyon
91 Linden Park, Manchester.
M19 2PG

ROCHDALE BRANCH OF THE ROYAL SCOTTISH COUNTRY DANCE SOCIETY

Aims & Activities: See the RSCDS on page 47.
Membership: 26.

✍ Secretary: Mr D. Ewart
Oakenslaw Cottage, 39 Tonacliffe Road, Whitworth, Rochdale.
OL12 8SS

☎ 01706 343584

ST NINIAN'S SCOTTISH COUNTRY DANCE SOCIETY

Aims & Activities: See the RSCDS on page 47.

✍ Secretary: Miss A. Williams
258 Brantingham Road,
Chorlton-cum-Hardy, Manchester
M21 1QZ

☎ 0161 881 5934

THISTLE SOCIETY, WIGAN

Aims & Activities: See the RSCDS on page 47.

✍ Secretary: Miss K. Dunbar
Dunabban, 7 Ruskin Crescent,
Abram, Wigan.
WN2 5PX

☎ 01924 861539

WOODFORD SCOTTISH COUNTRY DANCE GROUP

Aims & Activities: See the RSCDS on page 47.

✍ Secretary: Mrs E. Tone
177 Bramhall Moor Lane, Hazel
Grove, Stockport SK7 5BB

☎ 0161 483 8579

HAMPSHIRE

ANDOVER SCOTTISH DANCE CLUB

Aims & Activities: See the RSCDS on page 47.

✍ Secretary: Miss E. A. Childs
Siwa, The Ox Drove, Picket
Place, Andover.
SP11 6ND

BASINGSTOKE SCOTTISH COUNTRY DANCING CLUB

Aims & Activities: See the RSCDS on page 47.

✍ Secretary: Mrs M. Williams
9 Jackdaw Close, Kempshott,
Basingstoke.
RG22 8QW

CLAN MACGILL

Aims & Activities: To promote the clan spirit. Overseas links. Historical. Genealogical. Social.
Membership: Open to those bearing the name MacGill, or its variants, also those connected by descent or marriage.

✍ President: Viscount of Oxfuird
Hill House, St Mary Bourne,
Hampshire.
SP11 6BG

CLAN MONTGOMERIE

Aims & Activities: To collect historical and genealogical clan records. To promote overseas links. Annual Gathering.
Membership: Open to all bearing the name Montgomerie in its various spellings, and to those related by marriage or descent.

✍ Chieftain: The Earl of Eglinton
The Dutch House, West Green
Road, Hartley Wintney.
RG27 8JN

EASTLEIGH – ROWAN SCOTTISH COUNTRY DANCERS

Aims & Activities: See the RSCDS on page 47.

✍ Secretary: Mr T. Stewart
Tigh-na-Daraich, 162
Hiltingbury Road,
Chandlers Ford, Eastleigh.
SO53 1NS

FAREHAM SCOTTISH COUNTRY DANCERS

Aims & Activities: See the RSCDS on page 47.

✍ Secretary: Mrs P. Machin
18 Manor Way, Lee-on-Solent.
PO13 9JH
☎ 01705 550714

FLEET SCOTTISH COUNTRY DANCE SOCIETY

Aims & Activities: See the RSCDS on page 47.

✍ Secretary: Mrs V. Hansford
Glenburn, 1 Tudor Way,
Church Crookham, Fleet.

FORDINGBRIDGE SCOTTISH DANCING CLUB

Aims & Activities: See the RSCDS on page 47.

✍ Secretary: Ms B. McConnell
10 Fir Tree Hill, Alderholt,
Fordingbridge.
SP6 3AY
☎ 01425 657242

GLAYVA SCOTTISH DANCERS

Aims & Activities: See the RSCDS on page 47.

✍ Secretary: M J. McGrigor
28 Gilkicker Road, Alverstoke,
Gosport.
PO12 2UN
☎ 01795 583994

HAVANT REEL CLUB

Aims & Activities: See the RSCDS on page 47.

✍ Secretary: Mrs Elizabeth Dean
79 Sunnymead Drive,
Waterlooville.
PO7 6BW
☎ 01705 253752

ISLE OF WIGHT CALEDONIAN SOCIETY

Aims & Activities: Social and to encourage interest in Scottish heritage. See the RSCDS on page 47.

✍ Secretary: Mrs A. Robertson. 139
Staplers Road
Newport, Isle of Wight.
PO30 2DJ
☎ 01983 522739

NEW FOREST SCOTTISH COUNTRY DANCERS

Aims & Activities: See the RSCDS on page 47.

✍ Secretary: Mrs P. Perkins
Oakfield, 10 Rhinefield Close,
Brockenhurst.
SO42 7SU

PORTSMOUTH AND DISTRICT CALEDONIAN SOCIETY

Aims & Activities: Social and to encourage interest in Scottish heritage. See the RSCDS on page 47.

✍ Secretary: Mrs S. Chaney
The Gabled House, 5 Ashburton
Road, Alverstoke, Gosport.
PO12 2LH
☎ 01705 581960

PORTSMOUTH – DRAYTON ST ANDREWS SCOTTISH COUNTRY DANCE CLASS

Aims & Activities: See the RSCDS on page 47.

✍ Secretary: Mr C. Hills
13 East Cosham Road, Cosham,

Portsmouth.
PO6 2BP
☎ 01705 371639

Ryde, Isle of Wight.
PO33 1HP
☎ 01983 567010

SOUTHAMPTON SCOTTISH ASSOCIATION

Aims & Activities: Social and to encourage interest in Scottish heritage. See the RSCDS on page 47.
✍ Secretary: Mr J. Tubbs
5 Hinkler Road, Thornhill Park, Southampton.
SO2 6FR
☎ 01703 463996

SOUTHSEA REEL CLUB

Aims & Activities: See the RSCDS on page 47.
✍ Secretary: Mrs K. Lawmon
19 Nicholson Way, Havant.
PO9 3AZ
☎ 01705 450265

TADLEY SCOTTISH COUNTRY DANCING CLUB

Aims & Activities: See the RSCDS on page 47.
✍ Secretary: Mrs N. Scott
September Cottage, Brimpton Common, Reading.
RG7 4RT

WAVERLEY SCOTTISH DANCERS

Aims & Activities: See the RSCDS on page 47.
✍ Secretary: Mrs C. Cruden
2 Bere Close, Chandlers Ford, Eastleigh.
SO5 3QU
☎ 01703 267317

WIGHT SCOTTISH DANCERS

Aims & Activities: See the RSCDS on page 47.
✍ Secretary: Mrs S. Saunders
Leyton, 25 St Johns Wood Road,

WINCHESTER BRANCH OF THE ROYAL SCOTTISH COUNTRY DANCE SOCIETY

Aims & Activities: See the RSCDS on page 47.
Membership: 41.
✍ Secretary: Sue Ayland
2 Nettlestone, Netley Abbey, Southampton.
SO3 5FG
☎ 01703 454325

HEREFORD AND WORCESTER

BLACK MOUNTAIN REEL CLUB

Aims & Activities: See the RSCDS on page 47.
✍ Secretary: Mrs J. Davies
Fermain, Woodleigh Road, Ledbury HR8 2BG
☎ 01531 632096

BROMSGROVE SCOTTISH COUNTRY DANCE GROUP

Aims & Activities: See the RSCDS on page 47.
✍ Secretary: Mrs D. M. Manson
29 Salop Road, Redditch.
B97 4PS
☎ 01527 541317

DROITWICH AND DISTRICT SCOTTISH SOCIETY

Aims & Activities: Social and to encourage interest in Scottish heritage. See the RSCDS on page 47.
✍ Secretary: Mrs B. M. Thorp
9 Beech Avenue, Worcester.
WR3 8PZ

HEREFORD SCOTTISH COUNTRY DANCE CLUB

Aims & Activities: See the RSCDS on page 47.

✍ Secretary: Mrs Joan White
The Old Coach House,
Llanwye Close, Hereford.
HR1 1XX
☎ 01432 266867

HEREFORDSHIRE BRANCH OF THE ROYAL SCOTTISH COUNTRY DANCE SOCIETY

Aims & Activities: See the RSCDS on page 47.
Membership: 82.

✍ Secretary: Mrs M. Rintoul
The Rowans, 84 Chapel Street,
Abergavenny, Gwent.
NP7 8BL
☎ 01873 853658

HEREFORDSHIRE BURNS CLUB

Founded: 1910.
Aims & Activities: To cherish the memory of Burns and foster a love of his works. Social. Annual Burns Dinner. Overseas links.
Affiliations: The Burns Federation, No. 446.

✍ Secretary: J. J. Marshall
7 Somers Walk, Tupsley, Hereford.
HR1 10X

INKBERROW SCOTTISH COUNTRY DANCE CLUB

Aims & Activities: See the RSCDS on page 47.

✍ Secretary: Major O. O. Davidson
High Barr, High Street,
Inkberrow.
WR7 4DU
☎ 01386 792772

LEOMINSTER SCOTTISH DANCERS

Aims & Activities: See the RSCDS on page 47.

✍ Secretary: Mrs P. Mainwaring
Conway, Newlands Drive,
Leominster.
HR6 8PR
☎ 01586 614470

MALVERN SCOTTISH DANCING CLUB

Aims & Activities: See the RSCDS on page 47.

✍ Secretary: Mrs J. Graham
16 Knoll Lane, Poolbrook,
Malvern.
WR14 3JU
☎ 01684 574923

PERSHORE SCOTTISH COUNTRY DANCE SOCIETY

Aims & Activities: See the RSCDS on page 47.

✍ Secretary: Miss A. Wood
13 Tithe Court, Middle Littleton,
Evesham.
WR11 5LR
☎ 01386 833480

ROSS REEL CLUB

Aims & Activities: See the RSCDS on page 47.

✍ Secretary: Mrs J. Reed
Willow Tree Cottage, Leys Hill,
Ross-on-Wye.
HR9 5QU
☎ 01600 890834

WORCESTER SCOTTISH COUNTRY DANCE SOCIETY

Aims & Activities: See the RSCDS on page 47.

✍ Secretary: Mr J. Burnett
12 Chase End Close, Worcester.
WR5 2BY
☎ 01905 352604

WYRE FOREST SCOTTISH COUNTRY DANCE CLUB

Aims & Activities: See the RSCDS on page 47.
✍ Secretary: Mrs T. Oldroyd
422 Chester Road North,
Kidderminster.
DY10 1TB
☎ 01562 824626

HERTFORDSHIRE

BERKHAMPSTEAD STRATHSPEY AND REEL CLUB

Aims & Activities: See the RSCDS on page 47.
✍ Secretary: Mrs M. Buckell
36 Rambling Way, Potten End,
Berkhampstead.
HP4 2SF
☎ 01442 877651

BISHOPS STORTFORD CALEDONIAN SOCIETY

Aims & Activities: Social and to encourage interest in Scottish heritage.
Affiliations: The Royal Scottish Country Dance Society, (page 47).
✍ Secretary: Mrs M. MacHardy
Rose Isle, Sawbridgeworth Road,
Hatfield Heath.
CM22 7DR
☎ 01279 730711

HARPENDEN SCOTTISH COUNTRY DANCING CLUB

Aims & Activities: See the RSCDS on page 47.
✍ Secretary: Mr P. George
120 Clarence Road, St Albans.
AL1 4NW
☎ 01727 843001

NORTH HERTS REEL CLUB

Aims & Activities: See the RSCDS on page 47.
✍ Secretary: Mrs J. K. Warburton
17 Victoria Road, Shefford.
SG17 5AL
☎ 01462 812691

SOUTH-EAST HERTS SCOTTISH COUNTRY DANCE SOCIETY

Aims & Activities: See the RSCDS on page 47.
✍ Secretary: Mrs M. Cole
6 Beane Road, Watton-at-Stone.
SG14 3RG
☎ 01920 830389

ST ALBANS AND MID-HERTS CALEDONIAN SOCIETY

Aims & Activities: Social and to encourage interest in Scottish heritage. See the RSCDS on page 47.
✍ Secretary: Mr C. Walker
Pinetops, Birklands Lane, St
Albans.
AL1 1EE
☎ 01727 822143

WATFORD AND WEST HERTS SCOTTISH SOCIETY

Aims & Activities: Social and to promote interest in Scottish heritage. See the RSCDS on page 47.
✍ Secretary: Mr S. Kreloff
26 Chilcott Road, Watford.
WD2 5LE
☎ 01923 661905

HUMBERSIDE

BRIDLINGTON AND THE WOLDS CALEDONIAN SOCIETY

Founded: 1947.
Aims & Activities: Aims & activities. To promote interest in Scotland and

Scottish heritage and in particular Scottish literature and the works of Robert Burns.
Affiliations: The Burns Federation, No. 722.
✍ Secretary: Mrs Margaret MacFarlane
Highbank, 8 Glaisdale Close, Marton Park, Bridlington.
YO16 5FG

CLAN HUSTEAIN

Aims & Activities: To promote awareness of the clan and its history.
✍ Sir I. B. Macdonald of Sleat
Thorpe Hall, Rudston, Driffield.
YO25 0JE

GRIMSBY AND CLEETHORPES BURNS CLUB

Founded: 1968.
Aims & Activities: Social. Annual Gathering. To perpetuate the memory of Robert Burns.
Affiliations: The Burns Federation, No. 1037.
✍ Secretary: Mrs M. Dickens
14 St Nicholas Drive, Wybers Wood, Grimsby.
DN37 9QA

GRIMSBY AND DISTRICT CALEDONIAN DANCE CLASS

Aims & Activities: See the RSCDS on page 47.
✍ Secretary: Mrs I. M. Parkes
7 Windermere Avenue, Fairfield, Grimsby.
DN33 3BN
☎ 01472 825385

GRIMSBY AND DISTRICT CALEDONIAN SOCIETY

Founded: 1906.
Aims & Activities: To promote friendly relations between Scots and those of Scots descent in the Grimsby area.

To encourage appreciation of the works of Robert Burns. Annual Gathering.
Affiliations: The Burns Federation, No. 746.
✍ Secretary: Mrs I. M. Parkes
7 Windermere Avenue, Fairfield, Grimsby.
DN33 3BN

GRIMSBY SCOTTISH COUNTRY DANCE CLUB

Aims & Activities: See the RSCDS on page 47.
✍ Secretary: Mrs J. Gamon
30 St Peter's Grove, Laceby, Grimsby.
DN37 7HD
☎ 01472 872684

HULL SCOTS SOCIETY OF ST ANDREW

Founded: 1976.
Aims & Activities: To promote interest in Scottish heritage and in particular the work of Robert Burns. Annual Gathering.
Affiliations: The Burns Federation, No. 987.
✍ Secretary: Ms Jeanette Dewar
89 Deal Road, Swanland, Hull.
HU14 3QH

HUMBERSIDE BURNS SOCIETY

Founded: 1970.
Aims & Activities: To follow the philosophy of Burns. Social. Charitable. Educational. Historical. Annual Gathering.
Affiliations: The Burns Federation, No. 943.
Membership: Open to all interested in the aims.
✍ Secretary: Mrs Dorothy McEwan
37 Claremont Avenue, Hull.
HU6 7NE

ISLE OF MAN

ISLE OF MAN SCOTTISH COUNTRY DANCE GROUP

Aims & Activities: See the RSCDS on page 47.
✍ Secretary: Mr & Mrs D. Shimmin
Sea Haven, The Vollan,
Promenade, Ramsey.
IM8 3UP

RAMSEY SCOTTISH DANCING GROUP

Aims & Activities: See the RSCDS on page 47.
✍ Secretary: Mrs B. Saville
Windsor House, Windsor Mount,
Ramsey.
☎ 01624 814417

KENT

CLAN ROBERTSON

Aims & Activities: To promote the clan spirit around the world. To collect and preserve historical and genealogical clan records. Social. Annual Gathering. Overseas links.
Membership: Open to those bearing the name Robertson and those related by marriage or descent.
✍ Secretary: A. G. H. Robertson
The Breach Farm, Goudhurst
Road, Cranbrook.
TN17 2LJ

CLIFTONVILLE – ISLE OF THANET SCOTTISH COUNTRY DANCERS

Aims & Activities: See the RSCDS on page 47.
✍ Secretary: Mrs L. Cross
60 Bradstow Way, Broadstairs.
TN10 1AJ
☎ 01843 861850

DOVER AND EAST KENT SCOTTISH SOCIETY

Aims & Activities: Social and to promote interest in Scottish heritage including the work of Robert Burns. Annual dinner.
Affiliations: The Burns Federation, No. 918.
✍ Secretary: John Darrant
54 Charles Lister Court, London Road, Dover.
CT17 0TP

MEDWAY AND DISTRICT CALEDONIAN ASSOCIATION

Aims & Activities: Social and to encourage interest in Scottish heritage. See the RSCDS on page 47.
✍ Secretary: Mrs S. Orr
Elmhora, Upnor Road, Upper Upnor, nr Rochester.
ME2 4XE
☎ 01634 711265

ORPINGTON AND DISTRICT CALEDONIAN SOCIETY

Aims & Activities: Social and to promote interest in Scottish heritage. See the RSCDS on page 47.
✍ Secretary: Miss L. M. Clark
24 Burford Road, Bromley.
BR1 2EZ

ROYAL TUNBRIDGE WELLS BRANCH OF THE ROYAL SCOTTISH COUNTRY DANCE SOCIETY

Aims & Activities: See the RSCDS on page 47.
Membership: 150.
✍ Secretary: Mrs E. Orr
10 Oaklands Road, Groomsbridge.
TN3 9SB
☎ 01892 864531

SEVENOAKS REEL CLUB

Aims & Activities: See the RSCDS on page 47.

✍ Secretary: Miss M. Talbot
12 Quakers Hall Lane, Sevenoaks.
TN13 3TR
☎ 01732 450574

TONBRIDGE WELLS AND CROWBOROUGH SCOTTISH COUNTRY DANCE GROUP

Aims & Activities: See the RSCDS on page 47.

✍ Secretary: Mr R. R. Brisley
White Heather, Stone Quarry Road, Chelwood Gate, nr Hayward's Heath, West Sussex.
RH17 7LP
☎ 01825 740533

LANCASHIRE

BURNLEY AND DISTRICT CALEDONIAN SOCIETY

Aims & Activities: Social. Annual Gathering. To encourage interest in the work of Robert Burns.
Affiliations: The Burns Association: Number 417.

✍ Secretary: Mrs I. Smith
9 Mount Road, Burnley.
BB11 2LA

CLITHEROE AND DISTRICT CALEDONIAN SOCIETY

Aims & Activities: Social and to promote interest in Scottish heritage. See the RSCDS on page 47.

✍ Secretary: Mr J. Cameron
Woodhaven, Whalley Banks, Whalley.
BB6 0JL
☎ 01254 823808

FYLDE SCOTTISH COUNTRY DANCING SOCIETY

Aims & Activities: See the RSCDS on page 47.

✍ Secretary: Mrs J. Jagger
53 Northgate, Blackpool.
FY2 9LT
☎ 01253 351117

LYTHAM ST ANNES SCOTTISH COUNTRY DANCE SOCIETY

Aims & Activities: See the RSCDS on page 47.

✍ Secretary: Mrs B. Carr
18 Commonside, Andsell, Lytham St Annes.
☎ 01253 735135

MACDONALD SOCIETY

Aims & Activities: To promote the clan spirit. To collect and preserve clan records. Genealogical. Historical. To strengthen overseas links.
Membership: Open to those bearing the name MacDonald and to members of the clan septs, also those connected by marriage or descent.

✍ Secretary: John McDonald
31 Carr Meadow, Bamber Bridge, Preston.
PR5 8MR

NELSON AND ACCRINGTON SCOTTISH COUNTRY DANCE SOCIETY

Aims & Activities: See the RSCDS on page 47.

✍ Secretary: Mrs L. Edington
31 Laund Gate, Fence, Burnley.
BB12 9PL
☎ 01282 615514

NORTH WEST CRAVEN BRANCH OF THE ROYAL SCOTTISH COUNTRY DANCE SOCIETY

Aims & Activities: See the RSCDS on page 47.

Membership: 90.
✍ Secretary: Mrs E. Bradshaw
Dale Bank, The Square, Ingleton, Carnforth.
LA6 3EG
☎ 01524 241986

PENWORTHAM SCOTTISH COUNTRY DANCE CLASS

Aims & Activities: See the RSCDS on page 47.
✍ Secretary: Mr S. R. Brown
17 Lark Avenue, Penwortham, Preston.
PR1 9RQ
☎ 01772 748034

PLEYDELL DANCE GROUP

Aims & Activities: See the RSCDS on page 47.
✍ Secretary: Lillian Pleydell
126 Railway Street, Nelson.
BB9 9AL
☎ 01282 698366

PRESTON AND DISTRICT CALEDONIAN SOCIETY

Aims & Activities: Social and to encourage interest in Scottish heritage. See the RSCDS on page 47.
✍ Secretary: Mrs M. F. Smith
64 Tulketh Road, Ashton, Preston.
PR2 1AQ
☎ 01772 729547

RIBBLE VALLEY BRANCH OF THE ROYAL SCOTTISH COUNTRY DANCE SOCIETY

Aims & Activities: See the RSCDS on page 47.
Membership: 59.
✍ Secretary: Mr C. D. Bainbridge
Pleasant View, Tockholes, Darwen.
BB3 0NY
☎ 01254 704554

THORNTON CLEVELEYS AND DISTRICT SCOTTISH SOCIETY

Founded: 1951.
Aims & Activities: To promote interest in Scottish heritage and the work of Robert Burns. Social. Annual gathering.
Affiliations: The Burns Federation, No. 754.
✍ Secretary: Mrs M. H. Campbell
13 Wolverton Avenue, Blackpool.
FY2 9NT

LEICESTERSHIRE

LEICESTER BRANCH OF THE ROYAL SCOTTISH COUNTRY DANCE SOCIETY

Aims & Activities: See the RSCDS on page 47.
Membership: 84.
✍ Secretary: Mrs P. Hood
10 Honeycomb Close, The Beeches, Narborough.
LE9 5PS
☎ 0116 2841532

LEICESTER CALEDONIAN SOCIETY

Founded: 1877.
Aims & Activities: Social. To foster friendly relations between Scots in the Leicester area. To encourage interest in Scottish literature and the work of Robert Burns. Highland dancing. Annual Gathering.
Affiliations: The Royal Scottish Country Dance Society and the Burns Federation, No. 461.
✍ Secretary: Mrs E. Woodfield
Martlets, Top End, Great Dalby, Melton Mowbray, Leicester.
LE14 2HA

MARKET HARBOROUGH SCOTTISH COUNTRY DANCING SOCIETY

Aims & Activities: See the RSCDS on page 47.

✍ Secretary: C. P. A. Elphick
Lazonby, 9 Little Lunnon, Dunton Bassset, Lutterworth.
LE17 5JR
☎ 01455 209446

LINCOLNSHIRE

GAINSBOROUGH AND DISTRICT CALEDONIAN SOCIETY

Aims & Activities: Social and to promote interest in Scottish heritage, including the works of Robert Burns. Annual Dinner.
Affiliations: The Burns Federation, No. 887.

✍ Secretary: Mr Lew W. Reid
14 Newlands Court,
Gainsborough.
DN21 1QX

LINCOLN CALEDONIAN SOCIETY

Aims & Activities: Social and to encourage interest in Scottish heritage. See the RSCDS on page 47.

✍ Secretary: Mrs E. Clarkson
4 Dene Close, Skellingthorpe,
Lincoln.
☎ 01522 686901

LINCOLN SCOTTISH COUNTRY DANCE ASSOCIATION

Aims & Activities: See the RSCDS on page 47.

✍ Secretary: Mrs Burkinshaw
40 Albion Crescent, Lincoln.
LN1 1EB
☎ 01522 53193

STAMFORD SCOTTISH DANCE CLUB

Aims & Activities: See the RSCDS on page 47.

✍ Secretary: Mrs J. Green
37 Highlands Way, Stamford.

LONDON

CALEDONIAN CLUB TRUST LTD

Founded: 1952.
Aims & Activities: Social. Annual Gathering.
Affiliations: The Burns Federation, No. 1063.

✍ Secretary: P. J. Varney
9 Halkin Street, London.
SW1X 7DR

CLAN CATHCART

Aims & Activities: To promote the clan spirit worldwide. To collect and preserve hostorical and genealogical clan records and memorabilia. Social.
Membership: Open to those with the name Cathcart, or its variants, and to those related by descent or marriage.

✍ The Chieftain: Major General
The Earl of Cathcart
2 Pembroke Gardens, London.

CLAN GRIERSON

Aims & Activities: To further the clan spirit around the world. To preserve all genealogical and historical clan records. Annual Gathering.
Membership: Open to those of the name Grierson and those related by descent or marriage.

✍ The Chieftain: Sir Michael
Grierson of Lag
Bt., 40c Palace Road, London.

CLAN MACDONALD OF CLANRANALD

Aims & Activities: To promote the clan spirit. To collect the clan records, both Genealogical and Historical. Overseas Links.

Membership: Open to all members of the Macdonald of Clanranald clan and those related by marriage or descent.

✍ The Chieftain: Ranald A. Macdonald of Clanranald
55 Compton Road, London.

CLAN MACPHERSON

Founded: 1939.

Aims & Activities: To foster clan spirit and communication worldwide. To study and preserve clan history and tradition. To acquire and hold property in the Badenoch area of Scotland as well as objects of interest to the clan. Overseas links. Annual Gathering. Charitable. Historical. Social.

Membership: Open to all bearing the name or connected with the clan.

✍ Secretary: 81 Runnymede London.
SW19 2PG

CLAN NICOLSON

Aims & Activities: To promote the clan spirit throughout the world. To collect and preserve the clan historical and genealogical records. Social. Charitable. Overseas links.

Membership: Open to members of the Nicolson clan and those bearing that name, or variants of it, also to those related by descent or marriage.

✍ Secretary: Lord Carnock
90 Whitehall Court, London.
SW1A 2EL

ELSTREE AND BOREHAMWOOD REEL CLUB

Aims & Activities: Social. See the RSCDS on page 47.

✍ Secretary: Miss M. Fouracre
171 Dunraven Drive, The Ridgeway, Enfield, Middlesex. EN2 8LN

☎ 0181 367 4201

HARROW AND DISTRICT CALEDONIAN SOCIETY

Founded: 1928.

Aims & Activities: To encourage social intercourse amongst the Scottish community in Harrow. To foster interest in the works of Robert Burns.

Affiliations: The Burns Federation, No. 492.

✍ Secretary: Ms Sheena Henderson
92A Kenton Road, Kenton, Harrow, Middlesex.
HA9 9AE

LONDON BRANCH OF THE ROYAL SCOTTISH COUNTRY DANCE SOCIETY

Aims & Activities: See the RSCDS on page 47.

Membership: 975.

✍ Secretary: Mrs H. Brown
6 Wells Drive, London.
NW9 8DD

☎ 0181 205 0958

LONDON WEEKEND SCHOOL GROUP

Aims & Activities: See the RSCDS on page 47.

✍ Secretary: Mrs H. U. Brown
6 Wells Drive, Kingsbury, London.
NW9 8DD

✆ 0181 205 0958

MORLEY COLLEGE SCOTTISH COUNTRY DANCING CLUB

Aims & Activities: See the RSCDS on page 47.
✍ Treasurer: Sheila Elkin
7 Sussex Gardens, Highgate,
London.
N6 4LY
☎ 0181 348 7604

SHEEN SCOTTISH COUNTRY DANCE GROUP

Aims & Activities: See the RSCDS on page 47.
✍ Secretary: Mr B. Cresswell
34 Cresswell Road, Twickenham.
Middlesex.
TW1 2DZ
☎ 0181 892 0471

SIDCUP AND DISTRICT CALEDONIAN ASSOCIATION

Aims & Activities: Social and to encourage an interest in Scottish heritage.
Affiliations: The Royal Scottish Country Dance Society, (page 47).
✍ Secretary: Mr T. Boorman
15 Old Farm Road West, Sidcup,
Kent.
☎ 0181 302 2974

ST ANDREWS SOCIETY

Aims & Activities: Social and to encourage an interest in Scottish heritage. See the RSCDS on page 47.
✍ Secretary: Miss A Raffan
2 Erridge Road, Merton Park,
London.
SW19 3JB
☎ 0181 540 1755

WHITE HEATHER SCOTTISH DANCERS

Aims & Activities: See the RSCDS on page 47.
✍ Secretary: B. Baker

39 Burnham Road, Chingford,
London.
E4 8PD
☎ 0181 529 5121

MERSEYSIDE

LIVERPOOL BRANCH OF THE ROYAL SCOTTISH COUNTRY DANCE SOCIETY

Aims & Activities: See the RSCDS on page 47.
Membership: 81.
✍ Secretary: Mrs J. Baker
7 Primrose Road, Liverpool.
L18 2HE
☎ 0151 722 9207

LIVERPOOL BURNS CLUB

Founded: 1924.
Aims & Activities: Social. To encourage interest in the literarature of Robert Burns. Annual Gathering.
Affiliations: The Burns Federation, No. 366.
✍ Secretary: Mrs Hazel Bishop
29 Charterhouse Road,
Liverpool.
L25 8ST

SOUTHPORT BRANCH OF THE ROYAL SCOTTISH COUNTRY DANCE SOCIETY

Aims & Activities: See the RSCDS on page 47.
Membership: 103.
✍ Secretary: Mrs J. Reid
5 Palmerston Road, Southport.
PR9 7AQ

WALLASEY SCOTTISH DANCE GROUP

Aims & Activities: See the RSCDS on page 47.
✍ Secretary: Mrs Halls

14 Waterpark Road, Prentom,
Birkenhead.
L42 9NZ

WIRRAL BRANCH OF THE ROYAL SCOTTISH COUNTRY DANCE SOCIETY

Aims & Activities: See the RSCDS on
page 47.
Membership: 84.
✍ Secretary: Mr J. Henderson
18 Hazelwood, Greasby, Wirral.
L49 2RQ
☎ 0151 678 1961 (home)
☎ 0151 703 9504 (business)

NORFOLK

NORWICH BRANCH OF THE ROYAL SCOTTISH COUNTRY DANCE SOCIETY

Aims & Activities: See the RSCDS on
page 47.
Membership: 114.
✍ Secretary: Mrs M. J. Daniels
166 Earlham Green Lane,
Norwich.
NR5 3RD

NORTHAMPTONSHIRE

CORBY STEWARTS AND LLOYDS' BURNS CLUB

Founded: 1944.
Aims & Activities: Social. Annual
Gathering. To perpetuate the memo-
ry of Robert Burns.
Affiliations: The Burns Federation,
No. 606.
✍ Secretary: J. Gray
23 Ollerton Walk, Corby.
NN17 1UP

GRAMPIAN ASSOCIATION

Founded: 1969.
Aims & Activities: Social. Annual
Gathering.
Affiliations: The Burns Federation,
No. 1053.
✍ Secretary: J. Marriot
14 Bognor Road, Corby.

HAZEL TREE BURNS CLUB

Founded: 1970.
Aims & Activities: Social. Annual
Gathering. To perpetuate the memo-
ry of Robert Burns.
Affiliations: The Burns Federation,
No. 1072.
✍ Secretary: T. J. Starrs
27 Newark Drive, Corby.
NN18 0ES

NORTHAMPTON TOWN AND COUNTY SCOTTISH SOCIETY

Founded: 1973.
Aims & Activities: Aims & activities.
Social. To encourage interest in
Scottish heritage. Annual Gathering.
Affiliations: The Burns Federation,
No. 1051.
✍ Secretary: F. R. Perkins
182 Kingsthorpe Grove,
Northampton.
NN2 6PD

SGIAN DHU CEILIDH CLUB

Founded: 1973.
Aims & Activities: Social. Annual
Gathering. To perpetuate the memo-
ry of Robert Burns.
Affiliations: The Burns Federation,
No. 1075.
✍ Secretary: D. K. Fraser
3 Hunt Street, Corby.
NN18 9LE

NORTHUMBERLAND

BEDLINGTON AND DISTRICT BURNS CLUB

Founded: 1934.
Aims & Activities: Social. Annual Gathering. To promote interest in the works of Robert Burns.
Affiliations: The Burns Federation, No. 534.
✍ Secretary: James K. Stewart
2 East Riggs, Bedlington.
NE22 5SH

CHOPPINGTON BURNS CLUB

Founded: 1848.
Aims & Activities: Social and to perpetuate the memory of Burns.
Affiliations: The Burns Federation, No. 699.
Membership: Open to anyone interested in the aims of the club.
✍ Secretary: Mrs E. Scott
82 Stirling Drive, Bower Grange, Bedlington.

CLAN HANNAY SOCIETY

Founded: 1960.
Aims & Activities: To foster clan and family ties throughout the world. To collect and preserve relics, records and traditions and to preserve as a clan possession the 16th-century Sorbie Tower in Galloway. To strengthen overseas links. Annual gathering. Social. Historical.
Affiliations: Associated Societies: Hanna, Hannay, Hannah Clan Society (USA).
Publications: Newsletter.
Membership: Open to all bearing the name Hannay, Hannah, or Hanna, or connected with the clan by descent or marriage.
✍ Secretary: 7 Oxted Cose
Framlington.
NE23 9YE

NORTHUMBERLAND AND DURHAM CALEDONIAN SOCIETY

Founded: 1924.
Aims & Activities: Social. Educational. Annual Highland ball. To promote and practise Scottish country dancing. To perpetuate the memory of Robert Burns.
Affiliations: The Burns Federation, No. 745.
Membership: Open to all interested in the aims of the society.
✍ Secretary: Mrs J. M. Harper
7a Osbaldeston Gardens,
Gosforth, Newcastle-upon-Tyne.
NE3 4JE

SEAHOUSES SCOTTISH COUNTRY DANCING GROUP

Aims & Activities: See the RSCDS on page 47.
✍ Secretary: Mrs E. Braidford
7 Osborne Gardens, Seahouses.
NE68 7UF
☎ 01665 721396

TYNEDALE COUNTRY DANCE CLUB

Aims & Activities: See the RSCDS on page 47.
✍ Secretary: P. Quince
34 Glamis Crescent, Lockhaugh, Rowlands Gill, Tyne & Wear.
NE39 1AT
☎ 01207 542441

WHITTINGHAM GAMES

Aims & Activities: To organise annual professional games and sports in the area of Whittingham.
Affiliations: The Scottish Games Association, (page 74).
✍ Secretary: R. Herdman
Riverdale House, Townfoot, Rothbury.
NE66 7NX
☎ 01669 621121

NOTTINGHAMSHIRE

COTGRAVE BURNS CLUB

Founded: 1977.
Aims & Activities: Social. Annual Gathering. To perpetuate the memory of Robert Burns.
Affiliations: The Burns Federation, No. 963.
✍ Secretary: Mrs Elizabeth Ferns
4 Flagholme, Cotgrave.
NG12 3PE

MANSFIELD AND DISTRICT CALEDONIAN SOCIETY

Aims & Activities: Social and to encourage interest in Scottish heritage. See the RSCDS on page 47.
✍ Secretary: Mrs M. Erskine
16 Southpark Avenue, Mansfield.
NG18 4PL

NEWARK AND DISTRICT CALEDONIAN SOCIETY

Founded: 1923.
Aims & Activities: Social and to encourage interest in Scottish heritage. To encourage appreciation of Scottish literature, in particular the works of Robert Burns. Annual Gathering.
Affiliations: The Burns Federation, No. 329.
✍ Secretary: Mrs Elizabeth Hamilton
27 Macauley Drive, Balderton, nr Newark.
NG24 3QJ

NEWARK SCOTTISH COUNTRY DANCE SOCIETY

Aims & Activities: See the RSCDS on page 47.
✍ Secretary: Mrs S. Eyton-Williams
Heather House, Maltkiln Road, Fenton, Lincoln.
☎ 01427 718091

NOTTINGHAM BRANCH OF THE ROYAL SCOTTISH COUNTRY DANCE SOCIETY

Aims & Activities: See the RSCDS on page 47.
Membership: 95.
✍ Secretary: Mrs M. Oliver
The Old Dockyard, 52A The Wharf, Shardlow, Derby.
DE72 2HG
☎ 01332 799482

NOTTINGHAM SCOTTISH ASSOCIATION

Founded: 1901.
Aims & Activities: Social. To foster the Scottish spirit, traditions and customs. Charitable and historical. Annual Gathering.
Affiliations: The Burns Federation, No. 17.
Membership: Open to Scots by birth or descent, (to grandparents).
✍ Secretary: Mrs J. D. Willey
6 Moss Side,
Nottingham.
NG11 7EL

RETFORD AND DISTRICT CALEDONIAN SOCIETY

Founded: 1949.
Aims & Activities: Social. Annual Gathering.
Affiliations: The Burns Federation, No. 720.
✍ Secretary: Mrs Mary Isaacs
41 Armstrong Road,
Retford.
DN22 6QX

WORKSOP BURNS AND CALEDONIAN CLUB

Aims & Activities: Social and to encourage interest in Scottish heritage particularly the poetical works of Robert Burns. Annual Dinner.
Affiliations: The Burns Federation, No. 878.

✍ Secretary: Mr Thomas H. English
166 Raymoth Lane, Worksop.
S81 7BY

OXFORDSHIRE

ABINGDON SCOTTISH COUNTRY DANCE CLUB

Aims & Activities: See the RSCDS on page 47.
✍ Secretary: Mr J. Armstrong
Cutts End Cottage, Appleton Road, Cumnor.
OX2 9QH
☎ 01865 865208

BANBURY AND DISTRICT CALEDONIAN SOCIETY

Aims & Activities: Social and to encourage interest in Scottish heritage. See the RSCDS on page 47.
✍ Secretary: Mr K. Young
Saint Brannock, Sideleigh Road, Bodicote, Banbury.
OX15 4AY
☎ 01285 262858

CLAN SINCLAIR

Aims & Activities: To promote the clan spirit worldwide. To collect and preserve genealogical and historical records. Overseas links. Annual Gathering.
Membership: Open to those bearing the name Sinclair, or variants of it.
✍ Chieftain: The Earl of Caithness
Finstock Manor, Finstock.
OX7

HARWELL A.E.R.E. AND DISTRICT CALEDONIAN SOCIETY

Aims & Activities: Social and to encourage interest in Scottish heritage. See the RSCDS on page 47.
✍ Secretary: Lilian Morris

15 Cherbury Green Grove, nr Wantage, Oxford.
OX12 0DP

OXFORD UNIVERSITY SCOTTISH DANCE SOCIETY

Aims & Activities: See the RSCDS on page 47.
✍ Secretary: Mr D. Cummins
9 Annesley Road, Rose Hill, Oxford.
OX4 4JH
☎ 01865 772474

OXFORDSHIRE BRANCH OF THE ROYAL SCOTTISH COUNTRY DANCE SOCIETY

Aims & Activities: See the RSCDS on page 47.
Membership: 92.
✍ Secretary: Mrs B. King
13 Stevenson Drive, Abingdon.
OX14 1SN
☎ 01235 532202

WITNEY SCOTTISH COUNTRY DANCERS

Aims & Activities: See the RSCDS on page 47.
✍ Secretary: Mrs B. Peace
68 Woodstock Road, Witney.
OX8 6DY
☎ 01993 702339

SHROPSHIRE

CLAN LENNOX

Aims & Activities: To collect genealogical and historical clan records. To promote overseas links. Annual Gathering.
Membership: Open to of the Lennox clan and those related by descent or marriage.
✍ Secretary: E. J. H. Lennox

Pools Farm, Downton-on-the-
Rock, Ludlow.
SY8 2HU

SHREWSBURY SCOTTISH DANCERS

Aims & Activities: See the RSCDS on
page 47.
✍ Secretary: Dr J. W. Duff
Jubilee Cottage, Harmer Hill,
Shrewsbury.
SY4 3DZ
☎ 01939 290326

TELFORD CALEDONIAN SOCIETY

Aims & Activities: Social and to
encourage an interest in Scottish heritage. See the RSCDS on page 47.
✍ Secretary: Mrs A. E. Drummond
22 Horsechestnut Drive,
Shawbirch, Telford.
TF5 0LN
☎ 01952 257002

SOMERSET

CLAN MATHESON SOCIETY

Founded: 1961.
Aims & Activities: To foster the clan
spirit worldwide. To strengthen over-
seas links. Historical. Social.
Publications: Clan Matheson
Newsletter.
Membership: Open to all interested in
the clan.
✍ Secretary: Standerwick Court
Frome.
BA11 2PP

SOMERSET BRANCH OF THE ROYAL SCOTTISH COUNTRY DANCE SOCIETY

Aims & Activities: See the RSCDS on
page 47.
Membership: 38.

✍ Secretary: Mr H. Barnes
Pendle, Hillway, Charlton,
Mackrell,
Somerton.
TA11 6AN
☎ 01458 223596

TAUNTON CALEDONIAN SOCIETY

Aims & Activities: Social and to
encourage interest in Scottish heritage. See the RSCDS on page 47.
✍ Secretary: Miss J. M. Glanville
113 Darby Way, Bishops Lydeard,
Taunton.
TA4 3BB
☎ 01823 433191

WEST SOMERSET YEOMANRY REELS CLUB

Aims & Activities: See the RSCDS on
page 47.
✍ Secretary: Miss P. Cotton
Lower Farm, West Bradley, nr
Glastonbury.
BA6 8LT

YEOVIL – ST MICHAEL'S SCOTTISH COUNTRY DANCE CLUB

Aims & Activities: See the RSCDS on
page 47.
✍ Secretary: Mrs M. Bezzant
Bancombe House, Bancombe
Road, Somerton.
TA11 6SB
☎ 01458 272955

STAFFORDSHIRE

CHESTERTON SCOTTISH DANCE SOCIETY

Aims & Activities: See the RSCDS on
page 47.
✍ Secretary: Mrs N. James

15 Derby Road, Talke,
Stoke-on-Trent.
ST7 1SG
☎ 01278 782843

ENDON SCOTTISH DANCE SOCIETY

Aims & Activities: See the RSCDS on page 47.
✍ Secretary: Mrs B. H. Atkins
Rydal, 6 Lingfield Avenue, Brown Edge, Stoke-on-Trent.
ST6 8RD
☎ 01782 502560

NUNEATON AND DISTRICT SCOTTISH SOCIETY

Founded: 1949.
Aims & Activities: Social and to encourage interest in Scottish heritage. Annual Gathering.
Affiliations: The Royal Scottish Country Dance Society and the Burns Federation, No. 777.
✍ Secretary: Mr B. Crosbie
Ivy Cottage, 48 Main Street, Peckleton.
LE9 7RE
☎ 01455 822786

SALTIRE SCOTTISH COUNTRY DANCE GROUP

Aims & Activities: See the RSCDS on page 47.
✍ Secretary: Mrs E. Ray
Cornerways, 29 Farm Road, Finchfield,
Wolverhampton.
WV3 8EL
☎ 01902 763402

STAFFORD AND DISTRICT CALEDONIAN SOCIETY

Aims & Activities: Social and to encourage interest in Scottish heritage. See the RSCDS on page 47.
✍ Secretary: Mrs V. J. Sartin

29 Thornyfields Lane,
Castle Church, Stafford.
ST17 9YS

STONE SCOTTISH DANCING GROUP

Aims & Activities: See the RSCDS on page 47.
✍ Secretary: Mrs H. Leslie
Halfway House, Slindon,
Eccleshall, Stafford.
ST21 6QP
☎ 01782 791350

WOLVERHAMPTON CALEDONIAN SOCIETY WEDNESDAY CLUB

Aims & Activities: See the RSCDS on page 47.
✍ Secretary: Ms I. Morrison
Duddingston, 14 Woodcote Road, Tettenhall, Wolverhampton.
WV6 8LP
☎ 01902 755634

SUFFOLK

ANGLO-SCOTTISH SOCIETY OF IPSWICH

Aims & Activities: Social and to encourage interest in Scottish heritage. See the RSCDS on page 47.
✍ Secretary: Mrs S. McIntosh
65 Bridgewater Road, Ipswich.
IP2 9PR
☎ 01473 685986

BURY ST EDMUNDS AND DISTRICT BURNS CLUB

Aims & Activities: Social. To promote and encourage interest in the works of Burns. Annual Gathering.
Affiliations: The Burns Federation, No. 1092.
✍ Secretary: Mrs E. H. Palmer

4 Lincoln Green,
Bury St Edmunds.
IP33 2LL

BURY ST EDMUNDS CALEDONIAN SOCIETY REEL CLUB

Aims & Activities: See the RSCDS on page 47.
✍ Secretary: Dr M. Rae
72 Home Farm Lane,
Bury St Edmunds IP33 2QL
☎ 01284 763055

CLAN CHISHOLM

Founded: 1951.
Aims & Activities: To foster the clan spirit. To promote overseas links. Historical. Social.
Affiliations: Branches in Edinburgh, Inverness, London, Australia, USA.
Publications: Annual clan journal.
Membership: Open to all bearing the name or coonnected with the clan by descent.
✍ Chieftain: Chisholm of Chisholm
Silver Willows, Bury St Edmunds.
IP28 8BY

TAM O'SHANTER BURNS CLUB

Aims & Activities: Social. Annual Gathering. To perpetuate the memory of Robert Burns.
Affiliations: The Burns Federation, No. 1099.
✍ Secretary: Robert Wardrop
24 Jubilee Court, Howton Road,
Bury St Edmunds IP33 2DD

WEST SUFFOLK CEILIDH CLUB

Aims & Activities: See the RSCDS on page 47.
✍ Secretary: Mrs Ann Bennoch
West Lodge, Mount Road,
Bury St Edmunds.
IP32 7PL
☎ 01284 763459

SURREY

ADDLESTONE AND DISTRICT SCOTTISH SOCIETY

Aims & Activities: Social and to encourage interest in Scottish heritage. See the RSCDS on page 47.
✍ Secretary: Mr A. Pearce
15 Sandalwood Avenue, Chertsey.
KT16 9PD
☎ 01932 564652

CAMBERLEY REEL CLUB

Aims & Activities: See the RSCDS on page 47.
✍ Secretary: Mr A. Pfeiffer
10 Greencroft, Clockhouse Road,
Farnborough.
☎ 01252 541631

CLAN STIRLING

Aims & Activities: To foster the clan spirit. Overseas links. Historical. Genealogical. Social.
Membership: Open to those bearing the name Stirling and its variants, also those related by descent or marriage.
✍ Secretary: Fraser J. Stirling
17 Park Row, Farnham.
GU9 7JH

CRANLEIGH SCOTTISH DANCE SOCIETY

Aims & Activities: See the RSCDS on page 47.
✍ Secretary: Mrs M. Potter
Derwen, Mapledrakes Road,
Ewhurst.
GU6 7QW
☎ 01483 277449

CROYDON AND DISTRICT BRANCH OF THE ROYAL SCOTTISH COUNTRY DANCE SOCIETY

Aims & Activities: See the RSCDS on page 47.
Membership: 151.
✍ Secretary: Miss J. Martin
19 Garrick Crescent, Park Hill, Croydon, Surrey.
CR0 5PW
☎ 0181 681 3968

EPSOM AND DISTRICT CALEDONIAN ASSOCIATION

Aims & Activities: Social and to encourage interest in Scottish heritage.
Affiliations: The Royal Scottish Country Dance Society, (page 47).
✍ Secretary: Mrs T. Mill
Amber Cottage, Grove Road, Epsom.
KY17 4DF
☎ 01372 724455

FARNHAM SCOTTISH COUNTRY DANCING CLUB

Aims & Activities: See the RSCDS on page 47.
✍ Secretary: Mrs I. Douglas
130 Tongham Road, Aldershot, Hampshire.
GU12 4AT

FRIMLEY GREEN SCOTTISH COUNTRY DANCE CLASS

Aims & Activities: See the RSCDS on page 47.
✍ Secretary: Mrs C. D. Brown
11 Carlyon Close, Mytchett, Camberley.
GU16 6JQ
☎ 01252 514789

REIGATE SCOTTISH COUNTRY DANCE CLUB

Aims & Activities: See the RSCDS on page 47.
✍ Secretary: Mrs I Dunn
11 Harlow Court, Wray Common Road, Reigate.
RH2 0RJ
☎ 01737 763971

RICHMOND CALEDONIAN SOCIETY

Aims & Activities: Social and to encourage interest in Scottish heritage. See the RSCDS on page 47.
✍ Secretary: Mr J. Frith
70 Clarence Road, Teddington.
TW11 0BW
☎ 0181 977 6195

SCOTTISH ASSOCIATION FOR WALLINGTON, CARSHALTON AND DISTRICT

Aims & Activities: Social and to encourage interest in Scottish heritage. See the RSCDS on page 47.
✍ Secretary: Mrs V. Meade
54 Bersersford Road, Cheam.
SM2 6ER
☎ 0181 642 4798

SELSDON SCOTTISH COUNTRY DANCE CLASSES

Aims & Activities: See the RSCDS on page 47.
✍ Secretary: Mrs S. Edie
9 Langley Road, Selsdon.
CR2 8ND

ST PHILIP'S SCOTTISH DANCERS

Aims & Activities: See the RSCDS on page 47.
✍ Secretary: Mrs J. Edgar
10 Park Lane East, Reigate.
RH2 8HN
☎ 01737 243165

SURBITON AND DISTRICT CALEDONIAN SOCIETY

Aims & Activities: Social and to encourage interest in Scottish heritage. See the RSCDS on page 47.
✍ Secretary: Mrs A. Bremner
23 The Manor Drive,
Worcester Park.
KT4 7L6
☎ 0181 337 3186

SUSSEX, EAST

ALDRINGTON SCOTTISH COUNTRY DANCE GROUP

Aims & Activities: See the RSCDS on page 47.
✍ Secretary: Mr J. Steer
57 Hangleton Road, Hove.
BN3 79H
☎ 01273 416893

ASHDOWN SCOTTISH COUNTRY DANCE CLUB

Aims & Activities: See the RSCDS on page 47.
✍ Secretary: Mr M. Copeman
Brook House, Burnt Oak,
Crowborough.
TN6 3SD
☎ 01892 655971

BRIGHTON AND HOVE SCOTTISH COUNTRY DANCE CLUB

Aims & Activities: See the RSCDS on page 47.
✍ Secretary: Miss T. Dunbar
98 Wick Hall, Furze Hill, Hove.
☎ 01723 771830

BRIGHTON BRANCH OF THE ROYAL SCOTTISH COUNTRY DANCE SOCIETY

Aims & Activities: See the RSCDS on page 47.

Membership: 126.
✍ Secretary: Mrs H. Goodwin
Flat 6, Sillwood Mansions, 9 Sillwood Place, Brighton.
BN1 2LH
☎ 01273 771061

CLAN KINCAID

Aims & Activities: To promote the clan spirit worldwide. Historical. Genealogical. Social.
Membership: Open to anyone bearing the name Kincaid, or connected to the clan by marriage or descent.
✍ Secretary: Mrs H.V. Kincaid
4a Bristol Gardens, Brighton.
BN2 5JR

HASTINGS AND ST LEONARD'S SCOTTISH REEL CLUB

Aims & Activities: See the RSCDS on page 47.
✍ Secretary: Mrs S. Plummer
1 Alexander Drive,
Bexhill-on-Sea.
TN39 3RR
☎ 01424 842757

SOUTHWICK SCOTTISH COUNTRY DANCE CLUB

Aims & Activities: See the RSCDS on page 47.
✍ Secretary: Mrs J. E. Rozzier
30 Grassmere Avenue,
Telscombe Cliffs, Peacehaven.
BN10 7BZ
☎ 01273 584933

SUSSEX, WEST

BOGNOR REGIS SCOTTISH COUNTRY DANCE CLUB

Aims & Activities: See the RSCDS on page 47.
✍ Secretary: Miss P. M. Harvey

10 Augburth Avenue, Aldwick,
Bognor Regis.
PO21 3DA
☎ 01243 262259

CRAWLEY SCOTTISH COUNTRY DANCING CLUB

Aims & Activities: See the RSCDS on
page 47.
✍ Secretary: R. N. Gray
   6 Bunting Close, Horsham.
   RH13 5PA
☎ 01403 264071

EAST GRINSTEAD SCOTTISH COUNTRY DANCE SOCIETY

Aims & Activities: See the RSCDS on
page 47.
✍ Mrs M. Sherar
   5 Windsor Place, East Grinstead.
   RH19 4RP
☎ 01342 311018

ST ANDREW'S REEL CLUB

Aims & Activities: See the RSCDS on
page 47.
✍ Secretary: Mrs P. Burgin
   Glenville House, 21 Glenville
   Road, Rustington, Littlehampton.
   BN16 2AU
☎ 01903 771661

WORTHING BRANCH OF THE ROYAL SCOTTISH COUNTRY DANCE SOCIETY

Aims & Activities: See the RSCDS on
page 47.
Membership: 46.
✍ Secretary: Mrs E. Chappell
   37 Comston Road,
   Goring-by-Sea.
☎ 01903 248155

TYNE AND WEAR

ARMSTRONG TRUST LTD

Aims & Activities: To research and collect information on the history and genealogy of the clan. To establish a museum. To acquire, restore and preserve clan property. To strengthen overseas links.
Affiliations: The Armstrong Clan Society.
Publications: The Armstrong News.
Membership: Open to all connected with the clan by descent or marriage.
✍ President: E. H. Armstrong
✍ Asst. Registrar: Phoebe
   Armstrong
   4 Oakland Road, West
   Monkseaton, Whitley Bay.
☎ 01912 533845

NEWCASTLE UNIVERSITY SCOTTISH COUNTRY DANCE SOCIETY

Aims & Activities: See the RSCDS on
page 47.
✍ Secretary: Mr P. Dunleavy
   18 Graham Park Road, Gosforth,
   Newcastle-upon-Tyne.
   NE3 4BH
☎ 0191 284 3633

NEWCASTLE-UPON-TYNE AND DISTRICT BRANCH OF THE ROYAL SCOTTISH COUNTRY DANCE SOCIETY

Aims & Activities: See the RSCDS on
page 47.
Membership: 360.
✍ Secretary: Mrs P. Cass
   34 Wenlock Drive, North Shields.
   NE29 9DH
☎ 0191 257 6882

SUNDERLAND BURNS CLUB

Founded: 1897.
Aims & Activities: Social. Annual

Gathering. Educational. To promote interest in the literature of Robert Burns.

Affiliations: The Burns Federation, No. 89.

✍ President: Mrs Anne Donnan
5 Buxton Gardens, Sunderland.
SR3 1LZ

WHITLEY BAY AND DISTRICT SOCIETY OF ST ANDREW

Founded: 1930.

Aims & Activities: Social. Annual Gathering. To promote interest in Scottish heritage. To perpetuate the memory of Robert Burns.

Affiliations: The Burns Federation, No. 696.

✍ Secretary: Albert Somerville
53 Woodburn Square,
Whitley Bay.
NE26 3JD

WARWICKSHIRE

BIRMINGHAM AND MIDLAND SCOTTISH SOCIETY

Founded: 1888.

Aims & Activities: To promote friendly intercourse between Scots in the area. To foster Scottish interests. To celebrate the birth of Robert Burns. To encourage the holding of Highland Games, the playing of the bagpipes, Highland dancing and similar Scottish activities.

Affiliations: The Burns Federation, No. 167.

✍ Secretary: Miss F. J. Mitchell
20 Meadow View, Moseley,
Birmingham.
B13 0AP

LEAMINGTON AND WARWICK CALEDONIAN SOCIETY

Founded: 1947.

Aims & Activities: Social. To encourage friendly relations between Scots in the area. Annual Gathering. To perpetuate the memory of Robert Burns.

Affiliations: The Burns Federation, No. 661.

✍ Secretary: Mrs Ann Haig
32 Lillington Close,
Leamington Spa.
CV32 7RN

ROYAL LEAMINGTON SPA BRANCH OF THE ROYAL SCOTTISH COUNTRY DANCE SOCIETY

Aims & Activities: See the RSCDS on page 47.

Membership: 69.

✍ Secretary: Mr A. Wright
Quorn Cottage, Church Road,
Grandborough, Rugby.
CV23 8DK
☎ 01788 814728 (home)
☎ 01203 563067 (business)

RUGBY SCOTTISH SOCIETY

Aims & Activities: Social and to encourage interest in Scottish heritage. See the RSCDS on page 47.

✍ Secretary: Mrs P. McAteer
Norcroft House, 91 Rugby Road,
Dunchurch.
CV22 6PQ

STRATFORD-UPON-AVON AND DISTRICT CALEDONIAN SOCIETY

Founded: 1947.

Aims & Activities: Social and to encourage interest in Scottish heritage. Annual Gathering.

Affiliations: The Royal Scottish Country Dance Society and The Burns Federation, No. 683.

✍ Secretary: Miss S. Cushing

23 Woodlands Road,
Stratford-upon-Avon.
CV37 0DH

TAM O'SHANTER BURNS CLUB

Aims & Activities: Social and to per-
petuate interest in the works of
Robert Burns. Annual Dinner.
Affiliations: The Burns Federation,
No. 845.
✍ Secretary: c/o Tam O'Shanter
Burns Club
Hertford Place, Coventry.
CV1 3JZ

TAMWORTH AND DISTRICT SCOTTISH SOCIETY

Founded: 1968.
Aims & Activities: Social. To promote
interest in Scottish heritage. Annual
Gathering.
Affiliations: The Burns Federation,
No. 1005.
✍ Secretary: Mrs E. Paterson
14 Highland Road, Erdington,
Birmingham.
B23 6PA

WEST MIDLANDS

BIRMINGHAM BRANCH OF THE ROYAL SCOTTISH COUNTRY DANCE SOCIETY

Aims & Activities: See the RSCDS on
page 47.
Membership: 209.
✍ Secretary: Mr E. E. Parkinson
168 Portland Road, Edgbaston,
Birmingham.
B16 9TD
☎ 0121 429 5714

CORRIEDON SCOTTISH COUNTRY DANCE GROUP

Aims & Activities: See the RSCDS on
page 47.
✍ Secretary: Mr L. Bulmer
17 Rosaville Crescent, Allesley,
Coventry.
CV5 9BP
☎ 01203 402927

COVENTRY AND DISTRICT CALEDONIAN SOCIETY

Founded: 1911.
Aims & Activities: To foster interest in
Scottish history and Scottish heritage.
To encourage study of the works of
Robert Burns. Annual Gatherings.
Social. Charitable. Educational.
Affiliations: The Burns Federation,
No. 559.
Membership: Open to those of Scots
descent.
✍ Secretary: Mr W. Lennox
10 Nordic Drift, Walsgrave,
Coventry.
CV2 2DE

KNOWLE SCOTTISH COUNTRY DANCE CLUB

Aims & Activities: See the RSCDS on
page 47.
✍ Secretary: Mr N. McDougall
67 St John's Close, Kowle,
Solihull.
B93 0NN
☎ 01564 775066

STOURBRIDGE AND DISTRICT SCOTTISH SOCIETY

Aims & Activities: Social and to
encourage interest in Scottish heritage. See the RSCDS on page 47.
✍ Secretary: Miss D. P. Parsons
26 South Avenue, Stourbridge.
DY8 3XY
☎ 01384 394464

SUTTON COLDFIELD BRANCH OF THE ROYAL SCOTTISH COUNTRY DANCE SOCIETY

Aims & Activities: See the RSCDS on page 47.
Membership: 61.
✍ Secretary: Mrs A. Willetts
  164 Green Lanes,
  Sutton Coldfield B73 5LT
☎ 0121 373 0513

WALSALL AND DISTRICT SCOTTISH SOCIETY

Founded: 1900.
Aims & Activities: Social. To encourage friendship between Scots in the area. Annual Gathering. To promote interest in the works of Robert Burns.
Affiliations: The Burns Federation, No. 296.
✍ Secretary: Dr M. Milne
  15 Portland Road, Aldridge,
  Walsall WS9 8NS

WEST MIDLANDS DISTRICT OF ENGLAND BURNS CLUB

Founded: 1972.
Aims & Activities: Social. To perpetuate the memory of Robert Burns.
Affiliations: The Burns Federation, No. 1036.
✍ Secretary: D. Jones
  23 Aynho Close, Mount Nod,
  Coventry.
  CV5 7HH

WOLVERHAMPTON AND DISTRICT CALEDONIAN SOCIETY

Founded: 1938.
Aims & Activities: Social. Annual Gathering. To foster interest in the works of Robert Burns.
Affiliations: The Burns Federation, No. 553.
✍ Secretary: Mrs Y. Pace
  40 Blakeley Avenue, Tettenhall,
  Wolverhampton.
  WV6 9HS

WOLVERHAMPTON BRANCH OF THE ROYAL SCOTTISH COUNTRY DANCE SOCIETY

Aims & Activities: See the RSCDS on page 47.
Membership: 26.
✍ Secretary: Mr D. G. Thomas
  13 Charterfield Drive,
  Kingswinford, Dudley.
  DY6 7RD
☎ 01384 271554 (home)
☎ 0121 559 5951 (business)

WOLVERHAMPTON BRANCH OF THE ROYAL SCOTTISH COUNTRY DANCE SOCIETY

Aims & Activities: See the RSCDS on page 47.
Membership: 35.
✍ Secretary: Mr R. Stephenson
  63 Himley Avenue, Dudley.
  DY1 2QP
☎ 01384 250937

WILTSHIRE

CLAN DURIE

Aims & Activities: To foster the clan spirit. To promote overseas links. To collect and preserve clan records and memorabilia. Genealogical. Historical. Social.
Membership: Open to all bearing the Durie name and those related by marriage or descent.
✍ Secretary: R. V. W. Durie
  Court House, Pewsey SN9

GORSHAM AND DISTRICT CALEDONIAN SOCIETY

Aims & Activities: Social and to encourage interest in Scottish heritage. See the RSCDS on page 47.
✍ Secretary: Mrs B. M. Laister
  4 The Beeches, Shaw, Melksham.
☎ 01225 702190

SWINDON AND DISTRICT SCOTTISH SOCIETY

Founded: 1946.

Aims & Activities: Social. To encourage interest in Scottish heritage. Highland dancing. Annual Gathering. To perpetuate the memory of Robert Burns.

Affiliations: The Burns Federation, No. 791.

✍ Secretary: B. L. Park
   63 Fairlawn, Swindon.
   SN3 6EU

SWINDON SCOTTISH COUNTRY DANCE CLUB

Aims & Activities: See the RSCDS on page 47.

✍ Secretary: Mrs I. Street
   Uplands, 31 High Street,
   Blunsdon, Swindon.
   SN2 4AG
☎ 01793 721285

YORKSHIRE, NORTH

HARROGATE PURPLE HEATHER CLUB

Aims & Activities: See the RSCDS on page 47.

✍ Mrs J. Morrison
   41 Almsford Oval, Harrogate.
   HG2 8EJ
☎ 01423 872234

HARROGATE SALTIRE SCOTTISH COUNTRY DANCE CLUB

Aims & Activities: See the RSCDS on page 47.

✍ President: Mr R. Williamson
   3 Windsor Court, Cavendish
   Avenue, Harrogate.
☎ 01423 508221

HARROGATE ST ANDREW'S SOCIETY

Founded: 1921.

Aims & Activities: To encourage friendly relations between Scots in the area. Social. Annual Gathering. To encourage interest in the work of Robert Burns.

Affiliations: The Burns Federation, No. 555.

✍ Secretary: Mrs Isobel Fairs
   23 Rudbeck Crescent, Harrogate.
   HG2 7AQ

HARROGATE STRATHSPEY AND REEL CLUB

Aims & Activities: See the RSCDS on page 47.

✍ Secretary: Ann Baranyai
   2 West Grove Road, Harrogate.
   HG1 2AD
☎ 01423 505625

NORTHALLERTON CALEDONIAN SOCIETY

Aims & Activities: Social and to encourage interest in Scottish heritage. See the RSCDS on page 47.

✍ Secretary: Mr M. Burt
   The Granary, Thornton-le-Moor,
   Northallerton.
☎ 01609 773429

RICHMOND BRANCH OF THE ROYAL SCOTTISH COUNTRY DANCE SOCIETY

Aims & Activities: See the RSCDS on page 47.

Membership: 86.

✍ Secretary: Mrs C. Middleton
   9 Frances Road, Richmond.
   DL10 4NF
☎ 01748 823331

SCARBOROUGH CALEDONIAN SOCIETY

Founded: 1934.
Aims & Activities: To promote understanding of Scottish history and Scottish heritage. To appreciate the works of Robert Burns. Social. Annual Gathering. Highland dancing.
Affiliations: The Royal Scottish Country Dance Society and the Burns Federation, No. 551.
Membership: Open to those of Scottish descent.
✍ Secretary: Mrs Patricia McNaughton
10 Trafalgar Road, Scarborough.
YO12 7QP

SCARBOROUGH CALEDONIAN SOCIETY SCOTTISH COUNTRY DANCE CLASS

Aims & Activities: See the RSCDS on page 47.
✍ Secretary: Miss Anne Dawson
15 Raincliffe Avenue, Scarborough.
YO12 5BU
☎ 01723 361767

SKIPTON AND DISTRICT CALEDONIAN SOCIETY

Founded: 1959.
Aims & Activities: Social and to encourage interest in Scotland and Scottish heritage, including the literature of Robert Burns. Annual Gathering.
Affiliations: The Burns Federation, No. 1023.
✍ Secretary: J. M. M. Smart
16 Turner Street, Barnoldswick, Lancashire.
BB8 6AT

ST ANDREW SOCIETY OF YORK

Founded: 1894.
Aims & Activities: Social. To promote friendly relations between Scots in the area. Annual Gathering. To encourage interest in the works of Robert Burns.
Affiliations: The Burns Federation, No. 718.
✍ Secretary: Alex C. Layhe
61 Eastfield Avenue, Haxby, York.
YO3 3EZ

WHITBY CALEDONIAN SOCIETY

Aims & Activities: Social and to encourage interest in Scottish heritage.
Affiliations: The Royal Scottish Country Dance Society, (page 47).
✍ Secretary: Mrs J. M. Osborne
6 Resolution Way, Whitby.
YO21 1NP
☎ 01947 603297

YORK SCOTTISH COUNTRY DANCE CLUB

Aims & Activities: See the RSCDS on page 47.
✍ Secretary: Mr A. J. Williams
84 Moor Lane. Dringhouses, York.
YO2 2QY
☎ 01904 709507

YORKSHIRE, SOUTH

BARNSLEY AND DISTRICT SCOTTISH SOCIETY

Founded: 1930.
Aims & Activities: Social. To promote friendly relations between Scots in the area. Annual Gathering. To promote interest in the literature of Robert Burns.
Affiliations: The Burns Federation, No. 439.
✍ Secretary: Mr L. Gibson
147 Pogmoor Road, Barnsley.
S70 6PT

CALEDONIAN SOCIETY OF DONCASTER

Founded: 1883.
Aims & Activities: To promote interest and understanding of Scottish history and Scottish heritage. Social. Annual Gathering. To encourage appreciation of the work of Robert Burns.
Affiliations: The Burns Federation, No. 556.
Membership: Open to those of Scottish descent.
✍ Secretary: Mrs L. Catchpole
35 Ardeen Road, Intake, Doncaster.
DN2 5ET

CALEDONIAN SOCIETY OF SHEFFIELD

Founded: 1883.
Aims & Activities: Social. To promote interest in Scottish history and heritage also to promote interest in the works of Robert Burns.
Affiliations: The Burns Federation, No. 405.
✍ Secretary: Richard A. Coghill
Tanwood, 37 Norton Park View, Sheffield.
S8 8GS

CLUMBER BURNS CLUB

Aims & Activities: Social and to promote interest in the works of Burns. Annual Dinner.
Affiliations: The Burns Federation, No. 922.
✍ Secretary: Mrs J. Jeavons
36 Brunswick Road, Broom Valley, Rotherham.
S60 2RH

DON VALLEY CALEDONIAN SOCIETY

Founded: 1971.
Aims & Activities: Scottish dancing. Piping. Social.

Affiliations: The Burns Federation, No. 972.
Membership: Open to those of Scottish descent.
✍ Secretary: Mrs Edith Ramsay
11 Basil Avenue, Armthorpe, Doncaster.
DN3 2AU

DONCASTER AND DISTRICT BRANCH OF THE ROYAL SCOTTISH COUNTRY DANCE SOCIETY

Aims & Activities: See the RSCDS on page 47.
Membership: 87.
✍ Secretary: Mr A. Jamieson
Tudor House, 11 Mill Lane, Westwoodside, Doncaster.
DN9 2AF
☎ 01427 752501

DONCASTER AND DISTRICT SCOTTISH COUNTRY DANCE SOCIETY

Aims & Activities: See the RSCDS on page 47.
Membership: Members 88.
✍ Secretary: Mr A. Jamieson
Tudor House, 11 Mill Lane, Westwoodside, Doncaster.
DN9 2AF
☎ 01427 752501

NORTH LINDSAY SCOTS SOCIETY

Founded: 1927.
Aims & Activities: To promote interest in Scottish heritage, including the work of Robet Burns. Social. Annual Gathering.
Affiliations: The Burns Federation, No. 706.
✍ Secretary: Mrs L. Hearne
29 Wiltshire Avenue, Burton-on-Stather, nr Scunthorpe.

RETFORD AND DISTRICT BRANCH OF THE ROYAL SCOTTISH COUNTRY DANCE SOCIETY

Aims & Activities: See the RSCDS on page 47.
Membership: 18.
✍ Secretary: Mrs A. Caudwell
32 Palmer Road, Retford, Notts.
DN22 6SS
☎ 01777 702071 (home)
☎ 01777 710641 (business)

ROTHERHAM AND DISTRICT SCOTTISH ASSOCIATION

Founded: 1924.
Aims & Activities: To foster Scottish culture. Highland dancing. Charitable. Educational. Historical. Social.
Affiliations: The Burns Federation, No. 454.
✍ Secretary: William Ingram
10 Mortain Road, Rotherham.
S60 39X

ROTHERHAM SCOTTISH COUNTRY DANCERS

Aims & Activities: See the RSCDS on page 47.
✍ Secretary: Miss M. Pearson
Woodleigh, Squires Lane,
Castleton, Sheffield.
S30 2WW
☎ 01433 620737

SCOTTISH PRESIDENTS ASSOCIATION

Aims & Activities: Social and to promote interest in Scottish heritage including the works of Robert Burns.
Affiliations: The Burns Federation, No. 917.
✍ Secretary: H. Millar MacDonald
8 Roxton Road, Sheffield.
S8 0BD

SHEFFIELD BRANCH OF THE ROYAL SCOTTISH COUNTRY DANCE SOCIETY

Aims & Activities: See the RSCDS on page 47.
Membership: 71.
✍ Secretary: Mrs N. Hutchinson
17 Everard Avenue, Bradway,
Sheffield.
S17 4LY
☎ 0114 2366723 (home)
☎ 0114 2824602 (business),

YORK AND NORTH HUMBERSIDE BRANCH OF THE ROYAL SCOTTISH COUNTRY DANCE SOCIETY

Aims & Activities: See the RSCDS on page 47.
Membership: 120.
✍ Secretary: Mrs H. Brown
Tir-Nan-Og, 8 Copper Beech
Close, Dunnington, York.
YO1 5PY
☎ 01904 488084

YORKSHIRE, WEST

BRADFORD REEL CLUB

Aims & Activities: See the RSCDS on page 47.
✍ Secretary: N. Campbell
60 Upper Wellhouse, Golcar,
Huddersfield.
HD7 4EU
☎ 01484 654507

BRIGHOUSE SCOTTISH COUNTRY DANCE CLUB

Aims & Activities: See the RSCDS on page 47.
✍ Secretary: Mr B. R. Wilson
6 Westacres, Lyndhurst Road,
Brighouse.
HD6 3SH
☎ 01484 722435

BURNS FEDERATION YORKSHIRE DISTRICT

Affiliations: The Burns Federation, No. 1102.

✍ Secretary: Mrs May McGuffog Brig-y-Don, 30 South Edge, Shipley.
BD18 4RA

FRASER SCOTTISH DANCERS

Aims & Activities: See the RSCDS on page 47.

✍ Secretary: Mrs J. Gooden
181 Bourne View Road,
Netherton, Huddersfield.
HD4 7JS
☎ 01484 661196

HUDDERSFIELD ST ANDREW SOCIETY

Founded: 1947.

Aims & Activities: To encourage interest in Scottish heritage, including the works of Robert Burns. Social. Annual Gathering.

Affiliations: The Burns Federation, No. 969.

✍ Secretary: B. K. Mitchell
7 Tanfield Road, Birkby,
Huddersfield.
HD1 5HG

ILKLEY SCOTTISH COUNTRY DANCE CLUB

Aims & Activities: See the RSCDS on page 47.

✍ Secretary: Mrs C. M. McDonald
25 Cleasby Road, Menston,
Ilkley.
LS29 6JE
☎ 01943 874497

KEIGHLEY SCOTTISH COUNTRY DANCE CLUB

Aims & Activities: See the RSCDS on page 47.

✍ Secretary: Mrs E. Ideson

15 Winston Avenue, Crosshill,
Keighley.
BD20 7DL
☎ 01535 632460

KIRKLEES SCOTTISH HIGHLAND SOCIETY

Founded: 1974.

Aims & Activities: Social. Annual Gathering. To perpetuate the memory of Robert Burns.

Affiliations: The Burns Federation, No. 945.

✍ Secretary: Mrs Elsie J. Medlen
34 Thorpe Lane, Almondbury,
Huddersfield.
HD5 8TA

LEEDS BRANCH OF THE ROYAL SCOTTISH COUNTRY DANCE SOCIETY

Aims & Activities: See the RSCDS on page 47.

Membership: 195.

✍ Secretary: Mrs C. M. McDonald
25 Cleasby Road, Menston,
Ilkley.
LS29 6JE
☎ 01943 874497

LEEDS CALEDONIAN SOCIETY

Founded: 1894.

Aims & Activities: To promote understanding of Scottish heritage and history and the literature of Robert Burns.

Affiliations: The Burns Federation, No. 548.

Membership: Open to those of Scottish descent.

✍ Secretary: A. Jeffers
6 Gascoigne Court,
Barwick-in-Elmet, Leeds.
LG15 4AY

LEEDS SCOTTISH COUNTRY DANCE CLUB

Aims & Activities: See the RSCDS on page 47.

✍ Secretary: Ms J. A. Kendall
85 Poplar Grove, Bradford.
BD7 4LL
☎ 01274 578141

LEEDS UNIVERSITY UNION SCOTTISH DANCE SOCIETY

Aims & Activities: See the RSCDS on page 47.

✍ Secretary: Mr A. Smith
18 Barkly Terrace, Beeston, Leeds.
☎ 0113 2715110

OTLEY AND DISTRICT CALEDONIAN SOCIETY

Aims & Activities: Social and to encourage interest in Scottish heritage including the works of Robert Burns. Annual Dinner.
Affiliations: The Burns Federation, No. 880.

✍ Secretary: Mrs Harriet Lee
Lyndhurst, Larkfield Road, Rawdon, Leeds.

PONTEFRACT AND DISTRICT CALEDONIAN SOCIETY

Founded: 1956.
Aims & Activities: To promote friendship amongst Scots in the area To encourage interest in Scottish heritage. Social. Charitable. Piping. Scottish country dancing.
Affiliations: The Royal Scottish Country Dance Society and the Burns Federation, No. 808.
Membership: Open to those over 16 who are Scots by birth, descent or marriage.

✍ Secretary: Mrs S. Cumming
5 Millhill Close, Darrington, Pontefract.
WF8 3BE

✍ Dance Club secretary: Mr G. Mort
16 The Croft, Badsworth, Pontefract.
WF9 1AS
☎ 01977 643039

ST ANDREW SOCIETY OF BRADFORD

Founded: 1886.
Aims & Activities: Social. Annual Gathering. To encourage friendship amongst Scots in the area. To promote interest in Scottish heritage, including the works of Robert Burns.
Affiliations: The Burns Federation, No. 812.

✍ Secretary: Dr Valerie Neasham
26 Carbotton Road, Greengates, Bradford.

WAKEFIELD CALEDONIAN SOCIETY

Founded: 1947.
Aims & Activities: Social. Annual Gathering. To encourage interest in Scottish heritage. To perpetuate the memory of Robert Burns.
Affiliations: The Burns Federation, No. 763.

✍ Secretary: Mrs K. J. Legget
52 Manor Rise, Walton, Wakefield.

WAKEFIELD CALEDONIAN SOCIETY SCOTTISH COUNTRY DANCE GROUP

Aims & Activities: See the RSCDS on page 47.

✍ Secretary: Mrs E. Young
76 Silcoates Lane, Wrenthorpe, Wakefield.
WF2 0NY
☎ 01924 378330

WALES

CLWYD

RUTHIN SCOTTISH COUNTRY DANCE SOCIETY

Aims & Activities: See the RSCDS on page 47.

✍ Secretary: Margaret Rogers
40a Well Street, Ruthin.
LL15 1AW
☎ 01824 707180

RUTHIN ST ANDREW SOCIETY

Aims & Activities: Social and to encourage interest in Scottish heritage. See the RSCDS on page 47.

✍ Secretary: Margaret Rogers
40a Well Street, Ruthin.
LL15 1AW
☎ 01824 707180

DYFED

PEMBROKESHIRE CALEDONIAN SOCIETY

Founded: 1948.
Aims & Activities: To promote friendship amongst Scots in Pembrokeshire. Annual Gathering. To encourage interest in the work of Robert Burns.
Affiliations: The Burns Federation, No. 940.
Membership: Open to all those of Scottish parentage. Associate membership open to those with one Scottish parent and spouses of members.

✍ Secretary: Mrs Kay Rosen
1 Canuset Close, Haken,
Milford Haven.
SA73 3NN

GLAMORGAN, MID

BRIDGEND AND DISTRICT SCOTTISH COUNTRY DANCING CLUB

Aims & Activities: See the RSCDS on page 47.

✍ Secretary: Mr A. J. Williams
48 The Verlands, Cowbridge,
South Glamorgan.
CF7 7BY
☎ 01466 773894

GLAMORGAN, SOUTH

CARDIFF CALEDONIAN SOCIETY

Aims & Activities: Social and to encourage interest in Scottish heritage. See the RSCDS on page 47.

✍ Secretary: Mr J. Gardner
12 Leven Close, Lakeside, Cardiff.
CF2 6DN
☎ 01222 756741

CARDIFF ST ANDREW'S SCOTTISH COUNTRY DANCE GROUP

Aims & Activities: See the RSCDS on page 47.

✍ Secretary: Mrs I. A Gardner
12 Leven Close, Lakeside, Cardiff.
CF2 6DN
☎ 01222 756741

RADYR SCOTTISH COUNTRY DANCERS

Aims & Activities: See the RSCDS on page 47.

✍ Secretary: Mrs C. M. Gray
35 Coryton Crescent,

Whitchurch, Cardiff.
CF4 7EQ
☎ 01222 614903

SOUTH WALES BRANCH OF THE ROYAL SCOTTISH COUNTRY DANCE SOCIETY

Aims & Activities: See the RSCDS on page 47.
Membership: 145.
✍ Secretary: Mrs l. Wilson
Pennant House, St Mary Church, Cowbridge.
CF7 7LW
☎ 01446 773894 (home)
☎ 01656 762085 (business),

GLAMORGAN, WEST

MUMBLES SCOTTISH COUNTRY DANCING GROUP

Aims & Activities: See the RSCDS on page 47.
✍ Secretary: Mr R. M. Forbes
3 Woodlands Terrace, Swansea.
SA1 6BR
☎ 01792 463871

SWANSEA ST ANDREW'S SCOTTISH COUNTRY DANCE SOCIETY

Aims & Activities: See the RSCDS on page 47.
✍ Secretary: Mrs J. Proudfoot
120 Woodcote, Killay, Swansea.
SA2 7AU
☎ 01792 299443

GWENT

ABERGAVENNY SCOTTISH COUNTRY DANCERS

Aims & Activities: See the RSCDS on page 47.
✍ Secretary: Mrs C. Dinsdakle
Crispin Cottage, Llandew, Rhydderch, by Abergavenny.
NP7 9TS
☎ 01873 840272

CWMBRAN SCOTTISH COUNTRY DANCE CLUB

Aims & Activities: See the RSCDS on page 47.
✍ Secretary: Mrs J. Cleaver
87 Bryn Milwr, Hollybush, Cwmbran.
NP44 7UU
☎ 01633 864404

NEWPORT SCOTTISH COUNTRY DANCE CLUB

Aims & Activities: See the RSCDS on page 47.
✍ Secretary: Mrs M. Davies
50 Anthony Drive, Caerleon, Newport.
NP6 1DS
☎ 01633 421128

GWYNEDD

CAERNARVONSHIRE AND ANGLESEY CALEDONIAN SOCIETY

Aims & Activities: Social and to encourage interest in Scottish heritage. See the RSCDS on page 47.
✍ Secretary: Mr B. Osborne
Foxbrush, Aber Pwll, Dinorwic.
LL56 4JZ
☎ 01248 670463

CLYNNOG THISTLE SCOTTISH DANCE GROUP

Aims & Activities: See the RSCDS on page 47.

✍ Secretary: Mrs J. Shaw
Dwlch Uchaf Nawr, Deindlen.
LL55 3EE
☎ 01286 870545

NORTH WALES SCOTTISH COUNTRY DANCE SCHOOL

Aims & Activities: See the RSCDS on page 47.

✍ Secretary: Mrs E. E. C. Brown
5 Anglesea Road, Great Orme, Llandudno.
LL30 2QB
☎ 01492 874415

POWYS

BUILTH WELLS SCOTTISH COUNTRY DANCE GROUP

Aims & Activities: See the RSCDS on page 47.

✍ Secretary: Mrs V. Sennett
Wyeburn House, Castle Street, Builth Wells.
LD2 3BN
☎ 01982 552907

NORTHERN IRELAND

ANTRIM

EAST ANTRIM BURNS ASSOCIATION

Aims & Activities: Social. Annual gathering. To perpetuate the memory of Robert Burns.
Affiliations: The Burns Federation, No. 1018.
✍ Secretary: Sam Cross
42 Glenvale Park, Glynn, Larne.
BT40 3EZ

PORTRUSH BRANCH OF THE ROYAL SCOTTISH COUNTRY DANCE SOCIETY

Aims & Activities: See the RSCDS on page 47.
Membership: 23.
✍ Secretary: Mrs F. Morrison
22 Westminster Park, Portstewart.
BT55 7JD
☎ 01265 832033 (home)
☎ 01265 4417 (business),

WHITEHEAD BRANCH OF THE ROYAL SCOTTISH COUNTRY DANCE SOCIETY

Aims & Activities: See the RSCDS on page 47.
Membership: 20.
✍ Secretary: Mrs A. Thompson
20 Windsor Avenue, Whitehead, Carrickfergus.
BT38 9RX

ARMAGH

PORTADOWN SCOTTISH COUNTRY DANCE SOCIETY

Aims & Activities: See the RSCDS on page 47.
✍ Secretary: Mrs E. Campbell
99 Kernan Gardens, Portadown, Craigavon.
BT63 5RA
☎ 01762 336121

BELFAST

BELFAST BRANCH OF THE ROYAL SCOTTISH COUNTRY DANCE SOCIETY

Aims & Activities: See the RSCDS on page 47.
Membership: 290.
✍ Secretary: Mrs L. Rankin
22 Ballynagarrick Road, Carryduff.
BT9 8LU
☎ 01232 812249 (home)
☎ 01232 797144 (business),

BELFAST BURNS CLUB

Founded: 1886.
Aims & Activities: Social. Annual Gathering. To perpetuate the memory of Robert Burns.
Affiliations: The Burns Federation, No. 15.
✍ Secretary: Miss Sheila Binns
8 Ballyfore Gardens, Ballyduff, Newtownabbey, County Antrim.
BT36 6XY

HARLAND AND WOLF BURNS CLUB

Founded: 1967.

Aims & Activities: Social. Annual Gathering.

Affiliations: The Burns Federation, No. 1010.

✍ Secretary: James Heron
2 Harland Park, Belfast.
BT4 1TZ

COUNTY DOWN

COMBER SCOTTISH COUNTRY DANCE CLUB

Aims & Activities: See the RSCDS on page 47.

✍ Secretary: Mrs P. Goodall
71 Mountain Road, Newtonards.
BT23 4UL
☎ 01247 813493

DOWNPATRICK SCOTTISH COUNTRY DANCE SOCIETY

Aims & Activities: See the RSCDS on page 47.

✍ Secretary: Mrs R. Wheeler
Portulla, 2 Finnebrogue,
Downpatrick.
☎ 01396 612730

CHANNEL ISLANDS

JERSEY

JERSEY CALEDONIA SCOTTISH COUNTRY DANCE GROUP

Aims & Activities: See the RSCDS on page 47.

✍ Secretary: Mrs H. M. McGugan
La Pelotte, Rue a Don, Grouville.
JE3 9GB

SCOTTISH SOCIETY OF JERSEY

Aims & Activities: Social. To promote friendship amongst the Scots or those of Scots descent resident in Jersey. Annual Gathering.

Affiliations: The Burns Federation, No. 1108.

✍ Secretary: Mrs C. Brown
Marine Villa, Roule de la Haule,
St Lawrence.
JE3 1BA

EUROPE

AUSTRIA

VIENNA BRANCH OF THE ROYAL SCOTTISH COUNTRY DANCE SOCIETY

Aims & Activities: See the RSCDS on page 47.
Membership: 29.
✍ Secretary: Mrs Marion Van Sickle
Mukenthalerweg 51, 1190 Vienna.
☎ 43 1 322565 (home)
☎ 43 328450 (business)

BELGIUM

CALEDONIAN SOCIETY OF BRUSSELS

Aims & Activities: To encourage all social activities likely to promote an interest in Scotland and Scottish heritage throughout the world.
Affiliations: The Burns Federation, No. 1061 and the St Andrew Society of Scotland.
✍ Secretary: Miss K. Macdonald
81 Rue du Duc, 1150 Brussels.
☎ 32 2 285 63 21

CALEDONIAN SOCIETY OF BRUSSELS COUNTRY DANCING

Aims & Activities: See the RSCDS on page 47.
✍ Secretary: Mr W. Frizzell
38 Avenue de Quebec, 1330 Rixensart, Brussels.
☎ 32 2 653 1198

FLEMISH CALEDONIAN SOCIETY

Aims & Activities: See the RSCDS on page 47.
✍ Secretary: Mr A. Gibbons
Avenue L. Bertrand 104/29F, 1030 Brussels.
☎ 32 2 242 2751

LID VAN DE ROYAL SCOTTISH PIPE BAND ASSOCIATION

Aims & Activities: Encouraging an interest in and the formation and organisation of pipe bands and piping and drumming, also participation in competitions and events in Highland Games.
Affiliations: The Royal Scottish Pipe Band Association, (page 59).
✍ Secretary: Koen Vanbesien
30 Pitoorsstraat, B-2110 Wljninegem.

ST ANDREW'S CHURCH SCOTTISH COUNTRY DANCE GROUP

Aims & Activities: See the RSCDS on page 47.
✍ Secretary: Mrs R. A. Campbell
68 Avenue d'Auderghem, Box 4, 1040 Brussels.
☎ 32 2 736 4238

DENMARK

POLYCARP DANCERS

Aims & Activities: See the RSCDS on page 47.
✍ Secretary: Mrs M. Petersen
Falkerslevvej 30, 4871 Horbelev.

ST ANDREW SOCIETY OF DENMARK

Founded: 1976.

Aims & Activities: To promote friendship between Denmark and Scotland and to further mutual knowledge of the two countries. Annual Gathering. Highland Games. Highland dancing. Historical. Charitable. Educational. Social.

Affiliations: The Royal Scottish Country Dance Society and The Burns Federation, No. 727.

Membership: Open to Scots living in Denmark and all with connections with Scotland.

✍ Secretary (dancing): Miss E. Hartzberg
Jydeholmen 35c, 3tv., DK-2720 Vanlose.
☎ 45 31 745 5324

✍ Burns Club: Lisc Rindel
Donnerupvek 6, Dk-2720 Vanlose.

FRANCE

ASSOCIATION DE DANSES ECOSSAISES DE ST QUAY PERROS Ñ SCOTS BONNET

Aims & Activities: See the RSCDS on page 47.

✍ Secretary: Mrs C. Louvet
Coz Moguero, F 22700 St Quay Perros.
☎ 33 96 91 18 21

CLUB DE DANSE ECOSSAISE

Aims & Activities: See the RSCDS on page 47.

✍ Secretary: Mrs M. Gros
52 Rue de l'Hermitage, 07500 Granges, Valence.
☎ 33 75 40 07 54

CLUB DE DANSE ECOSSAISE DE MONTPELLIER

Aims & Activities: See the RSCDS on page 47.

✍ Secretary: Nanon Vincent
4 Rue de l'Aubepine, 34070 Montpellier.

GORDON GROUP — BELZ

Aims & Activities: See the RSCDS on page 47.

✍ Secretary: Mr P. J. Rohrer
Le Champ de Ledu, 24370 Calviac en Perigord.

GROUPE DE DANSES ECOSSAISES DE LYONS

Aims & Activities: See the RSCDS on page 47.

✍ Secretary: Ms C. Orgeret
32 Avenue de Chateau, 69003 Lyon.
☎ 33 72 34 66 03

LE CHANDON D'ECOSSE

Aims & Activities: See the RSCDS on page 47.

✍ Secretary: Mme L. Chamoin
31 Rue Cavendish, 75019 Paris.
☎ 33 1 42 06 99 08

LES BALLERINS DE FRANCE

Aims & Activities: See the RSCDS on page 47.

✍ Secretary: J. S. Berthomiew
La Buissonnerie, 20 Rue de la Republique, Dampmart, 77400 Lagny.

LYON AND DISTRICT BURNS CLUB

Aims & Activities: Social and to encourage interest in Scottish heritage and work of Robert Burns. Annual Dinner.

Affiliations: The Federation of Burns Clubs, No. 1120.

🖎 Secretary: Ms Laura Swann
19 Allee de Chanterelles, St-Foy-Les-Lyon, 69110, Lyon.

PARIS BRANCH OF THE ROYAL SCOTTISH COUNTRY DANCE SOCIETY

Aims & Activities: See the RSCDS on page 47.
Membership: 92.

🖎 Secretary: Miss Noelle Thuvignon
19 Avenue du 8 Mai 1945, 95400 Villiers-le-Bell.

☎ 33 1 39 92 01 21

SCOTS KIRK

Aims & Activities: See the RSCDS on page 47.

🖎 Secretary: Miss N. Rendall
9 Rue de l'Epargne, 92320 Chatillon.

GERMANY

ANGLO GERMAN SCOTTISH COUNTRY DANCE GROUP

Aims & Activities: See the RSCDS on page 47.

🖎 Secretary: Mr A. Busse
Elchweg 26, W 4837 Verl 1.

CALEDONIAN SOCIETY OF HAMBURG, SCOTTISH COUNTRY DANCING SECTION

Aims & Activities: See the RSCDS on page 47.

🖎 Secretary: Mrs V. Puschmann
Freesienweg 40, 22395 Hamburg.

☎ 49 40 600 7710

CEILIDH DANCERS SCOTTISH COUNTRY DANCE CLUB

Aims & Activities: See the RSCDS on page 47.

🖎 Secretary: Ms S. Hegel
Innungswall 18 A, 3170 Gifhorn.

COLOGNE SCOTTISH COUNTRY DANCERS

Aims & Activities: See the RSCDS on page 47.

🖎 Secretary: Mrs A. Groenke
Albert-Kindle-Strasse 3, 50859 Koln.

☎ 49 221 478595

EMO DANCERS

Aims & Activities: See the RSCDS on page 47.

🖎 Secretary: Mr O. Thinius
Rosastr. 10, 45130 Essen.

FRANKFURT SCOTTISH COUNTRY DANCE CLUB

Aims & Activities: See the RSCDS on page 47.

🖎 Secretary: Mrs H. Mansky
Peter Bied Strasse 39, D-65929 Frankfurt.

☎ 49 69 302274

FREIBURG SCOTTISH COUNTRY DANCERS

Aims & Activities: See the RSCDS on page 47.

🖎 Secretary: Mrs R. Seidelmann
Hildstrasse 11, D-79102, Freiburg.

☎ 49 761 75628

MUNICH SCOTTISH ASSOCIATION

Aims & Activities: See the RSCDS on page 47.

🖎 Secretary: Sue Bollans
Keferstrasse 24B, 8080 Munchen.

☎ 49 89 391253

SCOTTISH COUNTRY DANCING SOCIETY OF BERLIN

Aims & Activities: See the RSCDS on page 47.

✍ Secretary: Frau A McLarren, Stindestrasse 23, 12167 Berlin.

☎ 49 30 7964625

TAMBURIN – STUTTGART GROUP

Aims & Activities: See the RSCDS on page 47.

✍ Secretary: S. Muller Geschaftstelle Rosenstrasse 40 7306 Denkendorf.

IRELAND

CLAN RUTHVEN

Aims & Activities: Overseas links. Social.

Membership: Open to members of the Ruthven clan and family and those bearing that name, or variants of it.

✍ President: The Earl of Gowrie Castlemartin, Kilcullen, County Kildare.

CORK SCOTTISH COUNTRY DANCE SOCIETY

Aims & Activities: See the RSCDS on page 47.

✍ Secretary: Mrs D. Payne 11 Hillcrest, Donnybrook, Douglas, County Cork.

☎ 353 21 361841

DUBLIN SCOTTISH COUNTRY DANCE CLUB

Aims & Activities: See the RSCDS on page 47.

✍ Secretary: Mr J. Gibson Tanglewood, The Nurseries, Delgany, County Wicklow.

☎ 353 287 7520

IRISH PIPE BAND ASSOCIATION

Aims & Activities: To encourage an interest in and the formation and organisation of pipe bands and piping and drumming, also participation in competitions and events in Highland Games.

Affiliations: The Royal Scottish Pipe Band Association, (page 59).

✍ Secretary: Enterprise Centre Melitta Road, Kildare, Ireland.

ITALY

CIVIS SCOTTISH COUNTRY DANCE GROUP

Aims & Activities: See the RSCDS on page 47.

✍ Secretary: Ms T. Edelman c/o Goethe Institute Library, 206 Piazza San Carlo 206, 10121 Torino.

☎ 39 11 662 84 75

SCOTTISH COUNTRY DANCE GROUP – ROME

Aims & Activities: See the RSCDS on page 47.

✍ Secretary: Mr J. Fitzpatrick Fisheries Dept., FAO of the UN, Via Della Terme di Caracalla, Rome 00100.

☎ 39 6 225 6510

SOCIETA DI DANZA

Aims & Activities: See the RSCDS on page 47.

✍ Secretary: Dr Fabio Mollica Via Calvart 10, 40129 Bologna.

☎ 39 51 371457

LUXEMBOURG

LUXEMBOURG SCOTTISH COUNTRY DANCE CLUB

Aims & Activities: See the RSCDS on page 47.
✍ Secretary: Ms. V. Craig
6 Grassbierg, L-6230 Bech G. D., Luxembourg.
☎ 352 79694

NETHERLANDS

CLANSMEN SCOTTISH COUNTRY DANCE GROUP

Aims & Activities: See the RSCDS on page 47.
✍ Secretary: Mrs M. McPhail
Ursulaland 1431, 2591 GW. The Hague.
☎ 31 70 382 1175

DELFT BRANCH OF THE ROYAL SCOTTISH COUNTRY DANCE SOCIETY

Aims & Activities: See the RSCDS on page 47.
Membership: 72.
✍ Secretary: Mr A. L. M. Boode
Elzendreefe 34, 3137 CC Vlaardingen.
☎ 31 10 474 1141 (home)
☎ 31 20 649 3752 (business)

GELDERMALSEN SCOTTISH COUNTRY DANCE GROUP

Aims & Activities: See the RSCDS on page 47.
✍ Secretary: Mrs A. Z Hootsen
Jacob de Ridderstaat 1. 4197 Bl Buurmalsen.
☎ 31 34 557 4879

GOUDA SCOTTISH COUNTRY DANCE SOCIETY

Aims & Activities: See the RSCDS on page 47.
✍ Secretary: Mr J. M. Feijtel
Ericalaan 28, 2803 BP, Gouda.
☎ 31 1820 26549

HAGUE DISTRICT BRANCH OF THE ROYAL SCOTTISH COUNTRY DANCE SOCIETY

Aims & Activities: See the RSCDS on page 47.
Membership: 55.
✍ Secretary: Mr H. van Zon
De Tol 421, 2266 EH Leidschendam.
☎ 31 70 320 2352 (home)
☎ 31 70 327 0557 (business)

LOWLAND HIGHLAND GAMES

Aims & Activities: To organise annual professional Highland Games and sports in the Netherlands.
Affiliations: The Scottish Games Association, (page 74).
✍ Secretary: A. Degeling
Peulen-straat 223, 3371 AM Hardinx-veld-Giessendam.

NEDERLANDSE ORGANISATIE VAN DOEDELZAKBANDS

Aims & Activities: To encourage an interest in and the formation and organisation of pipe bands and piping and drumming, also participation in competitions and events in Highland Games.
Affiliations: The Royal Scottish Pipe Band Association, (page 59).
✍ Secretary: Robert Hoogenhout
Assendorperdijk 86, 8012 EJ Zwolle.

PIPERS AND PIPE BAND SOCIETY OF AMSTERDAM

Aims & Activities: To encourage an

interest in and the formation and organisation of pipe bands and piping and drumming, also participation in competitions and events in Highland Games.

Affiliations: The Royal Scottish Pipe Band Association, (page 59).

✍ Secretary: Mieke Molenaar Finsenstraat 46, Amsterdam.

ROWAN TREE DANCERS

Aims & Activities: See the RSCDS on page 47.

✍ Secretary: Mr R. Meyer Ploegstede 1, 8171 HB Vaassen.

☎ 31 5788 2260

SCOTS CHURCH ROTTERDAM SCOTTISH COUNTRY DANCE CLUB

Aims & Activities: See the RSCDS on page 47.

✍ Secretary: Mr A. L. Boode Elzendreef 34, 3137 CC Vlardingen.

☎ 31 10 474 1141

SWILCAN SCOTTISH COUNTRY DANCE GROUP – UTRECHT

Aims & Activities: See the RSCDS on page 47.

✍ Secretary: Mrs M. Lambourne Vuurvliegweide 2, 3437 VT Nieuwegein.

☎ 31 34 024 7796

THISTLE CLUB OF SCOTTISH COUNTRY DANCING – EINDHOVEN

Aims & Activities: See the RSCDS on page 47.

✍ Secretary: Audrey Preston Picassohof 44, 5613 MC Eindhoven.

☎ 31 40 461029

NORWAY

CALEDONIAN SOCIETY OF NORWAY

Aims & Activities: To encourage all social activities likely to promote an interest in Scotland and Scottish heritage throughout the world.

Affiliations: The St Andrew Society of Scotland, (page 48).

✍ Secretary: David E. Brookes Revesporet 5b, 1347 Hosle.

OSLO SCOTTISH COUNTRY DANCE GROUP

Aims & Activities: See the RSCDS on page 47.

✍ Secretary: Jean Oeding Ostenga 30, 1349 Rykkin.

☎ 47 67138798

TANAGER SCOTTISH COUNTRY DANCE GROUP – STAVANGER

Aims & Activities: See the RSCDS on page 47.

✍ Secretary: Mrs C. Kemp Vidjevegen 2, 4056 Tanager.

☎ 47 51 696541

PORTUGAL

SCOTTISH COUNTRY DANCE GROUP OF PORTUGAL

Aims & Activities: See the RSCDS on page 47.

✍ Secretary: Mrs F. Rochette Rua Garcia de Orta, 70 2, 1200 Lisbon.

RUSSIA

CALEDONIAN SOCIETY OF MOSCOW

Aims & Activities: Social. Annual Gathering. To foster links with Scotland and people of Scottish origin in Russia. To serve as a focus for expatriate Scots in Russia.
Membership: Open to expatriate Scots and those with Scottish links.
✍ Dr Dimitri Fedosov
Institute of Universal History,
Russian Academy of Sciences,
Moscow.

ST ANDREWS SOCIETY RUSSIA

Founded: 1995
Aims & Activities: To promote the Scots identity and customs in Russia through fellowship between Scots, Russian nationals and citizens of all other countries who love Scotland.
Affiliations: The St Andrew Society, Burns Federation, The Royal Scottish Country Dance Society.
Publications: Internet home page: http://ourworld.compuserve.com/homepages/mmackie/
Membership: Around 40 families. Membership is open but voting is restricted to Scots.
✍ Chieftain: Mike Mackie
Dacha 60B, Line 2, Gerebryany Bor, 123103 Moscow.
☎ 7 095 501 2586900
© 7 095 501 2586920
✍ UK: c/o Mackie
FM Shell Neft, Moscow, Russia,
c/o Herald International
Mailings, PO Box 10235,
London.
SW19 3ZN
E 70673,3323@compuserve.com

ST PETERSBURG ASSOCIATION FOR INTERNATIONAL CO-OPERATION

Founded: 1949
Aims & Activities: To further cultural links between Russia and other countries. To arrange student and tourist exchanges and further contacts between schools. To provide interpreters for business. Charitable. Joint Burns suppers held every January.
Membership: Open to all.
✍ Margarita Mudrak
21 Fontanka, St Petersburg.
☎ 7 812 314 8327
© 7 812 311 4089
✍ Maggie MacAllister
Plain Tree Cottage, Houston,
Renfrewshire.
☎ 01505 690141

SPAIN

CLAN BOYD

Aims & Activities: Overseas links.
Membership: Open to members of the Boyd clan and family and those bearing that name, or variants of it, also to those related by marriage or descent.
✍ President: The Lord Kilmarnock
Casa de Mondrago, Ronda,
Malaga.

SCHIEHALLION GROUP

Aims & Activities: See the RSCDS on page 47.
✍ The Treasurer
Jerez 4, P4, 4B, E-28016, Madrid.
☎ 34 1 350 4793

SWEDEN

CALEDONIAN SOCIETY OF SWEDEN

Aims & Activities: To encourage all social activities likely to promote an interest in Scotland and Scottish heritage throughout the world.
Affiliations: The St Andrew Society of Scotland.
✍ Secretary: Julia Morton
   Box 159, 182 12 Dandergd.

GOTHENBURG BRANCH OF THE ROYAL SCOTTISH COUNTRY DANCE SOCIETY

Aims & Activities: See the RSCDS on page 47.
Membership: 26.
✍ Secretary: Ms Cecilia Fairall
   Bildstensgaten 61, S-423 47
   Torslanda.
☎ 46 1 563516 (home)
☎ 46 31 604038 (business)

STOCKHOLM BRANCH OF THE ROYAL SCOTTISH COUNTRY DANCE SOCIETY

Aims & Activities: See the RSCDS on page 47.
Membership: 43.
✍ Secretary: Ms G. Jansson
   Jaktvarvsplan 4, S-112 36.
☎ 46 08 653 97 52 (home)
☎ 46 08 785 83 32 (business)

STOCKHOLM CALEDONIAN DANCE CIRCLE

Aims & Activities: See the RSCDS on page 47.
✍ Secretary: Miss S. Brusling
   Nederstavagen 7, S-137 55
   Vasterhaninge.
☎ 46 8 500 371 37

SWEDISH-BRITISH SOCIETY

Aims & Activities: To encourage all social activities likely to promote an interest in Scotland and Scottish heritage throughout the world.
Affiliations: The St Andrew Society of Scotland.
✍ Secretary: Commodore Ulf Adlen
   Kommendorsgaten15, 114 48
   Stockholm.

THORBURN-MACFIE SOCIETY

Aims & Activities: Social and to encourage an interest in Scottish heritage for descendants of Thorburn or MacFie in Sweden.
✍ Secretary: Ulf M. Hagman
   Thorburn-MacFie Society,
   Uddevala.

SWITZERLAND

BADEN-BRUGG SCOTTISH COUNTRY DANCING CLUB

Aims & Activities: See the RSCDS on page 47.
✍ Secretary: Mrs M. Menzies
   Lourenstrasse 27, CH 5443,
   Niederrohrdorf.

BERN SCOTTISH COUNTRY DANCE GROUP

Aims & Activities: See the RSCDS on page 47.
✍ Secretary: Mrs S. Brawan-Fraser
   Beundeweg 8, CH-3033 Wohlen.
☎ 41 31 829 15 57

GENEVA SCOTTISH COUNTRY DANCE GROUP

Aims & Activities: See the RSCDS on page 47.
✍ Secretary: Mrs M. King
   7 Rue de Fribourg, 1202 Geneva.
☎ 41 22 732 75 53

SCOTTISH COUNTRY DANCE GROUP, BASEL

Aims & Activities: See the RSCDS on page 47.

✍ Secretary: Mrs J. Ogilvie-Steuri
St Gallen-Ring 206, 4054 Basel.
☎ 41 61 280 84 04

SWISS BURNS SOCIETY

Aims & Activities: To further the study of the works of Burns. Social. Annual Gathering.
Affiliations: The Burns Federation, No. 1080.
✍ Secretary: Daniel Ammann
Postfach 97
CH-7208 Malans.

ZURICH SCOTTISH COUNTRY DANCING CLUB

Aims & Activities: See the RSCDS on page 47.

✍ Secretary: Marlyn Villiger
Tannenweg 35, 4804 Wintertnor.
☎ 41 52 222 71 61

UKRAINE

ENGLISH SPEAKING LANGUAGE CLUB OF ODESSA

Aims & Activities: Social. To encourage the speaking of the English language, including the study of Robert Burns. Annual Gathering.
Affiliations: The Burns Federation, No. 1110.
✍ Secretary: Stanislav Kiselyov
English Speaking Club, PO Box 7, Odessa SU 270100.

UNITED STATES OF AMERICA

ALABAMA

ALABAMA HIGHLAND GAMES

Aims & Activities: These Games are usually held on the third Saturday in September in the Alabama Shakespeare Festival Grounds in the Wynton Blount Cultural Park, Montgomery. They include pipe bands, solo piping, Highland dancing and athletic events. Numerous other events include a Border Collie demonstration.

✍ Secretary: c/o PO Box 6075
Montgomery.
AL 36105

CLAN DOUGLAS SOCIETY OF NORTH AMERICA

Aims & Activities: To strengthen overseas links.
Membership: Open to those with the name Douglas and to those connected by descent or marriage.

✍ President: Rev. Melvyn. W.
Douglass
✍ Executive Secretary: Gilbert F.
Douglas Jr.
MD, 2009 Kentucky Avenue,
Birmingham AL 32516
☎ 1 205 922 9670

CLAN HUNTER ASSOCIATION

Aims & Activities: To strengthen Scottish and overseas links. Genealogical. Historical. Social.
Affiliations: The Clan Hunter Association, Scotland.
Membership: Open to those with the name Hunter and those connected by descent or marriage.

✍ Clan Officer USA: Charles M.
Hunter

PO Box 43062, Cahaba Heights
Branch, Birmingham.
AL 35243
☎ 1 205 967 0389

CLAN MACNEIL ASSOCIATION OF AMERICA SOUTH ATLANTIC BRANCH

Aims & Activities: To strengthen Scottish and overseas links. Genealogical. Historical. Social.
Membership: Open to all with the name MacNeil or that of one of its septs and to those related by descent or marriage.

✍ Comm: Louis McNeil Quigley
2021 Little John Drive, Oxford.
AL 36203

TARTAN HEIRS

Aims & Activities: See. The Royal Scottish Country Dance Society.

✍ Secretary: Ms M. S. Wynne
104 Broadway, No. 1
Birmingham.
AL 35209
☎ 1 205 942 7241

ALASKA

ALASKAN SCOTTISH CLUB

Aims & Activities: Social and to encourage an interest in Scottish heritage and to further interest in Scottish matters, including organising Highland Games.

✍ Secretary: c/o PO Box 3471
Anchorage.
AK 99510

ALASKAN SCOTTISH HIGHLAND GAMES

Founded: 1982.

Aims & Activities: These Games are usually held in late July or early August at Eagle River, Anchorage.

✍ Secretary: c/o Alaskan Scottish Club
PO Box 3471, Anchorage.
AK 99510

CLAN MACNEIL ASSOCIATION OF AMERICA ALASKA BRANCH

Aims & Activities: To strengthen Scottish and overseas links. Genealogical. Historical. Social.

Membership: Open to those bearing the name MacNeil or that of one of its septs and to those related by descent or marriage.

✍ Comm: Harry R. McNeal Sr.
3263 Repp Road, North Pole.
AK 99701

ARIZONA

AGNEW ASSOCIATION OF AMERICA

Aims & Activities: To collect genealogical information. To strengthen Scottish and overseas links. Genealogical. Social. Historical.

Affiliations: The Agnew Association, Scotland.

Publications: Quarterly.

Membership: Open to all bearing the name or connected with it.

✍ President: Col Jack P. Agnew
28981 West Worcester Road, Sun City.
AZ 93381
☎ 1 714 679 7664

ARIZONA HIGHLAND GAMES

Founded: 1966.

Aims & Activities: Generally held on the third Saturday in February in Phoenix at the Tempe Diablo Soccer Field.

✍ Secretary: Donald C. Wilkinson
4042 E. Indianola Avenue, Phoenix.
AZ 85018

ARMSTRONG CLAN SOCIETY

Aims & Activities: To strengthen Scottish and overseas links. Genealogical. Historical. Annual Gathering.

Affiliations: The Armstrong Trust.

Membership: Open to those with the name Armstrong and those related by descent or marriage.

✍ Commissioner
Western USA: Thomas A. Armstrong, 5813 East Cambridge Avenue, Scottsdale.
AZ 85257
☎ 1 602 945 3807

CALEDONIAN SOCIETY OF ARIZONA

Aims & Activities: Social and to encourage an interest in Scottish heritage and Scottish matters including organising an annual Highland Games.

✍ President: David R. Logan
5219 S. 44th Place, Phoenix.
AZ 85040

CLAN GUTHRIE

Aims & Activities: To strengthen Scottish and overseas links. Genealogical and Historical. Social. Annual Gathering.

Membership: Open to those with the name Guthrie and to those connected by descent or marriage.

✍ President: Harry L. Guthrie
5900 E. Thomas Road, H201, Scottsdale.
AZ 85251
☎ 1 602 946 1470

CLAN McBAIN

Aims & Activities: To strengthen Scottish and overseas links. Historical. Genealogical. Annual Gathering.
Membership: Open to all with the name McBain, or variant spellings, and to those connected by descent or marriage.
✍ J. H. McBain
  7025 North Finger, Rock Place, Tucson.

PHOENIX BRANCH OF THE ROYAL SCOTTISH COUNTRY DANCE SOCIETY

Aims & Activities: See the RSCDS on page 47.
Membership: 17.
✍ Secretary: Ms Harriet de View
  4608 West Maryland Avenue, Apt 137, Glendale.
  AZ 85301-4141
☎ 1 602 931 2545

TUCSON BRANCH OF THE ROYAL SCOTTISH COUNTRY DANCE SOCIETY

Aims & Activities: See the RSCDS on page 47.
Membership: 23.
✍ Secretary: Mr J. R. Lyon
  8951 E. Sierra Street, Tucson.
  AZ 85710
☎ 1 520 886 8699 (home)
☎ 1 520 621 6554 (business)

TUCSON HIGHLAND HAMES

Aims & Activities: Generally held annually in mid-November.
✍ Secretary: c/o PO Box 40665
  Tucson.
  AZ 85715

TUCSON SCOTTISH COUNTRY DANCE SOCIETY

Aims & Activities: See the RSCDS on page 47.

✍ Secretary: Mr C. Cartwright
  3910 North Stone Avenue, Tucson.
  AZ 85705
☎ 1 602 887 0875

ARKANSAS

ARKANSAS SCOTTISH COUNTRY DANCE SOCIETY

Aims & Activities: See the RSCDS on page 47.
✍ Secretary: Kathy Moore
  W. 27, Little Rock.
  AR 72204
☎ 1 501 663 5786

OZARK SCOTTISH FESTIVAL

Founded: 1980.
Aims & Activities: Organised by the Presbyterian College, itself founded in 1872, these Games are held at the College in early April.
✍ Secretary: c/o Arkansas College
  Batesville.
  AR 72501

CALIFORNIA

BEVERLY HILLS CLAN MACLEOD DANCERS

Aims & Activities: See the RSCDS on page 47.
✍ Secretary: Mrs A. Skipper
  1736 North Beverly Drive, Beverly Hills.
  CA 90210
☎ 1 310 276 8990

CALEDONIAN CLUB OF SAN FRANCISCO

Aims & Activities: Social and to foster an interest in Scottish matters and

Scottish heritage, including organising an annual Highland Gathering and Games.
✍ Secretary: John Dickson
13210 Merced Street, Richmond.
CA 94804

CALEDONIAN CLUB OF SAN FRANCISCO SCOTTISH GATHERING AND GAMES

Founded: 1966.
Aims & Activities: Generally held at Sonoma County Fairgroyund, Santa Rosa, seating 30,000 spectators, these Games are customarily held over the Labor Day weekend. They include the usual heavy events, athletic events, pipe bands, solo piping and Highland dancing, also fiddling. Notable for the US Caber championships.
✍ Secretary: John Dickson
13210 Merced Street, Richmond.
CA 94804

CALIFORNIA BRANCH OF THE CLAN MACNEIL ASSOCIATION OF AMERICA

Aims & Activities: Genealogical and Historical. To strengthen Scottish and overseas links. Associated to the Clan MacNeil Association, Scotland.
Affiliations: The Clan MacNeil Association, Scotland.
Membership: Open to those bearing the name MacNeil or that of one of its septs and to those related by descent or marriage.
✍ Comm: Frederick V. Neill
5614 Rockview Drive, Torrence.
CA 90505

CAMPBELL HIGHLAND GAMES

Founded: 1979.
Aims & Activities: Currently held in mid–October in Campbell. The town developed from the ranch bought by Ben Campbell in 1881. They include

the usual heavy events, pipe bands, solo piping and Highland dancing.
✍ Secretary: c/o Campbell
Chamber of Commerce
328 E. Campbell Avenue,
Campbell.
CA 95008

CENTRAL COAST GATHERING AND GAMES

Aims & Activities: These Games are usually held on the first Saturday in May in the El Chorro Regional Park, San Luis Obispo. They include the usual heavy events, piping and Highland dancing.
✍ Secretary: c/o PO Box 13954
San Luis Obispo.
CA 93406

CLAN BOYD SOCIETY

Aims & Activities: To strengthen Scottish and overseas links. Annual Gathering. Genealogical. Historical.
Membership: Open to those with the name Boyd and those related by descent or marriage.
✍ Secretary: Mrs W. R. Goddard
750 San Fernando Street,
San Diego.
CA 91206

CLAN DONNACHAIDH SOCIETY

Aims & Activities: Genealogical. Historical. To strengthen Scottish and overseas links. Annual Gathering.
Membership: Open to those with the name Robertson and those related by descent or marriage.
✍ Secretary: Ms Marjorie
Robertson Hale
PO Box 493 Brisbane.
CA 94005
☎ 1 415 782 8818

CLAN DONNACHAIDH SOCIETY NORTHERN CALIFORNIA BRANCH

Aims & Activities: To strengthen Scottish overseas links. Genealogical.
Membership: Open to those bearing the name Robertson or related by descent or marriage.
✍ The Rev John L. Duncan
PO Box 3231, Fairfield.
CA 94533
☎ 1 707 426 1045

CLAN FRASER ASSOCIATION CALIFORNIA

Aims & Activities: Historical and Genealogical. To strengthen Scottish and overseas links. Annual Gathering.
Membership: Open to those bearing the name Fraser, or related by marriage or descent.
✍ President: John S. Fraser
304 Cabrillo, San Clemente.
CA 92672
☎ 1 714 492 1794

CLAN GUNN SOCIETY OF NORTH AMERICA

Aims & Activities: Genealogical. Historical. To strengthen Scottish and overseas links. Annual Gathering.
Membership: Open to those named Gunn and those related by descent or marriage.
✍ Chairman: Martha Wilson Mayer
2090 Leland Way, Concord.
CA 94520
☎ 1 415 682 3749

CLAN MACNAB SOCIETY OF CALIFORNIA

Aims & Activities: To strengthen Scottish and overseas links. Historical. Genealogical. Annual Gathering.
Membership: Open to all of the name (in any spelling) or connected with the clan or its septs (Abbot, Abbotson,

Dewar, Gilfillan, Macandeoir) by descent or marriage.
✍ President: David W. McNabb
1929 Beloit Ave., Apt. 9,
Los Angeles.
CA 90025
☎ 1 213 478 2612

CLAN MACTAVISH ASSOCIATION

Aims & Activities: To strengthen Scottish and overseas links. Annual Gathering. Genealogical. Social.
Membership: Open to those named MacTavish or connected by descent or marriage.
✍ President: W. Alec McTavish
✍ Secretary: Myron McTavish
222 Katherine Avenue, Salinas.
CA 93901
☎ 1 408 422 4212

CLAN McCUBBIN SOCIETY

Aims & Activities: To strengthen Scottish and overseas links. Genealogical. Annual Gathering.
Membership: Open to all named McCubbin (in its various spellings) and to those related by descent or marriage.
✍ Secretary: A. Maxim Coppage
2497A Waiters Way, Concord.
CA 94520
☎ 1 415 825 9796

CONEJO VALLEY SCOTTISH SOCIETY

Aims & Activities: See the RSCDS on page 47.
✍ Secretary: Mrs V. Marshall
3136 Island View Drive, Ventura.
CA 93003
☎ 1 805 641 3962

JARDINE CLAN SOCIETY OF SOUTHERN CALIFORNIA

Aims & Activities: To strengthen

Scottish and overseas links. Genealogical and Historical.
Affiliations: Jardine Clan Society, Scotland.
Membership: Open to those with the name Jardine and to those related by marriage or descent.
✍ Mrs James Henry
528 N. Crescent Heights Bl,
Los Angeles.
CA 90048
☎ 1 213 658 7618

LA JOLLA SCOTTISH COUNTRY DANCE CLUB

Aims & Activities: See the RSCDS on page 47.
✍ Secretary: Mr D. Richards
1577 Calle Delicada, La Jolla.
CA 92037
☎ 1 619 454 5101

LOS ANGELES BRANCH OF THE ROYAL SCOTTISH COUNTRY DANCE SOCIETY

Aims & Activities: See the RSCDS on page 47.
Membership: 190.
✍ Secretary: Deanna St Amand
12744 Kahlenberg Lane,
North Hollywood.
CA 91607
☎ 1 818 761 4750

LOS ANGELES BURNS CLUB

Aims & Activities: Social and to promote interest in Scottish heritage iuncluding the works of Burns.
Affiliations: The Burns Federation, No. 1121.
✍ Mr J. G. Rennie
6634 Lautrec Place,
Rancho Palos Verdes.
CA 90275-5607

MILL VALLEY SCOTTISH COUNTRY DANCERS

Aims & Activities: See the RSCDS on page 47.
✍ Secretary: Mr J. M. Hird
81 Flicker Drive, Novato.
CA 94949
☎ 1 415 884 2716

MODESTO HIGHLAND GAMES AND GATHERING

Founded: 1982.
Aims & Activities: The Games are usually held in the Tuolumne River Regional Park on the first Saturday in June. They include the usual heavy events, athletic events, piping and Highland dancing.
✍ Secretary: c/o The St Andrew's Society of Modesto
PO Box 2545, Modesto.
CA 95351

MONTEREY HIGHLAND GAMES

Founded: 1970.
Aims & Activities: Usually held on the first Saturday in August in the Monterey Fairgrounds, they include the usual heavy events, pipe bands, solo piping and Highland dancing.
✍ Secretary: c/o The Scottish Society of Monterey Peninsula
PO Box 1633, Carmel.
CA 93921

MOWAT FAMILY INTERNATIONAL

Aims & Activities: Genealogical. Historical. To strengthen Scottish and overseas links. Annual Gathering.
Membership: Open to all with the name Mowat and those related by desent or marriage.
✍ President: Harry B. Mowat
PO Box 449, Denair.
CA 95316
☎ 1 209 667 4836

NORTHERN CALIFORNIA BRANCH OF THE CLAN MACRAE

Aims & Activities: To strengthen Scottish and overseas links. Genealogical. Historical. Annual Gathering.
Membership: Open to those with the name MacRae and to those connected by descent or marriage.
🖂 Commissioner: Donald Calavan
Macrae
PO Box 15724, Sacramento.
CA 95852

ORANGE COUNTY BRANCH OF THE ROYAL SCOTTISH COUNTRY DANCE SOCIETY

Aims & Activities: See the RSCDS on page 47.
Membership: 71.
🖂 Secretary: Pat Baur
19812 Sienna Lane, Yorba Linda.
CA 92686
☎ 1 714 970 6714

ORANGE COUNTY BURNS CLUB

Aims & Activities: Social. Annual Gathering. To perpetuate the memory of Robert Burns. Overseas links.
Affiliations: The Burns Federation, No. 1087.
🖂 Secretary: Milton Ferguson
16232 Osborne Street,
Westminster CA 92683

PACIFIC COAST PIPE BAND ASSOCIATION

Aims & Activities: Encouraging an interest in and the formation and organisation of pipe bands and piping and drumming, also participation in competitions and events in Highland Games.
Affiliations: The Royal Scottish Pipe Band Association, (page 59).
🖂 Treasurer: Mr D. Maich
2703 Apollo Drive, San Jose.
CA 95121

PACIFIC HIGHLAND CLAN GATHERING AND GAMES

Founded: 1979.
Aims & Activities: Currently held during the first weekend in October at San Bernardino County Junior Fairgrounds in Chino. They include heavy events, pipe bands, solo piping and Highland dancing.
🖂 President: John MacRae
Clans of Highlands Inc., 2308
Shady Hills Drive, Diamond Bar.
CA 91765

ROBERT BURNS CLUB OF SAN DIEGO

Founded: 1975.
Aims & Activities: Social. Annual Gathering. To perpetuate the memory of Robert Burns.
Affiliations: The Burns Federation, No. 941.
🖂 Secretary: Robert B. Carlyle
PO Box 90031-5, San Diego.
CA 92190

SACRAMENTO BRANCH OF THE ROYAL SCOTTISH COUNTRY DANCE SOCIETY

Aims & Activities: See the RSCDS on page 47.
Membership: 82.
🖂 Secretary: Gail Erwin
1078 Beaver Park Way, Galt.
CA 95632
☎ 1 209 745 9063

SAN DIEGO BRANCH OF THE ROYAL SCOTTISH COUNTRY DANCE SOCIETY

Aims & Activities: See the RSCDS on page 47.
Membership: 126.
🖂 Secretary: Mr W. Jordan
18331, Verano Place, San Diego.
CA 92128
☎ 1 619 487 4635

SAN DIEGO HIGHLAND GAMES

Founded: 1974.

Aims & Activities: San Diego is sister city to Edinburgh and these Games are currently held on the second Saturday in June, in the Rancho Santa Fe Park. They include heavy events, pipe bands, solo piping and Highland dancing as well as athletic events.

✍ Contact: San Diego Tourist Board

SAN FRANCISCO BRANCH OF THE ROYAL SCOTTISH COUNTRY DANCE SOCIETY

Founded: 1965.

Aims & Activities: See the RSCDS on page 47.

Membership: 407.

✍ Secretary: Mr A. Tweedly
155 California Avenue, G202,
Palo Alto.
CA 94306

☎ 1 415 328 5563 (home)
☎ 1 415 688 8144 (business)

SAN GABRIEL VALLEY BRANCH OF THE ROYAL SCOTTISH COUNTRY DANCE SOCIETY

Aims & Activities: See the RSCDS on page 47.

Membership: 105.

✍ Secretary: Lathon H. Wells
10965 Glenoaks Boulevard, Apt.
544, Pacoma.
CA 91331

☎ 1 818 897 2586 (home)
☎ 1 213 897 0231 (business)

SCOTTISH DANCE ENSEMBLE

Aims & Activities: See the RSCDS on page 47.

✍ Secretary: Mr R. Goss
16485 Main, Puente.
CA 91744-5545

SCOTTISH FIDDLERS OF CALIFORNIA

Founded: 1986.

Aims & Activities: Supports the teaching and performance of traditional Scottish fiddle music. Sponsors Valley of the Moon Scottish Fiddling School, also Scottish Fiddle music and dance competitions and three local groups. Offers lessons in Gaelic singing, and dance, as well as fiddle. Annual meeting is on Labor Day in Santa Rosa.

✍ President: Alasdair Fraser
1938 Rose Villa Street, Pasadena.
CA 91107

☎ 1 818 792 6323

SCOTTISH SOCIETY OF MONTEREY PENINSULA

Aims & Activities: Social and to promote interest in Scottish matters and Scottish heritage, also to hold an annual Highland games.

✍ Secretary: c/o Scottish Society of Monterey Peninsula
PO Box 1633, Carmel.
CA 93921

SCOTTISH SOCIETY OF SANTA BARBARA

Aims & Activities: Social and to encourage study of Scottish heritage, tradition and history, including the works of Robert Burns. Annual Gathering.

Affiliations: The Burns Federation, No. 1096.

✍ Secretary: Mrs Margaret E. Chisholm
871 Arbol Verde Street,
Carpinteria.
CA 93013

SOUTHERN CALIFORNIA ASSOCIATION OF THE CLAN MACNEIL ASSOCIATION OF AMERICA

Aims & Activities: Social, historical and genealogical. To strengthen Scottish and overseas links. Annual Gathering.
Membership: Open to those with the name MacNeil or that of one of its septs and to those related by descent or marriage.
✍ Chairman: Edward Richburg
2035 Rangeview Drive, Glendale.
CA 91201

ST ANDREW'S SOCIETY OF MODESTO

Aims & Activities: Social and to encourage interest in Scottish heritage and to organise an annual Gathering and Highland Games.
✍ Secretary: c/o St Andrew's
Society of Modesto
PO Box 2545, Modesto.
CA 95351

STRATHLEVEN SCOTTISH DANCERS

Aims & Activities: See the RSCDS on page 47.
✍ Secretary: Mrs R. Walsh-Tague
6222 Choctaw Drive,
Westminster.
CA 92683
☎ 1 714 890 1631

UNITED SCOTTISH SOCIETY

Aims & Activities: Social and to encourage interest in Scottish heritage, history and traditions, including the works of Burns. Annual Gathering.
Affiliations: The Burns Federation, No. 1088.
✍ Secretary: Mrs Nan Daley
653 N. Willowgrove Avenue,
Glendora.
CA 91740

UNITED SCOTTISH SOCIETY'S HIGHLAND GATHERING AND GAMES

Founded: 1927.
Aims & Activities: The fourth-oldest Highland Games currently being held in North America. Customarily held over the Memorial Day weekend in the Orange County Fairground.
✍ Contact: Orange Count Tourist Board

WAVERLEY DANCERS

Aims & Activities: See the RSCDS on page 47.
✍ Secretary: Christa Wilk
730 Muskingum Avenue,
Pacific Palisades.
CA 90272
☎ 1 310 454 0085

WESTERN UNITED STATES PIPE BAND ASSOCIATION

Aims & Activities: To encourage an interest in and the formation and organisation of pipe bands and piping and drumming, also participation in competitions and events in Highland Games.
Affiliations: The Royal Scottish Pipe Band Association, (page 59).
✍ General Secretary: Mr Scott MacDonald
28257 Via Luis, Leguna, Miguel.
CA 92656

YORKSHIRE ROSE SCOTTISH COUNTRY DANCERS

Aims & Activities: See the RSCDS on page 47.
✍ Secretary: Mrs M. Schlicter
PO Box 957, Brawley.
CA 92227
☎ 1 819 344 0728

COLORADO

LONG'S PEAK SCOTTISH HIGHLAND FESTIVAL

Founded: 1978.
Aims & Activities: These Games are customarily held over the first weekend after Labor Day. They take place in Estes Park beside Lake Estes beneath Long's Peak (14,256 ft) They include heavy events, pipe bands, solo piping and Highland dancing, also athletic events.
✍ The Secretary
c/o PO Box 1820, Estes Park.
CO 80517

ROCKY MOUNTAIN HIGHLAND GAMES

Founded: 1983.
Aims & Activities: Currently held over two days during the second weekend in August in the Highland Heritage Park in Denver they include the usual heavy events, pipe bands, solo piping and Highland dancing as well as an exhibition of Scottish Cattle. The Sword of the Rockies is awarded for the best Sword Dance.
✍ Secretary: c/o St Andrew's
Society
Charles Todd, 3606 E. Hindsdale Pk, Littleton.
CO 80122
✍ c/o St Andrew's Society
Charles Todd, 911 W. Belmont Place, Littleton.
CO 80123

SCOTTISH COUNTRY DANCERS OF COLORADO

Aims & Activities: See the RSCDS on page 47.
✍ Secretary: Mr J. Davies
3200 Silverthorne Drive, Fort Collins.
CO 80526-2728
☎ 1 970 223 7730

ST ANDREW SOCIETY OF COLORADO

Aims & Activities: Social. To encourage interest in Scottish heritage. To organise annual Highland Games.
Affiliations: The Royal Scottish Country Dance Society, (page 47).
✍ Treasurer: Martha Wallace
3180 Harlan Street,
Wheat Ridge.
CO 80214
☎ 1 303 238 4896

CONNECTICUT

CLAN FARQUHARSON SOCIETY

Aims & Activities: To strengthen Scottish and overseas links. Genealogical. Historical. Social.
Membership: Open to those with the name Farquharson and its variants, also those related by descent or marriage.
✍ President: John T. Fargason
203 Carmel Hill Road,
North Bethlehem.
CT 06751
☎ 1 203 266 5180

GREATER HARTFORD SCOTTISH COUNTRY DANCE GROUP

Aims & Activities: See the RSCDS on page 47.
✍ Secretary: Virginia Knight
168 West Mountain Road,
West Simsbury.
CT 06092
☎ 1 203 658 4160

NEW HAVEN BRANCH OF THE ROYAL SCOTTISH COUNTRY DANCE SOCIETY

Aims & Activities: See the RSCDS on page 47.
Membership: 106.
✍ Secretary: Marge Wills

24-1 Riverdale Landiung, PO
Box 431, Old Lyme.
CT 06371
☎ 1 203 434 0451

NEWTOWN SCOTTISH DANCERS

Aims & Activities: See the RSCDS on
page 47.
✍ Secretary: Ms J. Rawson
37 Bear Hills Road, Newtown.
CT 06470
☎ 1 203 426 4263

ROUND HILL HIGHLAND GAMES

Founded: 1923.
Aims & Activities: Third oldest of the
current Games and sometimes
known as the Cowal Games of the
US, they are usually held on the 4th
of July in Cranberry Park. They
include pipe bands, solo piping and
Highland dancing as well as the usual
heavy events and eleven-a-side soccer.
✍ Secretary: c/o PO Box 261
Belden Station, Norwalk.
CT 06850

ST ANDREW'S SOCIETY OF CONNECTICUT

Aims & Activities: Social and to
encourage an interest in Scottish
heritage, also to organise an annual
Highland Festival.
✍ The Secretary
c/o PO Box 1195, Litchfield.
CT 06759

ST ANDREWS SOCIETY OF CONNECTICUT SCOTTISH FESTIVAL

Founded: 1984.
Aims & Activities: Currently held on
the second weekend in October in
the Fairgrounds, Goschen. These
games include pipe bands, solo piping

and Highland dancing, also the usual
heavy events.
✍ Secretary: c/o St Andrew's
Society of Connecticut
PO Box 1195, Litchfield.
CT 06759

DELAWARE

CLAN MONTGOMERY SOCIETY

Aims & Activities: Genealogical.
Historical. Annual Gathering. To
strengthen overseas links.
Membership: Open to those bearing
the name Montgomery in its various
spellings and those related by descent
or marriage.
✍ President: John F. Montgomery
✍ Secretary: Rowan P. Perkins
701 Fiske Lane, Newark.
DE 19711
☎ 1 302 731 4346

COLONIAL HIGHLAND GATHERING AND INTERNATIONAL OPEN SHEEP-DOG TRIALS

Founded: 1960.
Aims & Activities: Presently held at the
Maryland Department of Natural
Resources site at Fair Hill on the
third Friday and Saturday in May. As
well as the customary events the
games include a heptathlon, fiddling
and a sheep to shawl contest.
✍ Secretary: c/o Colonial Highland
Gathering
20 Wakefield Drive, Newark.
DE 19711

FLORIDA

42ND OR ROYAL HIGHLAND REGIMENT

Aims & Activities: To perpetuate the memory and traditions of the 42nd or Royal Highland Regiment, the Black Watch.
✍ Captain: Paul Pace
4742 Arthur Street,
Palm Beach Gardens.
FL 433410
☎ 1 305 694 1398

BAIRD FAMILY SOCIETY

Aims & Activities: Genealogical. Historical. To strengthen overseas and Scottish links. Annual gathering.
Membership: Open to those with the name Baird and those related by marriage or descent.
✍ Convener: Mrs Byron O. Baird
1890 Choctaw Trail, Maitland.
FL 32751
☎ 1 305 647 1129

BREVARD SCOTTISH COUNTRY DANCERS

Aims & Activities: See the RSCDS on page 47.
✍ Secretary: Mrs J. Geist
960 Sunswept Road NE,
Palm Bay.
FL 32905
☎ 1 407 727 7752

BROWARD SCOTTISH COUNTRY DANCERS

Aims & Activities: See the RSCDS on page 47.
✍ Secretary: Mrs H. P. Welch
1731 SW 4th Avenue,
Pompano Beach.
FL 33060
☎ 1 305 781 1230

CALEDONIAN SCOTTISH COUNTRY DANCERS OF ORLANDO

Aims & Activities: See the RSCDS on page 47.
✍ Secretary: Mrs J. Eaton
2721 Mae Loma Court, Orlando.
FL 32806
☎ 1 407 898 6047

CHARLOTTE REED SCOTTISH COUNTRY DANCERS

Aims & Activities: See the RSCDS on page 47.
✍ Secretary: Mrs C. Reed
246 SW 42 Street, Cape Coral.
FL 33914

CLAN BARCLAY SOCIETY USA

Aims & Activities: Genealogical. Historical. To strengthen Scottish and overseas links. Annual Gathering.
Membership: Open to those bearing the name Barclay and those related by descent or marriage.
✍ President: Thomas W. Barkley
✍ Secretary: George H. Hawkins Sr.
PO Box 568491, Orlando.
FL 32856
☎ 1 305 422 8907

CLAN DONNACHAIDH OF FLORIDA

Aims & Activities: Genealogical. Historical. Annual gathering. To strengthen Scottish and overseas links.
Membership: Open to those named Robertson or connected by descent or marriage.
✍ President: David Reid
✍ Secretary: Mrs Allan J. Robertson
519 Queens Mirror Circle,
Casselberry.
FL 32707
☎ 1 305 699 9172

CLAN FORSYTH OF AMERICA

Aims & Activities: Genealogical. Historical. To strengthen Scottish and overseas links. Annual gathering.
Membership: Open to all named Forsyth (in its various spellings) or connected by descent or marriage.
✍ President: Percy G. Forsyth
    4667 Dolphin Drive, Lake Worth. FL 33463
☎ 1 305 439 5693

CLAN GREGOR SOCIETY

Aims & Activities: To strengthen Scottish and overseas links. Genealogical. Historical. Annual Gathering.
Membership: Open to all with the name Gregor (and its variations) or connected by descent or marriage.
✍ Chairman: Sheila McGregor
✍ US Rep: John Weliver
    26 David Drive, Rt 12, Ft Myers. FL 33908
☎ 1 813 466 4802

CLAN GUNN SOCIETY OF NORTH AMERICA

Aims & Activities: To strengthen Scottish and overseas links. Genealogical. Historical. Annual Gathering.
Membership: Open to those named Gunn and to those related by descent and marriage.
✍ President: Edwin O. Joiner
    1461 Bowman Street, Clermont. FL 32711
☎ 1 904 394 6548

CLAN HOME/HUME SOCIETY

Aims & Activities: To promote awareness of the clan history, background and connections in Scotland. Genealogical. To strengthen overseas and Scottish links.
Membership: Open to those of the Home/Hume clan.

✍ President: Albet C. Eaton
    2721 Mae Loma Court, Orlando. FL 32806
☎ 1 305 898 6047

CLAN JOHNSTON/E IN AMERICA

Aims & Activities: Genealogical. Historical. To strengthen Scottish overseas links.
Membership: Open to those with the name Johnston/e and those connected by marriage or descent.
✍ President: William P. Bailey Jr MD.
✍ Joiner: Sue Johnstone
    1461 Bowman St., Clermont. FL 32711
☎ 1 904 394 6548

CLAN MACKINTOSH OF NORTH AMERICA

Aims & Activities: To strengthen Scottish and overseas links. Genealogical. Historical. Annual Gathering.
Membership: Open to those beaing the name Mackintosh and to those related by marriage or descent.
✍ President: Mrs Alta M. Bearman
    2341 NE 48 Court,
    Lighthouse Point. FL 33064

CLAN MACNACHTAN ASSOCIATION

Aims & Activities: To promote Scottish and overseas links. To trace genealogical links. To promote awareness of the clan history. Annual Gathering.
Membership: Open to those bearing the Macnachtan name (in its various spellings) and those related by marriage or descent.
✍ National Membership Chairman:
    Carl McNaughton Messina
    405 N. 18th St, Jacksonville Beach FL 32250
☎ 1 904 246 7660

CLAN MACNAUGHTON

Aims & Activities: To promote awareness of the clan history, background and connections in Scotland. To strengthen Scottish and overseas links. Genealogical. Annual Gathering.

Membership: Open to those bearing the name MacNaughton and those related by marriage or descent.

✍ President: Robert A. Foster
  5700 Mariner Dr., 403 Tampa.
  FL 33609
☎ 1 813 872 6754

CLAN MACNEIL ASSOCIATION OF AMERICA FLORIDA BRANCH

Aims & Activities: To strengthen Scottish and overseas links. Annual gathering. Genealogical. Historical.

Membership: Open to those with the name MacNeil or that of one of its septs, also those connected by descent or marriage.

✍ Comm: Robert A. MacNeille
  12296 137th Street, North Largo.
  FL 33544

DUNEDIN HIGHLAND GAMES

Founded: 1966.

Aims & Activities: These Games generally take place in late March of early April and the festivities last a full week. Dunedin is the sister city to Stirling and is very conscious of its Scottish origins. The schools have pipe bands and these are naturally a feature of the Games, as well as the usual athletic and heavy events, pipe bands, solo piping and Highland dancing. The games also include a parade of tartans and a kilted mile. Many Canadians come south for the Games.

✍ Secretary: Dunedin Highland
  Games & Festival Committee
  Inc., PO Box 507, Dunedin.
  FL 33528-0507

FLORIDA NORTH BRANCH OF THE ROYAL SCOTTISH COUNTRY DANCE SOCIETY

Aims & Activities: See the RSCDS on page 47.

Membership: 56.

✍ Secretary: Patty Caddell
  4259 Phillips Hwy, Lot 70,
  Jacksonville.
  FL 32207
☎ 1 305 733 2904 (home)
☎ 1 739 9110 (business)

FLORIDA SOUTH BRANCH OF THE ROYAL SCOTTISH COUNTRY DANCE SOCIETY

Aims & Activities: See the RSCDS on page 47.

Membership: 107.

✍ Secretary: Helen P. Welch
  1731 SW 4th Avenue,
  Pompano Beach.
  FL 33060
☎ 1 305 781 1230

JACKSONVILLE SCOTTISH COUNTRY DANCERS

Aims & Activities: See the RSCDS on page 47.

✍ Secretary: Mrs P. Caddell
  4259 Phillips Hwy, Lot 70,
  Jacksonville.
  FL 32207

JARDINE CLAN SOCIETY SOUTH EAST

Aims & Activities: To promote awareness of the clan, their background and connections in Scotland and their part in Scottish history. To strengthen Scottish and overseas links. Genealogical. Annual Gathering.

Membership: Open to those with the name Jardine and those related by marriage or descent.

✍ President: Thomas P. Jardine
✍ Secretary: Mary Jo Jardine

3939 90th Terrace,
N. Pinnelas Park.
FL 33565
☎ 1 813 576 5728

MIAMI SCOTTISH COUNTRY DANCERS

Aims & Activities: See the RSCDS on page 47.
✍ Secretary: Mrs I. Ritchie
588 Palmetto Drive,
Miami Springs.
FL 33166
☎ 1 305 871 1635

NEW SMYRNA BEACH SCOTTISH COUNTRY DANCE GROUP

Aims & Activities: See the RSCDS on page 47.
✍ Secretary: Mrs T. Raymond
PO Box 124,
New Smyrna Beach.
FL 32170

ORLANDO BRANCH OF THE ROYAL SCOTTISH COUNTRY DANCE SOCIETY

Aims & Activities: See the RSCDS on page 47.
Membership: 37.
✍ Secretary: Mrs L. Senyk
Box 134, 1991 Sharpes.
FL 32959
☎ 1 407 636 2209

ORLANDO SCOTTISH HIGHLAND GAMES

Founded: 1978.
Aims & Activities: Currently held during the second weekend in January at the Central Florida Fairgrounds these are notable as the first Games of the year in the USA as well as being the third-largest in the south. They start with a ceilidh and whisky-tasting on the Friday and a golf tournament on the Sunday with the Games themselves held on the Saturday. They include the usual heavy and athletic events as well as pipe bands, solo piping and Highland dancing, also a sheepdog demonstration.
✍ Secretary: Orlando Scottish Highland Games
PO Box 300377, Fern Park.
FL 32730
☎ 1 407 339 3335

PALM BEACH SCOTTISH COUNTRY DANCERS

Aims & Activities: See the RSCDS on page 47.
✍ Secretary: Mrs M. Beach
4421 NW Fourth Court,
Plantation.
FL 33317

SALTIRE SCOTTISH COUNTRY DANCERS

Aims & Activities: See Royal Scottish Country Dance Society.
✍ Secretary: Mrs D. Shaw
8802 Andros Lane, Port Richey.
FL 34668
☎ 1 813 842 9662

SARASOTA SCOTTISH COUNTRY DANCERS

Aims & Activities: See the RSCDS on page 47.
✍ Secretary: Mrs G. Wiedorn
194 Sunaire Terrace, Nokomis.
FL 34275
☎ 1 813 485 7488

SCOTS-AMERICAN CLUB

Aims & Activities: Social and to encourage interest in Scottish tradition, history and heritage.
✍ Dr Robert V. Russell
100 NW 76th Ave, 104
Plantation.
FL 33317
☎ 1 305 583 3271

SCOTTISH AMERICAN SOCIETY OF SOUTH FLORIDA

Aims & Activities: Social and to encourage an interest in Scottish heritage, also to organise an annual Scottish Festival.
✍ Secretary: PO Box 633
   Miami Shores.
   FL 33158

SCOTTISH-AMERICAN SOCIETY

Aims & Activities: Social and to encourage interest in Scottish tradition, history and heritage.
✍ President: Desmond James Coady
✍ Secretary: Jean Cordovez
   2677 Carambola Road,
   West Palm Beach FL 33406
☎ 1 305 965 2562

SOUTH EAST FLORIDA SCOTTISH FESTIVAL

Founded: 1984.
Aims & Activities: Currently held on the first Saturday in March at Crandon Gardens, Key Biscayne. They include pipe bands, solo piping and Highland dancing. Special features include an 18th-century military encampment.
✍ Secretary: The Scottish American Society of South Florida
   PO Box 633, Miami Shores.
   FL 33158

SOUTHERN US PIPERS AND PIPE BAND ASSOCIATION

Aims & Activities: To encourage an interest in and the formation and organisation of pipe bands and piping and drumming, also participation in competitions and events in Highland Games.
Affiliations: The Royal Scottish Pipe Band Association, (page 59).
✍ President: Sandy Keith
   1070 Maclean Street, Dunedin.
   FL 33528

SPACE COAST SCOTTISH COUNTRY DANCERS

Aims & Activities: See the RSCDS on page 47.
✍ Secretary: Mrs L. Senyk
   Box 134, Sharpes.
   FL 32959
☎ 1 407 636 2209

ST ANDREW SOCIETY OF FLORIDA

Aims & Activities: Social and to encourage interest in Scottish tradition, history and heritage.
✍ Jack E. McDonald
   PO Box 1044, Stuart.
   FL 33495
☎ 1 305 287 3965

ST ANDREW SOCIETY OF TALLAHASSEE

Aims & Activities: Social and to encourage interest in the Scottish history, tradition and heritage.
✍ President: Bruce Montgomery
✍ Secretary: Jean Hozapfel
   PO Box 12034,
   Tallahassee.
   FL 32308
☎ 1 904 386 4953

ST ANDREW'S CEILIDH DANCERS

Aims & Activities: See the RSCDS on page 47.
✍ Secretary: Sharon Schwerzei
   2408 San Pedro Avenue,
   Tallahassee.
   FL 32304

ST ANDREW'S SOCIETY OF CENTRAL FLORIDA

Aims & Activities: Social and to encourage interest in Scottish tradition, history and heritage.
✍ President: Hamish Pollock Jr
✍ Membership Chairman: Robert J. Lowe

PO Box 1856, Winter Park.
FL 32790
☎ 1 305 831 4352

ST ANDREW'S SOCIETY OF FLORIDA

Aims & Activities: Social and to encourage interest in Scottish tradition, history and heritage.
✍ President: David Campbell
PO Box 663, Tampa.
FL 33601
☎ 1 813 228 4301

ST ANDREW'S SOCIETY OF PENSACOLA

Aims & Activities: See the RSCDS on page 47.
✍ Secretary: Mrs S. Hall
302 Camelia Street, Gulf Breeze.
FL 32561

ST ANDREW'S SOCIETY OF SARASOTA

Aims & Activities: Social and to encourage interest in Scottish tradition, history and heritage.
✍ President: John Ingram
PO Box 2592, Sarasota.
FL 33578
☎ 1 813 377 1118

STRATHLEVEN SCOTTISH COUNTRY DANCERS

Aims & Activities: See the RSCDS on page 47.
✍ Secretary: Ms M. McWhinnie
2336 Waterfall Drive,
Springhill.
FL 34608

STUART SCOTTISH COUNTRY DANCERS

Aims & Activities: See the RSCDS on page 47.
✍ Secretary: Maryalice McDonald

242 SE Edgewood Drive, Stuart.
FL 34996
☎ 1 407 287 3065

WHITE HEATHER DANCERS

Aims & Activities: See the RSCDS on page 47.
✍ Secretary: Christine Ruckdeschel
24479 Auduron Drive,
Brooksville.
FL 34601
☎ 1 407 898 6047

GEORGIA

ARMSTRONG CLAN SOCIETY

Aims & Activities: To promote awareness of the clan history, background and connections in Scotland and the Borders and their part in Scottish and Border history. To strengthen Scottish and overseas links. Genealogical. Annual Gathering.
Affiliations: The Armstrong Trust.
Membership: Open to those named Armstrong and to those related by marriage or descent.
✍ President: Col. H. H. Armstrong
1511 Stoneleigh Way,
Stone Mountain.
GA 30088
☎ 1 404 498 4220

ATLANTA BRANCH OF THE ROYAL SCOTTISH COUNTRY DANCE SOCIETY

Aims & Activities: See the RSCDS on page 47.
Membership: 130.
✍ Secretary: Ms S. Priest
3804 Cowan Circle, Acworth.
GA 30101-5109
☎ 1 404 974 4642 (home)
☎ 1 404 799 2558 (business)

AUGUSTA SCOTTISH COUNTRY DANCE SOCIETY

Aims & Activities: See the RSCDS on page 47.

✍ Secretary: Ms L. Whitehorne
3218 York Drive, Augusta.
GA 30909

BURNS CLUB OF ATLANTA

Founded: 1896.
Aims & Activities: Social and to encourage interest in the poetical works of Robert Burns. To celebrate Burns night and to encourage an interest in Scottish heritage.
Affiliations: The Burns Federation, No. 238.

✍ Secretary: Donald A. Mangerie
7170 Dunhill Terrace, Atlanta.
GA 30328
☎ 1 404 424 8000
✍ Mr Thomas R. Todd Jr.
265 Quiet Water Lane,
Dunwoody.
GA 30350

CALEDONIAN SOCIETY OF GREATER ATLANTA

Aims & Activities: Social and to encourage an interest in Scottish tradition, history and heritage.

✍ President: Raymond M. McTyre (FSA Scot)
3987 Indian Lakes Circle,
Stone Mountain.
GA 30083
☎ 1 404 292 6003

CLAN ANDERSON SOCIETY LTD

Aims & Activities: To promote awareness of the clan history, background and genealogical connections in Scotland. To strengthen Scottish and overseas links. Annual Gathering.
Membership: Open to those named Anderson and those related by descent or marriage.

✍ President: Edmund B. Anderson

350 Kensington Drive, Savannah.
GA 31405
☎ 1 912 355 5525

CLAN DONNACHAIDH SOCIETY OF THE SOUTH

Aims & Activities: To encourage interest in the clan history, background and connections in Scotland. To strengthen Scottish and overseas links. Genealogical. Annual Gathering.
Membership: Open to those named Robertson, or related by descent or marriage.

✍ President: Edwin B. Robertson
453 Hastings Way, Jonesboro.
GA 30236
☎ 1 404 477 7047

CLAN FORRESTER SOCIETY

Aims & Activities: To promote the clan spirit. To strengthen Scottish and overseas links. Historical. Genealogical. Annual gathering.
Membership: Open to those bearing the name Forrester and those related by marriage or descent.

✍ Secretary: Jerald Forrester
Route 6, Highway 81, Loganville.
GA 32049

CLAN FRASER SOCIETY OF N. A.

Aims & Activities: To promote interest in the clan history, background and the part the clan played in Scottish history. To strengthen Scottish and overseas links. Genealogical. Annual Gathering.
Membership: Open to those with the name Fraser and those related by descent or marriage.

✍ Chairman: Douglas J. Fraser
✍ Secretary: Mrs Julie Symes Powell
1065 McLynn Avenue, NE
Atlanta.
GA 30306
☎ 1 404 876 7030

CLAN HAY SOCIETY

Aims & Activities: To promote the clan spirit. Genealogical. Historical. To strengthen Scottish and overseas links. Annual gathering.
Membership: Open to those by the name of Hay and those related by marriage or descent.
✍ President: Ann Shirley
6309 Stillwater Drive, Atlanta.
GA 30274
☎ 404 997 5935

CLAN KEITH SOCIETY USA

Aims & Activities: To encourage the clan spirit. To promote awareness of thec clan history and genealogy. To strengthen Scottish and overseas links. Annual gathering.
Membership: Open to those with the name Keith and those related by marriage or descent.
✍ President: Darrell S. Keith
5505 Hill Road, Powder Springs.
GA 30073
☎ 1 404 943 6563

CLAN MACLAINE OF LOCHBUIE

Aims & Activities: To promote the clan spirit. Genealogical. Historical. To promote overseas and Scottish links. Annual gathering.
Membership: Open to those named Maclaine and hailing from Lochbuie, or those related by descent or marriage.
✍ James Maclaine
1773 Nancy Creek Bluff, Atlanta.
GA 30327
☎ 1 404 351 4956

CLAN MACTIRE

Aims & Activities: To promote the clan spirit. Historical. Genealogical. To strengthen Scottish and overseas links. Annual Gathering.
Membership: Open to those name Mactire and those connected by marriage or descent.
✍ Raymond M. McTyre (FSA Scot)
3987 Indian Lakes Circle,
Stone Mountain.
GA 30083
☎ 1 404 292 6003

CLAN McNAB SOCIETY OF AMERICA

Aims & Activities: To promote the clan spirit. Genealogical. Historical. To strengthen Scottish links. Annual gathering.
Membership: Open those named McNab (in its various spellings) and to those related by marriage or descent.
✍ Convener: Joseph N. McNabb
PO Box 1895, Stone Mountain.
GA 330086

ELLIOTT CLAN SOCIETY USA

Aims & Activities: To promote awareness of the clan history, background and connections in Scotland and their part in Scottish and Border history. To strengthen Scottish and overseas links. Genealogical. Annual Gathering.
Membership: Open to those with the name Elliott and those related by descent or marriage.
✍ President: Jim Elliott
3200, Habersham Road, NW
Atlanta.
GA 30305
☎ 1 404 233 1883

INNES CLAN SOCIETY

Aims & Activities: Genealogical. Historical. To strengthen Scottish and overseas links. Annual gathering.
Membership: Open to those bearing the name Innes and those related by descent or marriage.
✍ President: Joseph J. Innes

✍ Secretary: Susan Innes Kitchens
PO Box 492, Thomasville.
GA 31799

MOFFAT CLAN SOCIETY OF NORTH AMERICA

Aims & Activities: Genealogical.
Historical. To strengthen Scottish and
overseas links. Annual gathering.
Membership: Open to those by the
name of Moffat and those related by
marriage or descent.
✍ President: E. Albert Moffet
155 Maple Circle, Athens.
GA 30603
☎ 1 404 353 4729

ORDER OF THE TARTAN

Aims & Activities: Social and to
encourage interest in Scottish tradition, history and heritage.
✍ Convener: Ben Ramsay
PO Box 815, Columbus.
GA 31902
☎ 1 202 563 6017

SAVANNAH SCOTTISH COUNTRY DANCE GROUP

Aims & Activities: See the RSCDS on
page 47.
✍ Secretary: Mrs B. Young
6 Leaning Oaks Court, Savannah.
GA 31410
☎ 1 912 897 4862

SAVANNAH SCOTTISH HIGHLAND GAMES

Founded: 1978.
Aims & Activities: Generally held in
Old Fort Jackson (built in 1809) on
the first Saturday in May. They include
pipe bands, solo piping and Highland
dancing as well as heavy events.
✍ Secretary: Savannah Scottish
Games Inc.
PO Box 13435, Savannah.
GA 31416

SCOTTISH HARP SOCIETY OF AMERICA

Founded: 1983.
Aims & Activities: Promotes interest in
the Scottish harp and traditional
Scottish music. Teaches playing.
Conducts competitions and presents
scholarships.
Publications: Scottish Harp.
Membership: 100.
✍ Ed: Sandra Sparks: 1243 Druid
Place, No. 1, Atlanta.
GA 30307
☎ 1 404 659 3936

SHELLMAN GEORGIA HIGHLAND GAMES

Aims & Activities: These Games are
currently held on the third weekend
in November. They include pipe
bands, heavy events, solo piping and
Highland dancing.
✍ Secretary: c/o PO Box 532
Shellman.
GA 30324

ST ANDREW'S SOCIETY OF THE CITY OF SAVANNAH

Aims & Activities: Social and to
encourage and interest in Scottish
tradition, history and heritage.
✍ President: Lorton S. Livingston
624 E. 45th St, Savannah.
GA 31405
☎ 1 912 233 6460

STONE MOUNTAIN SCOTTISH FESTIVAL AND HIGHLAND GAMES

Founded: 1973.
Aims & Activities: These Games are
usually held over two days in mid-
October at the foot of the monolith-
ic 825ft-high granite Stone
Mountain. They include the usual
heavy events, pipe bands, solo piping
and Highland dancing as well as clan

challenge athletics and a sheepdog demonstration.
✍ Secretary: c/o PO Box 14023
Atlanta.
GA 30324

HAWAII

CALEDONIAN SOCIETY OF HAWAII

Aims & Activities: Social and to encourage an interest in Scottish tradition, history and heritage.
✍ President: Louis MacPhee
PO Box 4164, Honolulu.
HI 96813

CLANS OF HAWAII

Aims & Activities: Social and to encourage an interest in Scottish tradition, history and heritage.
✍ Chieftain: Peter McMorland
Sydserff
Waikoloa Village, Kamuela.
HI 96743
☎ 1 808 883 9306

HAWAII BRANCH OF THE ROYAL SCOTTISH COUNTRY DANCE SOCIETY

Aims & Activities: See the RSCDS on page 47.
Membership: 37.
✍ Secretary: Mary L. Godfrey
1419 Center Street, Honolulu.
HI 96816
☎ 1 808 737 1897

HAWAIIAN SCOTTISH ASSOCIATION

Aims & Activities: Social and to encourage an interest in Scottish heritage.
✍ Secretary: c/o 2615 S. King Street Suite 206, Honolulu HI 96826

HAWAIIAN SCOTTISH ASSOCIATION

Aims & Activities: Social and to encourage an interest in Scottish tradition, history and heritage.
✍ Chieftain: Stuart M. Cowan
1600 Grosvenor Center, 733 Bishop Street, Honolulu.
HI 96813
☎ 1 808 533 1767

HONOLULU HIGHLAND GAMES

Founded: 1982.
Aims & Activities: Currently held on the first Saturday in April at Kuroda Field, Fort de Russy. These Games include lawn bowling and spear throwing.
✍ Secretary: c/o The Hawaiian
Scottish Association
2615 S King Street, Suite 206, Honolulu.
HI 96826

IDAHO

BOISE SCOTTISH CALEDONIAN SOCIETY

Aims & Activities: Social and to encourage an interest in Scottish tradition, history and heritage.
✍ President: Jamie Thomson
2207 N. 17th St, Boise.
ID 83702
☎ 1 208 342 8680

ILLINOIS

BARRINGTON BURNS CLUB

Aims & Activities: Social and to encourage interest in the poetical works of Robert Burns. To celebrate Burns night and to encourage a wider interest in Scottish tradition, history and heritage.

✍ c/o PO Box 895
   Barrington.
   IL 60011

CHICAGO BRANCH OF THE ROYAL SCOTTISH COUNTRY DANCE SOCIETY

Aims & Activities: See the RSCDS on page 47.
Membership: 63.
✍ Secretary: Mr R. Gaston
   628 Sheridan Square, Evanston.
   IL 60202
☎ 1 708 475 4589 (home)
☎ 1 708 806 5312 (business)

CHICAGO SCOTTISH FESTIVAL

Aims & Activities: Currently held on the third Saturday and Sunday in October. These Games include pipe bands, solo piping and Highland dancing, also the usual heavy events and athletics.
✍ Secretary: c/o 26 E. Atteridge
   Road
   Lake Forest.
   IL 60045

CLAN ARCHIBALD FAMILY ASSOCIATION

Aims & Activities: To promote awareness of the family history, background and genealogical connections in Scotland and their place in Scottish history. To strengthen Scottish and overseas links.
Membership: Open to those by the name of Archibald and those related by marriage or descent.
✍ Elbert L. Archibald
   325 Greenwood, Evanston.
   IL 60201
☎ 1 312 864 5449

CLAN MACQUARRIE ASSOCIATION MIDWEST BRANCH

Aims & Activities: To promote knowledge of the clan history, and genealogy and their part in Scottish history. To strengthen Scottish and overseas links. Annual gathering.
Membership: Open to those bearing the name MacQuarrie (or its variants) and those related by marriage or descent.
✍ President: Gregory S. McQueary
✍ Chairman: Dr Roderick W.
   Clarke
   7490 Ryebrook Lane, Rockford.
   IL 61111
☎ 1 815 877 2424

CLAN McINTYRE ASSOCIATION

Aims & Activities: To promote the clan spirit. Genealogical. Historical. To strengthen Scottish and overseas links. Annual gathering.
Membership: Open to those bearing the name McIntyre and those related by descent or marriage.
✍ Secretary: W. Wells
   2230 Edwards street, Alton.
   IL 62002

EVANSTON SCOTTISH COUNTRY DANCERS

Aims & Activities: See the RSCDS on page 47.
✍ Secretary: Ms C. Shulski
   669 Happ Road, Northfield.
   IL 60093
☎ 1 708 441 8803

MID WEST PIPE BAND ASSOCIATION

Aims & Activities: To encourage an interest in and the formation and organisation of pipe bands and piping and drumming, also participation in competitions and events in Highland Games.

Affiliations: The Royal Scottish Pipe Band Association, (page 59).
✍ Secretary: Nancy Taylor
5450 N. Monitor, Chicago.
IL 60630

ROCKFORD BURNS CLUB

Aims & Activities: Social and to encourage interest in the poetical works of Robert Burns, also to celebrate Burns Night and to encourage a wider interest in Scottish tradition, history and heritage.
✍ President: Lester Hamilton
8974 Carradale Drive, Caledonia.
IL 61011
☎ 1 815 885 3902

INDIANA

42ND ROYAL HIGHLAND REGIMENT INC

Aims & Activities: Social and to encourage interest in the traditions and history of the 42nd Royal Highland Regiment, The Black Watch.
✍ Thomas J. Griffin
2043 South 9th Street, Lafayette.
IN 47905
☎ 1 317 474 8673

BRUCE INTERNATIONAL

Aims & Activities: To promote knowledge of the clan's part in Scottish history. To Genealogical. To strengthen Scottish and overseas links. Annual Gathering.
Membership: Open to those named Bruce or connected by descent or marriage.
✍ President: Rex A. Bruce
380 Western Drive, Bloomington.
IN 47401

CLAN MORRISON SOCIETY

Aims & Activities: To promote the clan spirit. Historical. Genealogical. To strengthen Scottish overseas links. Annual gathering.
Membership: Open those with the name Morrison and those related by marriage or descent.
✍ Jack H. Morrison
1699 Fuquay Road, Newburgh.
IN 47630
☎ 1 812 925 7800

INDIANA HIGHLAND GAMES

Aims & Activities: These Games are usually held on in the Zollner Stadium, Fort Wayne, on the second Saturday in July. They feature massed bands, pipe band competitions, solo piping and drumming and Highland dancing, the usual heavy events, athletics and also Border Collies.
✍ Secretary: Indiana Highland Games
Inc., 7020 Salge Drive,
Fort Wayne IN 46835
☎ 1 219 486 2658

LOUISVILLE SCOTTISH COUNTRY DANCE SOCIETY

Aims & Activities: See the RSCDS on page 47.
✍ Secretary: Mrs Corson
11111 Trealor Road, Memphis.
IN 47413

McCONNAUGHEY SOCIETY

Aims & Activities: To promote the clan spirit. Historical. Genealogical. Annual gathering.
Membership: Open to those named McConnaughey or related by marriage, or descent.
✍ President: Betty Buntin Matthews
✍ Secretary: Pat McConnaughay
PO Box 27051, Indianapolis.
IN 46227
☎ 1 317 786 4363

SCOTTISH CULTURAL SOCIETY OF FORT WAYNE

Aims & Activities: See the RSCDS on page 47.
✍ Secretary: Ms J. Brautzsch
2206 Parkland Drive, Fort Wayne. IN 46825
☎ 1 219 483 0870

SCOTTISH SOCIETY OF INDIANAPOLIS

Aims & Activities: Social and to encourage interest in Scottish tradition, history and heritage.
✍ President: Carter Carlisle Keith
4705 N. Broadway, Indianapolis. IN 46205
☎ 1 317 283 1978

IOWA

CLAN CUNNING ASSOCIATION

Founded: 1977.
Aims & Activities: Educational. Historical. Research.
Affiliations: The Council of Scottish Clans and Associations. The American Scottish Foundation.
Membership: 500. Open to those descendants of 12th-century Scottish clan Cunning, and those with variants or derivatives of the name.
✍ President: Willis Cunning
KTJ, 3824 Lanewood drive, Des Moines IA 5031-1
☎ 1 515 255 4594

SCOTTISH HERITAGE SOCIETY NORTH EAST IOWA

Aims & Activities: Social and to encourage interest in Scottish tradition, history and heritage.
✍ President: Karan Kelso
1617 Hawthorne Dr, Cedar Falls. IA 50613
☎ 1 319 277 2399

KANSAS

CLAN GALBRAITH ASSOCIATION OF NORTH AMERICA

Aims & Activities: To promote the clan spirit. Gnealogical. Historical. To strengthen Scottish and overseas links. Annual Gathering.
Membership: Open to those named Galbraith or related by descent or marriage.
✍ President: Robert L. Galbraith
✍ Secretary: Nadine G. Mauk
333 Coolidge, Wichita. KS 67204
☎ 1 316 838 7214

KANSAS CITY HIGHLAND GAMES

Founded: 1968.
Aims & Activities: Generally held on the first weekend in June these Games include amateur heavy events and drumming.
✍ Secretary: Kansas City Highland Games
PO Box 112, Shawnee Mission. KS 66222

KANSAS CITY ST ANDREW SOCIETY SCOTTISH COUNTRY DANCERS

Aims & Activities: See the RSCDS on page 47.
✍ Secretary: Mr S. Lebofsky
PO Box 3418, Kansas City. KS 66103
☎ 1 816 523 6851

STERLING SCOTS HERITAGE SOCIETY

Aims & Activities: Social and to encourage interest in Scottish tradition, history and heritage.
✍ President: Frances Calderwood
✍ Secretary: Carol Gene Brownlee
Sterling College, Box 158,

Sterling.
KS 67579
☎ 1 316 278 3202

TOPEKA ST ANDREW SOCIETY

Aims & Activities: Social and to encourage interest in Scottish tradition, history and heritage.
✍ President: James Duncan Wallace
706 Grandview, Topeka.
KS 66606
☎ 1 913 357 4196

KENTUCKY

CENTRAL KENTUCKY BRANCH OF THE ROYAL SCOTTISH COUNTRY DANCE SOCIETY

Aims & Activities: See the RSCDS on page 47.
Membership: 75.
✍ Secretary: Mr H. Lindsay
756 Green Ridge Lane,
Louisville.
KY 40207
☎ 1 502 905 5330

CLAN MACNEIL ASSOCIATION OF AMERICA KENTUCKY-TENNESSEE BRANCH

Aims & Activities: To strengthen Scottish and overseas links. Genealogical. Historical. Annual Gathering.
Membership: Open to those named MacNeil or belonging to one of the clan septs or related by marriage or descent.
✍ Commissioner: Bruce M. McNeill
3534 Kahlert Avenue, Louisville.
KY 40215

GLASGOW HIGHLAND GAMES

Founded: 1986.
Aims & Activities: Usually held in the Barren River State Resort Park over the last weekend in May. They are part of a full weekend of Scottish related activties, which include a tattoo, ceilidhs, a tartan ball and a Scottish country dance. The Games themselves include all the usual heavy events, pipe band competitions, solo piping and Highland dancing, athletic events and a five-mile run.
✍ Secretary: c/o 121 1/2 E. Main Street
PO Box 373, Glasgow.
KY 42142
☎ 1 502 651 3141

KENTUCKY SCOTTISH WEEKEND

Founded: 1983.
Aims & Activities: Usually held in the second weekend in May in the General Butler State Resort Park in Carrolton. The Games include pipe bands, solo piping and drumming Highland dancing and amateur athletics.
✍ Secretary: Kentucky Scottish Weekend
PO Box 91683, Louisville, KY 40291-0683 or Department of Parks, Frankfort.
KY 40601

LEXINGTON SCOTTISH COUNTRY DANCE SOCIETY

Aims & Activities: See the RSCDS on page 47.
✍ Secretary: Marilyn Rogers
4309 Cobblestone Knoll,
Lexington.
KY 40515

LOUISVILLE SCOTTISH COUNTRY DANCE SOCIETY

Aims & Activities: See the RSCDS on page 47.

✍ Secretary: Rusty Saunders
2349 Saratoga Drive, Louisville.
KY 40205
☎ 1 454 0171

SCOTTISH HERITAGE SOCIETY OF CENTRAL KENTUCKY

Aims & Activities: Social and to encourage interest in Scottish tradition, history and heritage.
✍ President: The Rev Carl Beiden
✍ Treasurer: Percilla Ewen
1413 Mt Rainer Drive,
Lexington.
KY 40502
☎ 1 606 273 2171

LOUISIANA

CALEDONIAN SOCIETY OF NEW ORLEANS

Aims & Activities: Social and to encourage interest in Scottish tradition, history and heritage.
✍ President: Herbert William
2815 Chestnut St, New Orleans.
LA 40115
☎ 1 504 895 7044

CALEDONIAN SOCIETY OF NEW ORLEANS SCOTTISH COUNTRY DANCERS

Aims & Activities: See the RSCDS on page 47.
✍ Secretary: Mrs W. Grubb 8131 Cohn Street
New Orleans.
LA 70118-2801
☎ 1 504 866 2220

CLAN MACNEIL ASSOCIATION OF AMERICA MISSISSIPPI/LOUISIANA BRANCH

Aims & Activities: To strengthen

Scottish and overseas links. Historical. Genealogical. Annual Gathering.
Membership: Open to those named MacNeil, or belonging to one of the septs, or related to the clan by descent or marriage.
✍ Comm: Dr David L. MacNeill
4400 General Meyer Ave., 309
New Orleans.
LA 70114

CLAN MAXWELL SOCIETY OF THE USA

Aims & Activities: To promote awareness of the clan history and their part in Scottish and Border history. To strengthen Scottish overseas links. Genealogical. Annual Gathering.
Membership: Open to those with the name Maxwell family or related by marriage or descent.
✍ Chieftain: Murvan M. Maxwell
✍ Secretary: Mrs Edith B. Maxwell
303 Audubon Blvd.,
New Orleans.
LA 70125
☎ 1 504 866 9753

CLAN SWINTON

Aims & Activities: To promote the clan spirit. Genealogical. Historical.
Membership: Open to those named Swinton or related by marriage or descent.
✍ President: John Swinton of that Ilk
2713 Orleans Boulevard,
Jefferson. LA

ST ANDREW SOCIETY OF LOUISIANA

Aims & Activities: Social and to encourage interest in Scottish tradition, history and heritage.
✍ President: John Fraser
2217 Wirth Place, New Orleans.
LA 70115
☎ 1 504 866 8019

MAINE

CLAN BORTHWICK ASSOCIATION

Aims & Activities: To strengthen Scottish and overseas links. Genealogical. Historical. Annual Gathering.
Membership: Open to those with the name Borthwick and those related by marriage or descent.
✍ Secretary: Joseph T. Borthwick
25 Lafayette Street, Calais.
ME 04619
☎ 1 207 454 3886

MAINE HIGHLAND GAMES

Founded: 1979.
Aims & Activities: The Games are currently held in mid-August at Thomas Point Beach, Brunswick. They include piping, Highland dancing, athletics, with demonstrations of Scottish country dancing, fiddling and sheepdog work.
✍ Secretary: c/o 298 York Street
York.
ME 03909

NEW ENGLAND BRANCH OF THE CLAN MACNEIL ASSOCIATION OF AMERICA

Aims & Activities: To promote awareness of the clan history and genealogy. To strengthen Scottish and overseas links.
Membership: Open to those named Macneil (or its variant spellings) or related by marriage or descent.
✍ Warren E. Blake
Box 969, Jefferson.
ME 04348

ST ANDREW'S SOCIETY OF MAINE

Aims & Activities: To encourage all social activities likely to promote an interest in Scotland, its history, traditions and Scottish heritage.
Affiliations: The St Andrew Society, Edinburgh.
✍ President: Harold Cooper
298 York Street, York.
ME 03909
☎ 1 207 363 5103

TRENTON ACADIAN SCOTTISH FESTIVAL

Founded: 1980.
Aims & Activities: Generally held in the third week end of July in the Acadia National Park. As well as the customary programme of events, the Games include a tomahawk event and a sheepdog demonstration.
✍ Contact: Trenton Tourist Board

MARYLAND

BALTIMORE SCOTTISH COUNTRY DANCERS

Aims & Activities: See the RSCDS on page 47.
✍ Secretary: Mrs N. Koppelman
6006 Hunt Ridge Road, Apt. 2521, Baltimore.
MD 21210
☎ 1 410 377 8765

CARRUTHERS CLAN SOCIETY

Aims & Activities: To promote the clan spirit. Genealogical. Historical. To strengthen Scottish and overseas links.
Membership: Open to those bearing that name, or variants of it.
✍ Secretary: Richard A. Crothers
227 Old Zion Road North East.
MD 21901
☎ 1 410 658 5482

CELTIC SOCIETY OF SOUTHERN MARYLAND

Aims & Activities: Social and to encourage interest in Scottish tradition, history and heritage. Annual Gathering.

✍ President: Benjamin R. Williams
PO Box 209, Prince Frederick.
MD 20678
☎ 1 301 535 0292

CLAN MACINTYRE

Aims & Activities: To promote the clan spirit and trace genealogical records in Scotland and the USA. To record the clan history: To hold an Annual Gathering.
Membership: Open to the members of the MacIntyre clan and all those bearing that name, or variants of it, also to those connected by descent or marriage, or those interested in the aims.

✍ President: James W. MacIntyre of Glencoe
15301 Pine Orchard Drive, Apartment 3H, Silver Spring.
MD

CLAN MAITLAND SOCIETY OF NORTH AMERICA

Aims & Activities: To promote the clan spirit and to record their part in Scottish history. Genealogical. To strengthen Scottish and overseas links. Annual Gathering.
Membership: Open to those bearing the name Maitland, or those related by marriage or descent.

✍ President: Sandra LaCroix
✍ Secretary: Mary Maitland Kelly
108 Lawson Road, Scituate.
MA 02066
☎ 1 617 545 2637

MARYLAND SCOTTISH SOCIETY

Aims & Activities: Social and to encourage interest in Scottish tradition, history and heritage.

✍ President: Dr George Merril
118 W. Melrose Avenue, Baltimore.
MD 21210
☎ 1 301 323 8128

McHENRY HIGHLAND FESTIVAL

Founded: 1990.
Aims & Activities: Presently held at the Garrett County Fairgrounds in the first weekend in June. These indoor Games include pipe bands and solo piping and Highland dancing. In addition there are sheepdog demonstrations and a golf tournament.

✍ Secretary: Deep Creek Lake/Garrett County Promotion Council
Courthouse, Oakland.
MD 21550
☎ 1 301 334 1948

MID-ATLANTIC BRANCH OF THE CLAN MACNEIL ASSOCIATION OF AMERICA

Aims & Activities: Genealogical. Historical. To strengthen Scottish and overseas links. Annual Gatherings.
Membership: Open to those bearing the name McNeil, or of one of the septs. or those related by marriage or descent.

✍ Charles E. MacNeill
19105 Canadian Court, Gaithersburg.
MD 20760

ROBERT BURNS SOCIETY OF ANNAPOLIS

Founded: 1974.
Aims & Activities: Social. Annual Gathering. To perpetuate the memory of Robert Burns.
Affiliations: The Burns Federation, No. 986.

✍ Secretary: PO Box 4185

Annapolis.
MD 21403

ST ANDREW'S SOCIETY OF BALTIMORE

Aims & Activities: Social and to encourage interest in Scottish tradition, history and heritage.
✍ President: Elliott W. Hudgins III
✍ Secretary: Arthur S. McAra
1335 Hickory Springs Circle,
Baltimore.
MD 21228
☎ 1 301 744 4281

ST ANDREW'S SOCIETY OF THE EASTERN SHORE

Aims & Activities: Social and to encourage interest in Scottish tradition, history and heritage. Overseas links.
✍ President: Virgil W. Maxwell
✍ Secretary: Katherine McInnis
PO Box 1364, Easton.
MD 21601
☎ 1 301 745 2783

MASSACHUSETTS

BERKSHIRE INDOOR HIGHLAND GAMES

Founded: 1984.
Aims & Activities: Currently held on the second Saturday in May and including children's events.
✍ Secretary: c/o PO Box 54
Pittsfield.
MA 01201

BOSTON BRANCH OF THE ROYAL SCOTTISH COUNTRY DANCE SOCIETY

Aims & Activities: See the RSCDS on page 47.
Membership: 350.

✍ Secretary: Jeanetta McColl
16 Maureen Road, Framingham.
MA 01701-4133
☎ 1 508 877 5028

BOSTON CALEDONIAN CLUB

Aims & Activities: To promote social activities likely to foster an interest in Scottish tradition, history and heritage.
✍ Chief: Herbert A. MacLeod
4 Iroquois Road, Arlington.
MA 02174
☎ 1 617 648 9031

CAPE BRETON GAELIC SOCIETY

Aims & Activities: Social and to encourage interest in Gaelic tradition, history and heritage.
✍ President: Margaret Morrison
495 North Street, Tewksbury.
MA 01876
☎ 1 617 858 3792

CLAN DRUMMOND SOCIETY OF NORTH AMERICA

Aims & Activities: To promote awareness of the clan history and trace genealogical records. To strengthen Scottish and overseas links. Annual gathering.
Membership: Open to those with the name Drummond and those related by descent or marriage.
✍ President:
Charles E. McRobbie Jr.
6 Bernard Lane, Methven.
MA 01844
☎ 1 617 682 0130

CLAN GILLESPIE SOCIETY

Aims & Activities: To promote the clan spirit and research clan connections in Scotland. Genealogical. Historical. To strengthen Scottish and overseas links.

Membership: Open to all bearing the name Gillespie and those related by birth or marriage.

✍ Chieftain: Dr R. J. M. Gillespie
100 Stanley St Attleboro Falls.
MA 02763

CLAN MACNICOL IN THE AMERICAS

Aims & Activities: To promote awareness of the clan history, background and connections in Scotland. To strengthen Scottish and overseas links. Annual Gathering.
Membership: Open to those bearing the name MacNicol (in all its variants) and to those connected by descent or marriage.

✍ Commissioner: Dr Murray Nicolson
60 Revolutionary Road,
Concord.
MA 01742

☎ 1 617 369 3416

✍ Membership Secretary: Forrester I. Nicolson
7 Wall St., Wellesley Hills.
MA 02181

☎ 1 617 237 5347

HIGHLAND LIGHT SCOTTISH SOCIETY

Aims & Activities: Social and to encourage interest in Scottish tradition, history and heritage.

✍ President: George F. Gregory
PO Box 341, Yarmouth Port.
MA 02675

☎ 1 617 362 5125

ST ANDREW'S SOCIETY OF BRIDGEWATER

Aims & Activities: Social and to encourage interest in Scottish tradition, history and heritage.

✍ Chieftain: Gene McLean
PO Box 203, Bridgewater.
MA 02324

ST ANDREW'S SOCIETY OF BRIDGEWATER

Aims & Activities: Social and to encourage interest in Scottish tradition, history and heritage. Annual Gathering.

✍ Chieftain: Gene McLean
PO Box 203 Bridgewater.
MA 02324

TAM O'SHANTER HIGHLAND GAMES

Aims & Activities: Currently held on the first Saturday in June at Romuva Park, Brockton.

✍ Secretary: c/o 200 Buckminster Drive
Norwood.
MA 02062

MICHIGAN

ALMA HIGHLAND FESTIVAL AND GAMES

Founded: 1968.
Aims & Activities: These Games are held at Alma College, which has its own pipe band, usually over the last weekend in May. Alma calls itself 'Scotland USA' and because of its position attracts entries from both the USA and Canada. As well as the usual events the Games include Pipe band championships, a farmer's walk, fiddling, soccer, a road run, a sheepdog demonstration and a craft fair.

✍ Secretary: c/o PO Box 506
Alma.
MI 48801

CLAN DONNACHAIDH MICHIGAN

Aims & Activities: To promote the clan spirit. Genealogical. Historical. To promote links with Scotland and overseas. Annual Gathering.

Membership: Open to those bearing the name Robertson and those related by marriage or descent.
✍ Edward Robinson
   8188 Potter Road, Davison.
   MI 48423
☎ 1 313 653 4275

CLAN MUNRO ASSOCIATION USA

Aims & Activities: To promote awareness of the clan history, background and connections in Scotland. To strengthen Scottish and overseas links. Annual Gathering.
Membership: Open to all bearing the name Munro (in its varied spellings) or related by marriage or descent.
✍ Secretary: Claire E. Monroe
   11131 Union Road, Route 2, Pittsford.
   MI 49271
☎ 1 517 523 2635

DETROIT BRANCH OF THE ROYAL SCOTTISH COUNTRY DANCE SOCIETY

Aims & Activities: See the RSCDS on page 47.
Membership: 70.
✍ Secretary: Cathie Lavery
   608 Sunset Lane,
   St Calir Shores, MI
☎ 1 810 296 3282
✍ Detroit Mailing Address:
   PO Box 931
   Royal Oak, MI 48068-0931

DETROIT BURNS CLUB

Founded: 1912.
Aims & Activities: Social. Annual Gathering. To promote interest in the literary work of Robert Burns.
Affiliations: The Burns Federation, No. 701.
✍ Secretary: Mrs Helen McCallum
   9352 Colorada, Livonia.
   MI 48150

DETROIT HIGHLAND GAMES

Founded: 1867.
Aims & Activities: The second oldest of the Highland Games held currently in the USA these are generally held on the first Saturday in August in the 83-acre historic Fort Wayne on the Detroit River, directly across from Windsor, Canada. They include the usual heavy events, Pipe bands, solo piping and Highland dancing. They are organised by the St Andrew's Society of Detroit with entirely volunteer support.
✍ Secretary: F. Michael Smith
   PO Box 32291, Detroit.
   MI 48232
☎ 1 313 832 1849
✍ Arthur Cheney
   1326 Mayfield, Livonia.
   MI 48150
☎ 1 313 42 4864

ROSEVILLE RED HACKLE DANCERS

Aims & Activities: See the RSCDS on page 47.
✍ Secretary: Ms M. Ross
   35793 Hilton, Fraser.
   MI 48026

SCOTTISH SOCIETY OF SOUTH WEST MICHIGAN

Aims & Activities: To promote social activities likely to foster an interest in Scottish tradition, history and heritage.
✍ President: Kenneth C. McAfee
✍ Secretary: Jean Hunter
   725 Wagner Dr. Apt 9,
   Battle Creek.
   MI 49017
☎ 1 616 963 3596

MINNESOTA

CLAN MACKINTOSH

Aims & Activities: To promote awareness of the family history, background and connections in Scotland. To strengthen Scottish and overseas links. Annual Gathering.
Affiliations: Clan Mackintosh, Scotland.
Membership: Open to those named Mackintosh or related by descent or marriage.
✍ Convener: James Elder
13010 W. Colfax Place, Butler.
WI 53007
☎ 1 414 781 7638

CLAN SINCLAIR ASSOCIATION

Founded: 1978.
Aims & Activities: Encourages a closer relationship between members. Offers help with genealogical research, disseminates information.
Membership: 450, comprising 300 families and 150 individuals. Open to descendants of the Sinclair family.
✍ President: David Sinclair
Nouschor
124 N 24th Ave. E, Duluth.
MN 55812
☎ 1 218 724 7761

ST ANDREW'S SOCIETY OF FARGO-MOORHEAD

Aims & Activities: Social and to encourage interest in Scottish tradition, history and heritage.
✍ President: Douglas Sillers
RR2, Moorhead.
MN 56560
☎ 1 218 233 4373

ST ANDREW'S SOCIETY OF MINNESOTA

Aims & Activities: Social and to encourage interest in Scottish tradi-

tion, history and heritage. To encourage closer links with Scotland.
✍ President: Sally Kerr Edstron
✍ Chairman: William D. Hannay
5432 North Willow Lane,
Brooklyn.
MN 55430
☎ 1 612 526 5386

ST PAUL SCOTTISH COUNTRY FAIR

Founded: 1972.
Aims & Activities: Currently held on the first Saturday in May in the grounds of Macalister College, which offers courses in piping and Highland dancing. This includes exhibitions by local artists.
✍ Secretary: Madison Sheely
Macalister College, 1600 Grand Avenue, St Paul.
MN 55105

TWIN CITIES ROYAL SCOTTISH COUNTRY DANCE SOCIETY

Aims & Activities: See the RSCDS on page 47.
Membership: 33.
✍ Secretary: K. Schwarzruck
2011 Ashland Avenue, St Paul.
MN 55104-5833
☎ 1 612 641 1569

MISSISSIPPI

HIGHLANDS AND ISLANDS SCOTTISH FESTIVAL

Aims & Activities: Generally held early in September at the Hiller Park in Biloxi.
✍ Secretary: c/o PO Box 431
Biloxi.
MS 39633

ORDER OF SCOTTISH DAMES

Aims & Activities: Social and to encourage an interest in Scottish history, tradition and heritage, especially on the distaff side.
✍ Sennachie: Mrs Bruce H. Nicholson
5614 Brentwood Drive, Jackson. MS 39211
☎ 1 601 956 2508

MISSOURI

BURNS CLUB OF ST LOUIS

Founded: 1905.
Aims & Activities: To promote interest in the literary work of Robert Burns. Social. Annual Gathering.
Affiliations: The Burns Federation, No. 220.
✍ Secretary: Mr T. E. Newton III
6242 Waterman Avenue, St Louis. MO 63130

CELTIC SOCIETY OF THE OZARKS BURNS CLUB

Aims & Activities: Social and to promote interest in Scottish heritage and the works of Burns.
Affiliations: The Burns Federation, No. 1122.
✍ Secretary: Dr J. C. Holsinger
2214 E. Cherryvale, Springfield. MO 65804-4524

KANSAS CITY ST ANDREW'S SOCIETY

Founded: 1964.
Aims & Activities: Social and to encourage interest in Scottish heritage, history and tradition. To perpetuate the memory of Robert Burns. Annual Gathering.
Affiliations: The Burns Federation, No. 1035; The Royal Scottish Country Dance Society.

✍ G. Morrison FSA Scot
5617 Northwest Adrian, Kansas City.
MO 64141-2751
✍ Karen Spaith
PO Box 1304, Kansas City.
MO 64141

SCOTTISH COUNTRY DANCERS

Aims & Activities: See The Scottish Country Dance Society.
✍ Secretary: Mr S. Lebofsky
PO Box 3418, Kansas City.
MO 66103
☎ 1 816 523 8581

SCOTTISH COUNTRY DANCERS OF ST LOUIS

Aims & Activities: See the RSCDS on page 47.
✍ Secretary: Mrs J. Lehr
11 Ballas Court, St Louis.
MO 63131-3038
☎ 1 314 432 2842

MONTANA

BILLINGS SCOTTISH COUNTRY DANCERS

Aims & Activities: See the RSCDS on page 47.
✍ Secretary: Ms G. Waples
4246 Marian Circle, Blue Creek route, Billings.
MT 59101
☎ 1 406 248 5260

BOZEMAN SCOTTISH COUNTRY DANCERS

Aims & Activities: See the RSCDS on page 47.
✍ Secretary: Mrs C. Wagner
50 Meagher Avenue, Bozeman.
MT 59715
☎ 1 406 587 7173

MISSOULA SCOTTISH COUNTRY DANCERS

Aims & Activities: See the RSCDS on page 47.

✍ Secretary: Pat Dolan
PO Box 945 Lolo.
MT 59847

☎ 1 406 272 0618

NEBRASKA

SCOTTISH COUNTRY DANCE GROUP OF OMAHA

Aims & Activities: See the RSCDS on page 47.

✍ Secretary: Betty Carter 3654
Avenue D
Council Bluffs.
IA 51501

☎ 1 1 712 323 4269

NEW HAMPSHIRE

CLAN DUNBAR

Aims & Activities: To promote awareness of the clan history, background and connections in Scotland. Genealogical. Historical. To strengthen Scottish and overseas links. Annual Gathering.
Membership: Open to those with the name Dunbar or related by descent or marriage.

✍ Chieftain: D. Dunbar Chaplin III
RFD 1, Box 668,
Center Barnstead.
NH 03225

☎ 603 269 4371

LOON MOUNTAIN HIGHLAND GAMES

Founded: 1976.
Aims & Activities: Customarily held over the three days of the weekend following Labor Day at the Loon Mountain Recreational Centre in the White Mountain National Forest. As well as the usual events they include Harp and Fiddle Championships, the Loon Mountain Stone Carry (240lb) a kilted race and an 18th-century military encampment. (74th Argyll Highlanders).

✍ Secretary: PO Box 130
Cambridge.
MA 02238-0130

NEW HAMPSHIRE SCOTTISH COUNTRY DANCE GROUP

Aims & Activities: See the RSCDS on page 47.

✍ Secretary: Mrs O'Donnell
40 Allen Road, Bow.
NH 03304-5007

NEW JERSEY

BONNIE BRAE HIGHLAND GAMES

Aims & Activities: Currently held on the second Saturday in June and including most of the usual events.

✍ Secretary: Director of
Development
Bonnie Brae, Millington.
NJ 07946

PRINCETON SCOTTISH COUNTRY DANCERS

Aims & Activities: See the RSCDS on page 47.

✍ Secretary: Mr R. Miller Jnr.
129 Susan Drive, Trenton.
NJ 08638

NEW MEXICO

NEW MEXICO BRANCH OF THE ROYAL SCOTTISH COUNTRY DANCE SOCIETY

Aims & Activities: See the RSCDS on page 47.
Membership: 58.
✍ Secretary: Cathy Turner
   PO Box 63, Los Alomos.
   NM 87544
☎ 1 505 984 3256

ST ANDREW SOCIETY OF NEW MEXICO

Aims & Activities: Social and to promote interest in   Scottish heritage, history and traditions, including the literary works of Robert Burns. Annual Gathering.
Affiliations: The Burns Federation, No. 1112.
✍ Secretary: R. L. Stevenson
   PO Box 40507, Albuquerque.
   NM 87196

NEW YORK

ADIRONDACK SCOTTISH GAMES

Founded: 1977.
Aims & Activities: Currently held at Crandall Park, Glen Falls, on the first Saturday in June. They include most of the usual events.
✍ Secretary: Harold Kirkpatrick
   492 Glen Street, Glen Falls.
   NY 121801

AMERICAN SCOTTISH FOUNDATION

Founded: 1956.
Aims & Activities: To build bonds of friendship and co-operation between Scottish and American people. To preserve   Scottish heritage and to bring into one general association as many as possible of the 22 million or more Americans of Scottish descent. Sponsors annual Scottish Ball.
Publications: Calling All Scots (quarterly).
Membership: Open to Americans of Scottish descent and to Scots living in the USA.
✍ President: Dr Charles H. Haws.
   PO Box 537
   Lennox Hill Sta., New York.
   NY 10021
☎ 1 212 605 0338
✆ 1 212 557 1685

AMHERST MUSEUM SCOTTISH FESTIVAL

Aims & Activities: Customarily held in mid-September at the Amherst Museum.
✍ Secretary: Amherst Museum
   Amherst.
   NY

BRUCE FAMILY

Aims & Activities: To promote awareness of the family background and connections in Scotland and their part in Scottish history. To strengthen Scottish and overseas links. Annual Gathering.
Membership: Open to all bearing the name Bruce and those connected by descent or marriage.
✍ Personal Representative of the Chief: Duncan A. Bruce
   185 E. 85th Street, New York.
   NY 10028
☎ 1 212 751 1812

BUFFALO BRANCH OF THE ROYAL SCOTTISH COUNTRY DANCE SOCIETY

Aims & Activities: See the RSCDS on page 47.
Membership: 42.
✍ Secretary: Mrs B. McCulloch

4177 Circle Court, Williamsville.
NY 14221
☎ 1 716 633 6066 (home)
☎ 1 716 845 2567 (business)

BURNS SOCIETY OF THE CITY OF NEW YORK

Aims & Activities: Social and to encourage study of the works of Robert Burns. Annual Gathering. Historical.
Affiliations: The Burns Federation, No. 1114.
✍ Secretary: Joseph R. Lester
PO Box 354, Chatham.
NY 07928

CAPITAL DISTRICT HIGHLAND GAMES

Founded: 1978.
Aims & Activities: Usually held on the Saturday before Labor Day in Altamont, a small town near Albany in a good rural setting. The Games include a Scottie dog competition.
✍ Secretary: 40 Terrace Avenue
Albany.
NY 12203

CENTRAL NEW YORK SCOTTISH GAMES

Founded: 1934.
Aims & Activities: The fifth oldest of the current Games held in the USA. They are usually held on the second Saturday in August at the Griffin Field on Lake Onondaga, near Liverpool. They are sponsored by the Clan Douglas and include all the usual events.
✍ Secretary: Joseph Walker
160 Stafford Avenue, Syracuse.
NY 13206

CLAN DUNBAR

Aims & Activities: To promote awareness of the clan history and trace genealogical records. To promote Scottish and overseas links. Annual Gathering.
Membership: Open to those bearing the name Dunbar, or related by descent or marriage.
✍ President: Sir Jean Dunbar of Mochrum Bt.
45-55 39th Street,
Long Island City.
NY

CLAN FERGUSSON SOCIETY OF NORTH AMERICA

Aims & Activities: To promote awareness of the clan history and Scottish connections. Genealogical. Historical. Annual Gathering.
Membership: Open to those named Fergusson (in its various spellings) or those connected by descent or marriage.
✍ President: Thomas Ferguson
6364 Gillis Road, Victor.
NY 14564
☎ 1 716 924 5284

GREATER NEW YORK BRANCH OF THE CLAN MACNEIL ASSOCIATION OF AMERICA

Aims & Activities: To increase knowledge of the clan history, background and connections in Scotland. To strengthen Scottish links. Annual Gathering.
Membership: Open to those bearing the Macneil name (or its variants) or connected by descent or marriage.
✍ David L. Fuss
30 Horatio Street, Apt. 2-B,
New York.
NY 10014

LONG ISLAND SCOTTISH GAMES

Founded: 1961.
Aims & Activities: Usually held on the lawn of Old Westbury Mansion and Gardens on the fourth Saturday in

August. These Games include the usual events.
🖎 Secretary: Long Island Scottish Games
30 Bluegrass Lane, Levittown.
NY 11756
☎ 1 516 883 9396

NEW YORK BRANCH OF THE ROYAL SCOTTISH COUNTRY DANCE SOCIETY

Aims & Activities: See the RSCDS on page 47.
Membership: 147.
🖎 Secretary: Mrs S. Freedman
2130 East 18th Street, Brooklyn.
NY 11229
☎ 1 718 336 5026

ROCHESTER SCOTTISH COUNTRY DANCERS

Aims & Activities: See the RSCDS on page 47.
🖎 Secretary: Ms A. G.Young
569 Eastbrooke Lane, Rochester.
NY 14618
☎ 1 716 473 6183

SAINT ANDREW'S SOCIETY OF THE STATE OF NEW YORK

Founded: 1756.
Aims & Activities: Social. Educational. Sponsors scholarship and an Almoners programme for graduate study. Maintains 700-volume Scottish library.
Membership: 1000: Staff: 1. Open to persons of Scottish birth or descent.
🖎 Office Manager: Eva Northcote
71 W. 23rd St, New York.
NY 10010
☎ 1 21 807 1730

SCOTIA DANCERS

Aims & Activities: See the RSCDS on page 47.
🖎 Treasurer: Mr R. Anthony

126 West 96th St, New York.
NY 10025
☎ 1 212 865 5338

SCOTTISH COUNTRY DANCE SOCIETY OF WESTCHESTER

Aims & Activities: See the RSCDS on page 47.
🖎 Secretary: Mr B. Percival
67 Burns Street, Forest Hills.
NY 11375
☎ 1 718 544 5768

NORTH CAROLINA

AMERICAN CLAN GREGOR SOCIETY

Aims & Activities: To promote the clan spirit. Genealogical. Historical. Annual Gathering.
Membership: Open to those bearing the name Gregor (in its various forms) or related by descent or marriage.
🖎 Chieftain Dr. Russell C. McGregor
249a S. Lake Shore Drive, Whispering Pines.
NC 28327
☎ 1 919 949 3119

CALEDONIAN FOUNDATION

Founded: 1988.
Aims & Activities: Promotes the establishment of an endowment to enable Scottish Opera to continue to maintain high standards of excellence and continue to improve in all its aspects. Seeks support in the USA for the maintenance of Balnain House in Inverness and the Theatre Royal in Glasgow. Supersedes American Friends of Scottish Opera, founded in 1976.

Membership: Open to individuals interested in building US support for the Scottish Arts.
✍ Executive Vice-President: Miss Duncan MacDonald
Scottish Heritage Center,
PO Box 564, Laurinburg.
NC 28352
☎ 1 919 277 5236

CAROLINA SCOTTISH COUNTRY DANCE SOCIETY

Aims & Activities: See the RSCDS on page 47.
✍ Secretary: Mr D. Burgess
321 Bay Tree Lane,
Raleigh.
NC 27615
☎ 1 919 847 5840

CHAPEL HILL SCOTTISH COUNTRY DANCE SOCIETY

Aims & Activities: See the RSCDS on page 47.
✍ Secretary: Mrs S. Coulter
1107 Buchanan Boulevarde,
Durham.
NC 27701
☎ 1 919 286 7278

CHARLOTTE SCOTTISH COUNTRY DANCE SOCIETY

Aims & Activities: See the RSCDS on page 47.
✍ Secretary: Ms K. Burns
4741 Hedgemore Drive,
Apt. 2-G, Charlotte.
NC 28209-3251
☎ 1 704 399 8060

CLAN FORBES SOCIETY

Aims & Activities: To promote awareness of the clan history, background and connections in Scotland. To strengthen Scottish links. Genealogical. Historical. Annual Gathering.

Membership: Open to those bearing the name Forbes or those connected by descent or marriage.
✍ President: Ernest T. Forbes III
PO Box 18193, Asheville.
NC 28814
☎ 1 704 255 8810

CLAN GRAHAM SOCIETY

Aims & Activities: To encourage awareness of the clan history, background and connections in Scotland and the Borders. To strengthen Scottish and overseas links. Annual Gathering.
Membership: Open to anyone bearing the name Graham, or connected with that name by descent or marriage.
✍ President: Richard Graham
✍ Membership Vice-President: Robert H. Howard
1228 Kensington Drive,
High Point.
NC 27260
☎ 1 919 8855789

CLAN MACNEIL ASSOCIATION OF AMERICA

Aims & Activities: To promote awareness of the clan history, background and connections in Scotland. To strengthen Scottish and overseas links. Annual Gathering.
Membership: Open to those bearing the name Macneil (or its variants) and those related by descent or marriage.
✍ President: Royce Neil McNeill FSA Scot.
✍ Secretary: Doris B. McNeill
1824 Stonyridge Drive, Charlotte.
NC 28208
☎ 1 704 399 1134

CLAN MACNEIL ASSOCIATION OF AMERICA CAROLINAS BRANCH

Aims & Activities: To promote the clan

spirit. Genealogical. Historical. Annual Gathering.

Membership: Open to those with the name MacNeil,or of one of the septs. or those connected by descent or marriage.

✍ Comm: John A. MacNeill Sr.
PO Box 339, Whitesville.
NC 29427

CLAN MACRAE SOCIETY OF NA

Aims & Activities: To improve awareness of the clan history, background and connections in Scotland. To strengthen Scottish links. Genealogical. Annual Gathering.

Membership: Open to those bearing the name MacRae, or connected by descent or marriage.

✍ President: Hugh MacRae II
3501 Oleander Drive,
PO Box 3145, Wilmington.
NC 28406
☎ 1 919 392 3300

CLAN MENZIES SOCIETY

Aims & Activities: To encourage the clan spirit. Gnealogical. Historical. To promote closer links with Scotland. Annual Gathering.

Membership: Open to those bearing the name Menzies (in its varied spellings) or related by marriage or descent.

✍ Secretary: David A. Mathewes
420 Long Branch, Cullowhee.
NC 28723
☎ 1 704 293 5229

FLORA MACDONALD HIGHLAND GAMES

Founded: 1977.

Aims & Activities: Generally held on the first weekend in October at Red Springs, they include the usual events and a re-enactment of Revolutionary War battles.

✍ Secretary: Flora Macdonald

Highland Games Inc.
PO Box 547, Red Springs.
NC 28377

GRANDFATHER MOUNTAIN HIGHLAND GAMES AND GATHERING OF SCOTTISH CLANS

Founded: 1956.

Aims & Activities: One of the best known and largest Games in the USA they are held in the superb setting of the MacRae Meadow beneath the Grandfather Mountain. They start on the Thursday and last four days over the first full weekend following the 4th of July. There is a picnic and opening ceremony on the Thursday followed by clan meetings and social events on the Friday. The Games themselves take place on the Saturday and Sunday, and include all the usual events as well as a parade of more than 100 clans and numerous traditional events. Scottish Heritage USA Inc are sponsors of the Games.

✍ Secretary: Cheryl Farthing
PO Box 2356, Banner Elk.
NC 28604
☎ 1 704 898 5286

GREENSBORO SCOTTISH COUNTRY DANCE SOCIETY

Aims & Activities: See the RSCDS on page 47.

✍ Secretary: Mr S. Arnett
3501 Kenmore Street,
Greensboro.
NC 27282
☎ 1 910 282 0764

HAYWOOD SCOTTISH DANCERS

Aims & Activities: See the RSCDS on page 47.

✍ Secretary: Mr D. A. Mathewes
RT1 Box 530, Canton.
NC 28716
☎ 1 704 648 4255

RALEIGH SCOTTISH DANCERS

Aims & Activities: See the RSCDS on page 47.
✍ Secretary: Mrs P. Johnston
215 S. E Maynard Road, Cary.
NC 27511
☎ 1 919 380 7707

ROBERT BURNS SOCIETY OF NORTH CAROLINA

Aims & Activities: Social and to perpetuate the memory of Robert Burns. Annual Gathering.
Affiliations: The Burns Federation, No. 826.
✍ The Secretary: PO Box 220605 Charlotte.
NC 2822-0605

SCOTTISH HERITAGE USA

Founded: 1965.
Aims & Activities: To recognise and enhance the original bonds of ancestral and national character among the peoples of Scotland and the United States. Works in co-operation with the National Trust for Scotland. Emphasis is on the exchange of people and ideas between Scotland and the US. Sponsors the annual Grandfather Mountain Highland Games in North Carolina.
✍ President: Alexander R. Hamilton. PO Box 4547 Pinehurst.
NC 28374
☎ 1 919 295 4448
✆ 1 919 295 3147

SHELBY SCOTTISH COUNTRY DANCERS

Aims & Activities: See the RSCDS on page 47.
✍ Secretary: Mrs E. Yates
1223 New Crest Lane, Shelby.
NC 28150
☎ 1 704 482 8253

WAXHAW SCOTTISH GAMES

Founded: 1980.
Aims & Activities: These Games are generally held in a large natural outdoor theatre on the last Saturday in October and include the usual events.
✍ Secretary: c/o Scottish Society of the Waxhaws Ltd.
Robert Burns Station,
PO Box 143, Waxhaw.
NC 28173

OHIO

CINCINATTI BRANCH OF THE ROYAL SCOTTISH COUNTRY DANCE SOCIETY

Aims & Activities: See the RSCDS on page 47.
Membership: 79.
✍ Secretary: Elizabeth Luzzo
PO Box 43097, Cincinnati.
OH 45243
☎ 1 513 793 6547

CLAN MATHESON SOCIETY

Aims & Activities: To encourage further knowledge of the clan background and connections in Scotland and their part in Scottish history. To strengthen Scottish and overseas links. Annual Gathering.
Membership: Open to all bearing the name Matheson or related by descent or marriage.
✍ Honorary Secretary: Leslie R. Matheson
3850 Laurel Glen Drive,
Broadway Heights.
OH 44147
☎ 1 216 562 5729

CLEVELAND HEIGHTS SCOTTISH COUNTRY DANCE GROUP

Aims & Activities: See the RSCDS on page 47.

✍ Secretary: Karl Augenstein
3586 Grosvenor Road, Cleveland Heights.
OH 44118

CLEVELAND SCOTTISH COUNTRY DANCE GROUP

Aims & Activities: See the RSCDS on page 47.
✍ Secretary: Mrs S. Utrata
1618 Wagar Road, Lakewood.
OH 44107
☎ 1 216 228 3265

DAYTON SCOTTISH COUNTRY DANCE SOCIETY

Aims & Activities: See the RSCDS on page 47.
✍ Secretary: Sue A. Michael
248 Foothill Drive, Brookville.
OH 75309
☎ 1 513 833 2833

GREAT LAKES BRANCH OF THE CLAN MACNEIL ASSOCIATION OF AMERICA

Aims & Activities: Genealogical. Historical. To promote closer links with Scotland and the clan overseas. Annual Gathering.
Membership: Open to those bearing the name MacNeil, or of one of its septs, or related by descent or marriage.
✍ Comm: Carolyn R. Neal
2538 Vaness Drive, Toledo.
OH 43615

LYNDHURST SCOTTISH COUNTRY DANCE GROUP

Aims & Activities: See the RSCDS on page 47.
✍ Secretary: Amy Clough
1031 Allston Road, Cleveland Heights.
OH 44121

OHIO SCOTTISH GAMES

Founded: 1978.
Aims & Activities: Generally held on the fourth Saturday in June at Oberlin College. They include the usual events as well as rugby and a kilted mile race.
✍ Secretary: Ohio Scottish Games
PO Box 21169, Cleveland.
OH 44121

SCOTTISH HERITAGE ASSOCIATION

Founded: 1885.
Aims & Activities: Promotes the perpetuation of Scottish tradition through the preservation of Scottish music, history and culture in the USA. Social activities include annual Burns night dinner, kirking of the Tartans, fish fries and others. (Formerly 1991 Clan Grant, No. 17 Order of Scottish Clans).
Membership: 115. Open to men of Scottish descent and others interested.
✍ Secretary: Joseph Clarke
28704 Knickerbocker Road,
Bay Village OH 44140
☎ 1 216 835 1713

OKLAHOMA

CLAN GRANT

Aims & Activities: To increase knowledge of the clan and its place in Scottish history. Genealogical. To strengthen the bonds with Scotland and clan members overseas. Annual Gathering.
Membership: Open to those bearing the name Grant or related by descent or marriage.
✍ Chief: James Jones
✍ Secretary: Alex W. Campbell
17 OSC, 7441 Hi View Drive,
N. Royalton OH 44133
☎ 1 216 237 6400

CLAN GREGOR SOCIETY GREAT LAKES CHAPTER

Aims & Activities: To promote awareness of the clan history, background and connections in Scotland. Genealogical. To encourage Scottish and overseas links. Annual Gathering.
Membership: Open to those bearing the name Gregor (or its variants) or related by descent or marriage.
✍ Chairman: Margaret M. Frost
20770 Lake Road, Rocky River.
OH 44116
☎ 1 216 333 1008

CLAN HANNA

Aims & Activities: To foster clan and family ties throughout the world. Annual Gathering. Associated with the Clan Hannay Society, Scotland.
Affiliations: Associated with the Clan Hannay Society, Scotland.
Membership: Open to all bearing the name of Hanna, Hannah, or Hannay, or those connected by descent or marriage.
✍ National Convener: The Rev James A. M. Hanna
The Manse, Oak Hill.
OH 45656
☎ 1 614 982 7507

OKLAHOMA SCOTTISH GAMES AND GATHERING

Founded: 1980.
Aims & Activities: Generally held on the fourth Saturday in September in Mannion Park 'The Friendly Games' have attendance figures of more than 5,000. Events include pipe bands, solo piping, Highland dancing and amateur heavy events, a tug-o'-war and children's competitions.
✍ Secretary: Ruth Rankin
PO Box 9796, Tulsa.
OK 74157-0796

TULSA CEILIDH DANCERS AND PIPERS

Aims & Activities: See the RSCDS on page 47.
✍ Secretary: Miss E. Lane
154 North Florence Place, Tulsa.
OK 74110

OREGON

ATHENA CALEDONIAN GAMES

Founded: 1899 and restarted 1976.
Aims & Activities: These Games are currently held on the second Saturday in July. They include a tattoo, a women's caber and rolling-pin toss and free beer for all spectators wearing the kilt.
✍ Secretary: Donald R. Duncan
PO Box 245, Athena.
OR 97813

CLAN MACNEIL ASSOCIATION OF AMERICA, PACIFIC NORTH-WEST BRANCH

Aims & Activities: To promote awareness of the clan history and genealogy. To encourage Scottish and overseas links. Annual Gathering.
Membership: Open to those bearing the name MacNeil, or of one of its septs, or connected by descent or marriage.
✍ Col. John H. Neilson
17830 N. E Everett Court,
Portland OR 97230

PORTLAND BRANCH OF THE ROYAL SCOTTISH COUNTRY DANCE SOCIETY

Aims & Activities: See the RSCDS on page 47.
Membership: 65.
✍ Secretary: Marie Keene
920 S. W. 13th Avenue, Portland.
OR 97205

☎ 1 503 647 5621 (home)
☎ 1 503 224 4410 (business)

PORTLAND HIGHLAND GAMES

Founded: 1952.
Aims & Activities: Currently held on the third Saturday in June in the grounds of the Mt Hood Community Centre. As well as the usual events they include a ladies' frying pan toss and a sheepdog demonstration.
✍ Secretary: Dixie McKendrick
4242 SW Shore Blvd.,
Lake Oswego.
OR 97034

PENNSYLVANIA

ASSOCIATION OF SCOTTISH GAMES AND FESTIVALS

Founded: 1981.
Aims & Activities: Has 67 Associate Groups who conduct Highland Games and competitions in the USA, including foot racing and caber tossing. Serves as a forum for the exchange of information between members. Seeks to ensure that the Highland Games in the USA are of high quality.
✍ President: William J. Reid Jr.
47 E. Germantown Pike,
Plymouth Meeting.
PA 19462
☎ 1 215 825 7268
✆ 1 215 825 8745

CELTIC CLASSIC

Aims & Activities: These Games are currently held over the last weekend in September.
✍ Secretary: Celtic Classic
437 Main Street, Suite 314,
Bethlehem.
PA 18018

CLAN GRANT SOCIETY

Aims & Activities: To promote awareness of the clan history, background and connections in Scotland. To strengthen Scottish and overseas links. Annual Gathering.
Membership: Open to those bearing the name Grant or associated by descent or marriage.
✍ Convener: George Grant
✍ Membership Secretary: Shirley Grant Smith
1207 Cavalier Lane, West Chester.
PA 19380

CLAN MACTHOMAS SOCIETY

Aims & Activities: To develop interest in the clan and to promote its welfare. Genealogical. Historical. To promote strong links with Scotland and with clan members overseas. Annual Gathering.
Membership: Open to all connected with the clan surnames: Combe, Combie, McCombe, McCombie, McColm, McComb, McComas, McComish, MacComie, Macomish, Tam, Thom, Thoms, Thomas, Thomson.
✍ John G. McComb
106 8th St, Milford PA 18337
☎ 1 717 296 8452

DELAWARE VALLEY BRANCH OF THE ROYAL SCOTTISH COUNTRY DANCE SOCIETY

Aims & Activities: See the RSCDS on page 47.
Membership: 137.
✍ Secretary: Amy Cummings-Leight
247 Franklin Avenue,
Sounderton.
PA 18964
☎ 1 215 723 8531 (home)
☎ 1 215 362 7432 (business)
✆ 1 215 368 5720

DELCO SCOTTISH GAMES

Founded: 1967.

Aims & Activities: Currently held at the Devon Horse Show Grounds on the third Saturday in June. As well as the usual events, including at least 20 pipe bands, solo piping and drumming, Highland dancing and heavy events, there are fiddling and crafts demonstrations and grandstand seating is provided on both sides.

✍ Secretary: 181 Foxcatcher Lane Medici.
PA 19063

DUNLOP/DUNLAP FAMILY SOCIETY

Aims & Activities: To increase knowledge of the Scottish origins and history of the family. Genealogical. To strengthen links with Scotland and family members overseas. Annual Gathering.

Membership: Open to those bearing the name Dunlop/Dunlap, or connected by marriage or descent.

✍ President: Captain James M. Dunlop
USN (ret).

✍ Secretary: Mrs Elsie Dunlap Harnish
46 Ashlea Gardens, New Holland.
PA 17557
☎ 1 717 354 9473

HARRISBURG SCOTTISH COUNTRY DANCE SOCIETY

Aims & Activities: See the RSCDS on page 47.

✍ Secretary: Mr R. Davidson
5530 Old Locust Lane,
Harrisburg.
PA 17109
☎ 1 717 545 5092

JOHN MORE ASSOCIATION

Aims & Activities: To promote awareness of the genealogical background and connections in Scotland.

Membership: Open to connections of the family of John More.

✍ President: Eric More Marshall
9831 Sidehill Road Northeast.
PA 16428
☎ 1 814 725 4915

LEHIGH VALLEY SCOTTISH COUNTRY DANCE SOCIETY

Aims & Activities: See the RSCDS on page 47.

✍ Secretary: Jane Matsinger
1714 Church View Road,
Coopersburg.
PA 18036
☎ 1 610 967 3205

LIGONIER HIGHLAND GAMES

Founded: 1959 by Clinton F. Macdonald.

Aims & Activities: Customarily held at Ligonier some miles east of Pittsburgh in the Idlewild Park, a heavily wooded, family amusement area, on the first Saturday after Labor Day. These Games include the usual heavy events, pipe bands, solo piping, Highland dancing, a tug-o'-war and also a sheepdog demonstration. Fiddling, harp-making and seven-a-side rugby are also included.

✍ Secretary: David L. Peet
359 Carlton Road, Bethel Park.
PA 15102
☎ 1 412 831 1408

NITTANY SCOTTISH DANCERS

Aims & Activities: See the RSCDS on page 47.

✍ Secretary: Ms C. Grigor
1954 Crabapple Drive,
State College.
PA 16801
☎ 1 814 237 5447

PITTSBURGH SCOTTISH COUNTRY DANCE SOCIETY

Aims & Activities: See the RSCDS on page 47.
✍ Secretary: Mrs L. Walters
  316 Parkway Drive, Pittsburgh.
  PA 15228
☎ 1 412 341 6775

ROBERT BURNS SCOTTISH CLUB OF ERIE

Founded: 1976.
Aims & Activities: Social.
Affiliations: The Burns Federation, No. 1073.
✍ Secretary: Mrs Sheila C. Sweet
  3527 Brierwood Drive, Erie.
  PA 16510

RHODE ISLAND

BURNS ANNIVERSARY COMMITTEE OF RHODE ISLAND

Founded: 1972.
Aims & Activities: Social. Annual Gathering. To perpetuate the memory of Robert Burns.
Affiliations: The Burns Federation, No. 1007.
✍ Secretary: Mrs E. S. MacLean
  88 Boxwood Avenue, Cranston.
  RI 02910

SOUTH CAROLINA

CHARLESTON SCOTTISH COUNTRY DANCERS

Aims & Activities: See the RSCDS on page 47.
✍ Secretary: Dr M. Mitcham
  860 Robert E. Lee Boulevard, Charleston.
  SC 29412
☎ 1 803 762 4859

CHARLESTON SCOTTISH GAMES AND HIGHLAND GATHERING

Founded: 1972, but Charleston had the first St. Andrew Society in the USA in 1729.
Aims & Activities: Currently held at Boone Hall Plantation in Mt Pleasant on the third Saturday in September. The Games include all the usual events, pipe bands, solo piping and drumming, Highland dancing and athletic and heavy events. In 1990 a competitor established a world record for sheaf-tossing.
✍ Secretary: Scottish Society of Charleston
  PO Box 10932, Charleston.
  SC 29411

CLAN HAMILTON

Aims & Activities: To promote the clan spirit. To encourage interest in the clan and their part in Scottish history. Genealogical. To strengthen Scottish and overseas links. Annual gathering.
Membership: Open to those bearing the name Hamilton or related by descent or marriage.
✍ President: James A. Hamilton Jr
✍ Secretary: Philip G. Dixon
  10 E Second South Street, Summerville.
  SC 29483
☎ 1 803 873 2430

CLAN MORRISON OF NORTH AMERICA

Aims & Activities: Historical. Genealogical. To strengthen the bonds with the clan in Scotland and with members overseas. Annual Gathering.
Membership: Open to those bearing the name Morrison, or related by descent or marriage.
✍ Chairman: John C. Morrison Jr., PO Box 14933, Surfside Beach SC 29587
☎ 1 803 650 0413

PALMETTO SCOTTISH COUNTRY DANCE SOCIETY

Aims & Activities: See the RSCDS on page 47.
✍ Secretary: Mrs L. Lockhart
708 Corn Hill Road, Columbia.
SC 29210
☎ 1 803 798 2206

ROBERT BURNS SOCIETY OF MID COLUMBIA

Founded: 1958.
Aims & Activities: Social. Annual Gathering. To perpetuate the memory of Robert Burns.
Affiliations: The Burns Federation, No. 994.
✍ Secretary: PO Box 1953
Columbia.
SC 29202

SCOTTISH SOCIETY OF CHARLESTON

Aims & Activities: Social and to encourage interest in Scottish heritage, also to organise annual Highland Games.
✍ Secretary: Scottish Society of Charleston
PO Box 10932, Charleston.
SC 29411

TENNESSEE

CLAN HENDERSON SOCIETY

Aims & Activities: To promote the clan spirit and encourage interest in the clan background and history in Scotland. Genealogical. To strengthen the bonds between members in Scotland and overseas. Annual gathering.
Membership: Open to those bearing the name Henderson (or its variants) and those related by descent or marriage.

✍ Convener: Walter M. Parrish Jr.
922 Kirkwood Lane, Nashville.
TN 37204
☎ 1 615 385 2654

CLAN MAXWELL SOCIETY OF THE USA

Aims & Activities: To promote knowledge of the part played by the clan in the history of Scotland and the Borders. Genealogical. To strengthen links between Scotland and clan members overseas.
Membership: Open to those bearing the name Maxwell and those related by descent or marriage.
✍ President: Laurence Maxwell Long
246 DeLee Drive, Kingsport.
TN 37663
☎ 1 615 239 8426

GREAT SMOKY MOUNTAINS GATLINBURG HIGHLAND GAMES

Founded: 1985.
Aims & Activities: Currently held over the third weekend in May the Games include the usual events and a women's kilted mile.
✍ Secretary: PO Box 84
Gatlinburg.
TN 37738

HAMILTON SCOTTISH COUNTRY DANCERS

Aims & Activities: See the RSCDS on page 47.
✍ Secretary: Mr C. Bissell
1006 Tower Place, Nashville.
TN 37204
☎ 1 615 292 8233

HOUSE OF GORDON

Aims & Activities: To promote the clan spirit. Genealogical. Historical. To strengthen links between clan members in Scotland and overseas. Annual Gathering.

Membership: Open to those bearing the name Gordon or related by marriage or descent.

✍ President: Charles O. Gordon
PO Box 1676, Johnson City.
TN 37605
☎ 1 615 928 2191

MEMPHIS SCOTTISH COUNTRY DANCERS

Aims & Activities: See the RSCDS on page 47.

✍ Secretary: Mr J. F. Schultz
2182 Gorham Place,
Germantown.
TN 38139
☎ 1 901 754 2419

TEXAS

AUSTIN SCOTTISH COUNTRY DANCE SOCIETY

Aims & Activities: See the RSCDS on page 47.

✍ Secretary: Mrs S. Harriman
19 North Peak Road, Austin.
TX 78746-5544
☎ 1 512 327 2869

BLUEBONNET SCOTTISH COUNTRY DANCERS

Aims & Activities: See the RSCDS on page 47.

✍ Secretary: Judi Schroeder
7418 Pipers Creek, San Antonio.
TX 78251-1430
☎ 1 210 684 7782

CEILIDH COUNTRY DANCERS OF FORT WORTH

Aims & Activities: See the RSCDS on page 47.

✍ Secretary: Vernon Wellman

5909 Sandra, Fort Worth.
TX 76133
☎ 1 817 292 2094

CLAN BRODIE ASSOCIATION

Aims & Activities: To promote awareness of the clan history, background and connections in Scotland. To strengthen Scottish and overseas links. Genealogical. Annual Gathering.

Affiliations: Clan Brodie, Scotland.

Membership: Open to those bearing the name Brodie (or its variants).

✍ National Convener: Edward F. Brodie
2602 S. Braeswood 4701
Houston.
TX 33625
☎ 1 713 663 6129

CLAN MACPHERSON

Aims & Activities: To promote the clan spirit. Genealogical. Historical. Annual gathering.

Affiliations: Clan Macpherson, Scotland.

Membership: Open to those named Macpherson (in its various forms) and those related by descent or marriage.

✍ Secretary: James F. Macphearson
4357 Echo Glen Drive, Dallas.
TX 75244
☎ 1 214 239 4090

DALLAS CALEDONIAN COUNTRY DANCE GROUP

Aims & Activities: See the RSCDS on page 47.

✍ Secretary: Averil Vestal
14330 Shoredale Lane, Dallas.
TX 75234
☎ 1 214 247 8962

DALLAS SCOTTISH HIGHLAND GAMES

Founded: 1972.

Aims & Activities: These Games are generally held on the first Saturday in September and include all the usual events, pipe bands, solo piping, Highland dancing and the heavy events.

✍ Secretary: Robert C. Forbes
    8523 San Leanardo Drive, Dallas.
    TX 75218

HEATHER AND THISTLE SOCIETY

Aims & Activities: Social. Annual Gathering to perpuate the memory of Robert Burns. Overseas links.
Affiliations: The Burns Federation, No. 1045.

✍ Chieftain: PO Box 980684
    Houston.
    TX 77098-0684

HOUSTON BRANCH OF THE ROYAL SCOTTISH COUNTRY DANCE SOCIETY

Aims & Activities: See the RSCDS on page 47.
Membership: 80.

✍ Secretary: Barbara Hazilwood
    5946 Willowbend Boulevard,
    Houston.
    TX 77096
☎ 1 713 729 0384

HOUSTON HIGHLAND GAMES

Founded: 1967.

Aims & Activities: Currently held in the grounds of St. Thomas Episcopal School on the second Saturday in May. With only 700 pupils the school has its own pipe band and Highland dancing is compulsory. The Games, not surprisingly, include pipe bands, solo piping and drumming, Highland dancing and the usual heavy events. They also include a sheepdog demonstration and a Viking raid on Scottish Highlanders, and more unusually Morris dancers and Clog hoppers!

✍ Secretary: Houston Highland
    Games Association
    PO Box 66, Bel Aire.
    TX 77401

SALADO HIGHLAND GAMES

Founded: 1981.

Aims & Activities: Currently held during the second full weekend in November on the village green in this former stage-coach town these Games attract a large attendance and include sheep dog trials as well as the usual events.

✍ Secretary: Central Texas Area
    Museum Inc
    Salado.
    TX 76571

TABARD INN BURNS CLUB

Aims & Activities: Social. To improve knowledge of the works of Robert Burns. Annual Gathering.
Affiliations: The Burns Federation, No. 1082.

✍ Secretary: Peter Thurmond
    907 NCNB Center Building,
    Tyler.
    TX 75702

TEXAS BRANCH OF THE CLAN MACNEIL ASSOCIATION OF AMERICA

Aims & Activities: To strengthen Scottish and overseas links. Genealogical. Historical. Annual Gathering.
Membership: Open to those bearing the name MacNeil, or of one of its septs, and those connected by descent or marriage.

✍ Comm: Howard G. MacNeil
    4012 Harlan Wood, Forth Worth.
    TX 76109

WEST TEXAS HIGHLAND GAMES

Founded: 1982.

Aims & Activities: Organised by the Scottish Heritage Society and currently held in the Garden and Arts Centre in Lubbock on the second Saturday in October. These small Games are preceded by a golf tournament.

✍ Secretary: PO Box 2081
Lubbock.
TX 79408

UTAH

PAYSON SCOTTISH FESTIVAL

Founded: 1987.

Aims & Activities: Currently held on the second Saturday in July in the City Park. The Games are preceded by a golf tournament and include the usual events as well as a women's fry-pan toss and rolling-pin throwing contest.

✍ Secretary: 300 South
Payson.
UT 84651

QUEECHEE SCOTTISH FESTIVAL

Founded: 1972.

Aims & Activities: Recently held at the Queechee Polo Field beside the river bisecting this small town on the third Saturday in August. The Games include most of the usual events, also seven-a-side rugby, deerhound coursing, a kilted mile, a ladies rolling-pin toss and an egg and spoon race.

✍ Secretary: Scotland-by-the-Yard
Queechee.
UT 05059

SALT LAKE CITY SCOTTISH COUNTRY DANCERS

Aims & Activities: See the RSCDS on page 47.

✍ Secretary: Ms M. Veranth
4460 Ashford Drive,
Salt Lake City.
UT 84124
☎ 1 801 278 5826

UTAH SCOTTISH ASSOCIATION

Aims & Activities: Social and to encourage interest in Scottish heritage, also to organise an annual Scottish Festival and Highland Games.

✍ Secretary: Utah Scottish
Association: 483 8th Avenue
Salt Lake City.
UT 84103

UTAH SCOTTISH FESTIVAL AND HIGHLAND GAMES

Founded: 1974.

Aims & Activities: Recently held in the Jordan River Park in Salt Lake City in mid-June. The Games include the usual events and a women's stone throw and Scottish baking contest.

✍ Secretary: Utah Scottish
Association
483 8th Avenue, Salt Lake City.
UT 84103

VERMONT

CLAN BELL DESCENDANTS

Aims & Activities: To strengthen overseas links. Annual Gathering. Genealogical. Historical.

Membership: Open to those with the name Bell, or those related by descent or marriage.

✍ President: Sid Bell
PO Box 451, Springfield.
VT 05156
☎ 1 802 885 3151

VERMONT INTERNATIONAL HIGHLAND GAMES

Founded: 1984.

Aims & Activities: Currently held on the third Saturday in June at Essex Junction. The Games include pipe bands, solo piping and drumming, Highland dancing, and the usual heavy events. Other features are clarsach playing and fiddling.

✍ Secretary: PO Box 692
Essex Junction.
VT 05452

VIRGINIA

CLAN FRASER ASSOCIATES

Aims & Activities: To promote knowledge of the clan history, background and connections in Scotland. Genealogical. To strengthen Scottish and overseas links. Annual Gathering.

Membership: Open to those with the name Fraser or related by descent or marriage.

✍ Secretary: John A. Fraser III
105 W. Masonic View Avenue,
Alexandria.
VA 22301
☎ 1 703 548 2884

CLAN IRWIN ASSOCIATION

Aims & Activities: To promote the clan spirit and closer links with Scotland. Genealogical. Historical. Annual Gathering.

Membership: Open to those bearing the name Irwin (or its variants) and those related by marriage or descent.

✍ President: Ralph R. Irwin
✍ Secretary: Karen Irvine Lewis
2674 N. Upshur St., Arlington.
VA 22207
☎ 1 703 243 5823

CLAN MACMILLAN, APPALACHIAN BRANCH

Aims & Activities: Historical. Genealogical. To strengthen links with Scotland and overseas.

Membership: Open to those with the name MacMillan or related by descent or marriage.

✍ President: David McMillan III
905 Mulberry Road, Martinsville.
VA 24112
☎ 1 703 632 4642

CLAN MUNRO ASSOCIATION

Aims & Activities: To promote the clan spirit worldwide. To encourage interest in the history of the clan and its genealogy. To promote stronger links with Scotland and other clan members. Annual Gathering.

Membership: Open to those named Munro (or its variants) or related by descent or marriage.

✍ Chairman: James H. Monroe
Ben Eagles, Rt 2. Box 233K,
Leesburg.
VA 22075
☎ 1 703 777 8667

COUNCIL OF SCOTTISH CLANS AND ASSOCIATIONS

Founded: 1974.

Aims & Activities: Promotes communication amongst persons and groups interested in Scottish affairs and culture. Serves as information centre on Scottish activities. Maintains computerised listings of Scottish clans and organisations.

✍ President: Craig R. Scott
PO Box 4016, Merrifield.
VA 22116-4016
☎ 1 703 406 8776

EASTERN UNITED STATES PIPE BAND ASSOCIATION

Aims & Activities: Encouraging an interest in and the formation and organisation of pipe bands and piping and drumming, also participation in competitions and events in Highland Games.

Affiliations: The Royal Scottish Pipe Band Association, (page 59).

✍ Treasurer: Donald R. Werth
7234 Whiston Drive, Springfield.
VA 22153

MID-ATLANTIC BRANCH OF THE CLAN DONNACHAIDH SOCIETY

Aims & Activities: Genealogical. Historical. To promote the clan spirit around the world. Annual gathering.
Membership: Open to those with the name Robertson, or those related by descent or marriage.

✍ President: Jim Fargo
PO Box 92, Springfield.
VA 22150

MURRAY CLAN SOCIETY

Aims & Activities: To promote awareness of the clan history, background and connections in Scotland. To strengthen Scottish and overseas links. Annual Gathering.
Membership: Open to those bearing the name Murray or related by marriage or descent.

✍ President: Lt. Col. Richard D. Murray USAF (Ret)
7801 Willowbrook Rd.,
Fairfax Sta. VA 22039
☎ 1 703 323 8162

NORTHERN VIRGINIA BRANCH OF THE ROYAL SCOTTISH COUNTRY DANCE SOCIETY

Aims & Activities: See the RSCDS on page 47.
Membership: 71.

✍ Secretary: Mimi Rodel
3730 Ingalls Avenue, Alexandria.
VA 22302
☎ 1 703 379 6921 (home)
☎ 1 301 424 0800 (business)

RICHMOND SCOTTISH COUNTRY DANCERS

Aims & Activities: See the RSCDS on page 47.

✍ Secretary: Barbara Benedict
2761 East Brigstock Road,
Midlothian.
VA 23113
☎ 1 804 378 0042

SCOTTISH COUNTRY DANCERS OF TIDEWATER

Aims & Activities: See the RSCDS on page 47.

✍ Secretary: Ms A. Harris
7692 Bull Run Court, Norfolk.
VA 23518-4616
☎ 1 804 587 4126

SCOTTISH SOCIETY OF RICHMOND

Aims & Activities: Social. To encourage those of Scottish descent to join together and to disseminate information regarding Scotland's history and heritage.

✍ President: Jeffry E. Kelso
PO Box 26831, Richmond.
VA 23261
☎ 1 804 329 4936

SCOTTISH SOCIETY OF THE VIRGINIA HIGHLANDS

Aims & Activities: To encourage interest in Scottish tradition, history and heritage. Social. Annual Gathering.
Membership: Open to those with Scottish blood, or interested in the aims.

✍ President: Myron C. White Jr
✍ Membership Chairman: Harriet H. Smith
3347 Pamlico Dr SW, Roanoke.
VA 24018
☎ 1 703 774 8640

ST ANDREW'S SOCIETY OF TIDEWATER

Aims & Activities: To promote awareness of the Scottish tradition, history and heritage. Social. Annual Gathering.
Membership: Open to those of Scottish descent, or interested in the aims.
✍ President: Dr Edward A. McLeod
✍ Secretary: John G. Ferguson
  2321 Hunt Neck Trail,
  Virginia Beach.
  VA 23456
☎ 1 804 468 0809

ST ANDREW'S SOCIETY OF WILLIAMSBURG

Aims & Activities: Social. To promote friendship amongst those with Scottish blood and to encourage interest in Scottish tradition, and heritage. Annual Gathering.
✍ President: Col. Paul J. Ritchie
  PO Box 533, Williamsburg.
  VA 23187
☎ 1 804 229 8832

TIDEWATER SCOTTISH FESTIVAL AND CLAN GATHERING

Founded: 1979.
Aims & Activities: Currently held by the sea in early June in the Norfolk Botanical Gardens, where the International Festival of Roses is also held. Apart from the usual features these Games include clan games, Scottish deerhound coursing and Scottish dog breeds.
✍ Secretary: Tidewater Scottish Festival
  PO Box 2000, Virginia Beach.
  VA 23452

VIRGINIA SCOTTISH GAMES

Founded: 1974.
Aims & Activities: Customarily held in Alexandria, sister city to Dundee, in the Episcopal High School over the fourth weekend in July. Despite their comparatively recent origins these have now become one of the major Games. Apart from the usual events including pipe bands, solo piping and drumming, Highland dancing and the customary heavy events and athletics, these Games also feature the US National Harp and Clarsach Championships, Scottish deerhound coursing and celebrity haggis hurling.
✍ Secretary: Virginia Scottish Games Association
  Box 1338, Alexandria.
  VA 22313

WASHINGTON BRANCH OF THE ROYAL SCOTTISH DANCE SOCIETY

Aims & Activities: See the RSCDS on page 47.
Membership: 118.
✍ Secretary: Mr J. McRae
  2214 S. Randolf Street, Arlington.
  VA 22204
☎ 1 703 920 2412

WILLIAMSBURG SCOTTISH COUNTRY DANCERS

Aims & Activities: See the RSCDS on page 47.
✍ Secretary: Mr J. F. Millar
  Newport House, 710 South Henry Street, Williamsburg.
  VA 23185
☎ 1 804 229 1775

WILLIAMSBURG SCOTTISH FESTIVAL

Founded: 1978.
Aims & Activities: Customarily held on the campus of the College of William and Mary at the end of September. This is the second-oldest college in the USA, founded in 1693. Competitors and spectators can also visit the nearby historic area of

Williamsburg. The Games themselves include the usual features — pipe bands, solo piping and drumming, Highland dancing, heavy events and athletics, as well as a Scottish sheepdog demonstration.

✍ Secretary: Scottish Festival Inc.
PO Box 866, Williamsburg.
VA 23187

WASHINGTON

ARMSTRONG CLAN ASSOCIATION

Founded: 1969.
Aims & Activities: To promote awareness of the clan history, background and genealogical connections in Scotland. To strengthen Scottish and overseas links. Annual Gathering.
Affiliations: The Armstrong Trust.
Membership: Open to all bearing the name Armstrong or related by descent or marriage.
✍ Administrator:
William S. Armstrong V
9811 NE 91st Avenue, Vancouver.
WA 98662
☎ 1 206 256 5299

BELLINGHAM HIGHLAND GAMES

Founded: 1960.
Aims & Activities: Recently held on the first Saturday in June the Games include pipe bands, solo piping and Highland dancing as well as the usual heavy events and other features.
✍ Secretary: Isla Paterson
639 Hunters Pt Drive,
Bellingham.
WA 98225

BELLINGHAM SCOTTISH COUNTRY DANCERS

Aims & Activities: See the RSCDS on page 47.
✍ Secretary: Dr T. T. Read
1901-38th Street, Bellingham.
WA 98226
☎ 1 360 734 1295

CALEDONIAN AND ST ANDREW'S SOCIETY

Aims & Activities: Social and to encourage interest in Scottish tradition, history and heritage.
✍ President: Rick Murchie
4131 13th Ave NE 705, Seattle.
WA 98105
☎ 1 206 633 4769

PACIFIC NORTH-WEST HIGHLAND GAMES

Founded: 1945.
Aims & Activities: Recently held in mid-August at the King County Fairgrounds, Enumclaw. These Games are organised by the Seattle Highland Games Association and include the customary features as well as a hay bale toss.
✍ Secretary: Sharon Rirelis
8802 Meridian Avenue, N. Seattle.
WA 98102
☎ 1 206 522 2874

SAN JUAN ISLAND SCOTTISH COUNTRY DANCERS

Aims & Activities: See the RSCDS on page 47.
✍ Secretary: Mrs B. Dann
371 Olympic View Lane,
Friday Harbor.
WA 98250

SEATTLE BRANCH OF THE ROYAL SCOTTISH COUNTRY DANCE SOCIETY

Aims & Activities: See the RSCDS on page 47.
Membership: 136.
✍ Secretary: Mr M. Hanson
c/o RSCDS, PO Box 2084, Seattle.
WA 98111
☎ 1 206 283 8133

SPOKANE SCOTTISH COUNTRY DANCERS

Aims & Activities: See the RSCDS on page 47.
✍ Secretary: Mr J. Stuart
W. 2917 Holyoke Avenue, Spokane.
WA 99208-4524
☎ 1 509 448 3050

SPOKANE SCOTTISH FESTIVAL AND TATTOO

Founded: 1958.
Aims & Activities: Currently held at the Riverfront Park on the last Saturday in July. The Games include the usual features as well as a tug-o'-war and a keg toss.
✍ Secretary: Mary Alward
418 E 11th St, Spokane.
WA 99202

ST ANDREW SOCIETY OF THE INLAND EMPIRE

Aims & Activities: Social and to encourage interest in Scottish tradition, history and heritage.
✍ President: Randal T. Fisher
PO Box 9687, Spokane.
WA 99205
☎ 1 509 467 8001

TACOMA HIGHLAND GAMES

Founded: 1968.
Aims & Activities: These Games are customarily held in mid-June in the Frontier Park.
Membership: Only open to residents from Washington, Oregon and Idaho.
✍ Secretary: Joyce Denton
241 E 63rd St, Tacoma WA 98404

TACOMA SCOTTISH COUNTRY DANCERS

Aims & Activities: See the RSCDS on page 47.
✍ Secretary: Mr G. Tomlin
4321 N. 9th Street, Tacoma.
WA 98406
☎ 1 206 752 8043

VANCOUVER USA SCOTTISH COUNTRY DANCERS

Aims & Activities: See the RSCDS on page 47.
✍ Secretary: Mrs P. Ingram
1521 NE 97th Avenue, Vancouver.
WA 98664
☎ 1 206 892 4366

VASHON ISLAND STRAWBERRY FESTIVAL AND HIGHLAND GAMES

Founded: 1984.
Aims & Activities: Currently held on the second Saturday in July. This small farming community had elebrated their strawberry festival for several years before local Scots added the Games to the day. The Games include a fiddling demonstration.
✍ Secretary: Sr Sterling Hill
10450 15th Avenue, SW Seattle.
WA 98746

WEST VIRGINIA

ST ANDREW'S SOCIETY OF WEST VIRGINIA

Aims & Activities: Social and to

encourage interest in Scottish tradition, history and heritage.
- ✍ President: Dr Dorsey D. Ellis
  1009 Woodmont Drive, S.
  Charleston.
  WV 25309
- ☎ 1 304 768 3498

WISCONSIN

MADISON SCOTTISH COUNTRY DANCERS

Aims & Activities: See the RSCDS on page 47.
- ✍ Secretary: Jean Willett
  5329 Milward Drive, Madison.
  WI 53711
- ☎ 1 608 273 8546

MILWAUKEE SCOTTISH COUNTRY DANCERS

Aims & Activities: See the RSCDS on page 47.
- ✍ Secretary: Miss K. Boyle
  3614 S. 35th Street, Milwaukee.
  WI 53221
- ☎ 1 414 643 1531

ROBERT BURNS CLUB OF MILWAUKEE

Founded: 1979.
Aims & Activities: Social and to encourage interest in the poetical works of Robert Burns. To celebrate

Burns night and to encourage a wider interest in Scottish tradition, history and heritage.
Affiliations: The Burns Federation, No. 1070.
- ✍ Secretaries: William H. Olson
  8162 N. Seneca Road, Fox Point.
  WI 53217
- ☎ 1 414 352 4579
- ✍ Miss Wendy Wilson-Taylor
  4125 West Cherrywood Lane,
  Brown Deer WI 53209

ST ANDREW'S SOCIETY OF MADISON

Aims & Activities: Social and to encourage interest in Scottish tradition, history and heritage.
- ✍ President: William W. Ferguson
  PO Box 1322, Madison.
  WI 53701
- ☎ 1 608 222 4231

WYOMING

SCOTTISH SOCIETY OF SOUTH-EAST WYOMING

Aims & Activities: Social. To encourage interest in Scottish tradition, history and heritage. Annual Gathering.
Membership: Open to those of Scottish descent.
- ✍ President: Alex Blane
  4201 Carla Drive, Cheyenne.
  WY 82009
- ☎ 1 307 632 3953

CANADA

ALBERTA

ATHABASCA SCOTTISH COUNTRY DANCE CLUB

Aims & Activities: See the RSCDS on page 47.
✍ Secretary: Mr M Rogers
    Box 1124, Athabasca T0G 0B0

CALGARY BRANCH OF THE ROYAL SCOTTISH COUNTRY DANCE SOCIETY

Aims & Activities: See the RSCDS on page 47. To preserve and further the practice of traditional Scottish country dancing. Promote overseas links and an annual Gathering. Social.
Membership: Open to all over 16 interested in the aims and objects of the Branch. Junior associate members: currently 68.
✍ Secretary: Susan Sherman
    PO Box 1471, Station M,
    Calgary.
    T2P 2L6
☎ 1 403 286 5216 (home)
☎ 1 403 237 3211 (business)

CALGARY BURNS CLUB

Founded: 1976.
Aims & Activities: Social. To perpetuate the memory of Robert Burns.
Affiliations: The Burns Federation, No. 946.
✍ Secretary: Andy Hay
    2 Brandy Lane, 1401-19 Street
    SW, Calgary T2W 3E7

CALGARY HIGHLAND GAMES

Founded: 1976.
Aims & Activities: To hold annual Highland Games in Calgary.

✍ Secretary: Andy Hay
    2 Brandy Lane, 1401-19 Street
    SW, Calgary.
    T2W 3E7

CALGARY SCOTTISH COUNTRY DANCE SOCIETY

Aims & Activities: See the RSCDS on page 47.
✍ Secretary: PO Box 1202
    Station Rd.,
    Calgary.
    T2P 2K9
☎ 1 403 246 0106

CANMORE HIGHLAND GAMES

Aims & Activities: To organise annual professional Highland Games and sports in the area of Canmore.
Affiliations: The Scottish Games Association, (page 74).
✍ Secretary: Sandy Bunch
    Box 2887,
    Canmore.
☎ 1 03 678 2015

EDMONTON BURNS CLUB

Founded: 1921.
Aims & Activities: Social. Annual Gathering. To encourage interest in the works of Robert Burns.
Affiliations: The Burns Federation, No. 571.
✍ Secretary: Robert M. Allan MBE
    32 Greer Crescent St, Albert.
    T8N 1T8

EDMONTON SCOTTISH COUNTRY DANCE CLUB

Aims & Activities: See the RSCDS on page 47.
✍ Secretary: Miss M. Cook

202, 12319 Jasper Avenue,
Edmonton.
T5N 4A7
☎ 1 493 488 1062

1021 Elliot Road South,
Lethbridge.
T1K 3V1
☎ 1 403 320 0357

EDMONTON SCOTTISH SOCIETY

Founded: 1921.
Aims & Activities: Social. Annual Gathering. To promote interest in Scottish heritage. To encourage study of the work of Robert Burns.
Affiliations: The Burns Federation, No. 1009.
✍ Secretary: Robert M. Allan MBE
32 Greer Crescent St,
Albert.
T8N 1T8

EDMONTON SCOTTISH SOCIETY COUNTRY DANCERS

Aims & Activities: See the RSCDS on page 47.
✍ Secretary: Mrs H. Jenkins
11408 56th Avenue,
Edmonton.
T6H 0Y2
☎ 1 403 436 7011

GRANDE PRAIRIE SCOTTISH SOCIETY

Aims & Activities: To encourage interest in Scottish heritage. See the RSCDS on page 47.
✍ President: Mrs S. Rossol
Box 774, Grande Prairie.
T8V 3R5
☎ 1 403 532 6710
✍ Secretary: Mrs M. Fugard
Box 774, Grande Prairie.
T8V 3R5
☎ 1 403 532 8555

LETHBRIDGE SCOTTISH COUNTRY DANCE CLUB

Aims & Activities: See the RSCDS on page 47.
✍ Secretary: Dr J. Fraser

MEDICINE HAT BRANCH OF THE ROYAL SCOTTISH COUNTRY DANCE SOCIETY

Aims & Activities: See the RSCDS on page 47.
Membership: 23.
✍ Secretary: Patricia McFarlane
Box 447, Medicine Hat.
T1A 7G2
☎ 1 403 526 5149 (home)
☎ 1 403 529 8181 (business)

SCHIEHALLION SCOTTISH HERITAGE SOCIETY

Aims & Activities: Social and to promote interest in Scottish heritage, history and tradition, including the works of Robert Burns. Annual Gathering.
Affiliations: The Burns Federation, No. 1115.
✍ Secretary: Ms Winona Haliburton
152 Westwood Drive SW,
Calgary.
T3C 2W1

ST GILES SCOTTISH COUNTRY DANCE CLUB

Aims & Activities: See the RSCDS on page 47.
✍ Secretary: Mrs U. Lennam
2616-11 Avenue NW, Calgary.
T2N 1H7
☎ 1 282 8264

TARBOLTON CLUB, EDMONTON

Founded: 1967.
Aims & Activities: Social. Annual Gathering. To perpetuate the memory of Robert Burns.
Affiliations: The Burns Federation, No. 927.

✍ Secretary: Robert M. Allan MBE
32 Greer Crescent St, Albert.
T8N 1T8

BRITISH COLUMBIA

BURNS CLUB OF VANCOUVER

Founded: 1976.
Aims & Activities: Social. Annual Gathering. To perpeuate the memory of Robert Burns.
Affiliations: The Burns Federation, No. 1078.
✍ Secretary: W. R. B. Dyer
2749 Lawson Avenue,
West Vancouver.
V7V 2G5

CARIBOO SCOTTISH COUNTRY DANCE CLUB

Aims & Activities: Affiliated to The Royal Scottish Country Dance Society.
✍ Secretary: Jane Christie
Box 68, 108 Ranch.
V0K 2Z0
☎ 1 604 395 2323 (ext 4077)

GLENEAGLES SCOTTISH COUNTRY DANCE CLUB

Aims & Activities: See the RSCDS on page 47.
✍ Secretary: Anna Brown
1358 East 18th Street,
North Vancouver V7J IM3
☎ 1 604 985 5596

KELOWNA SCOTTISH COUNTRY DANCE GROUP

Aims & Activities: See the RSCDS on page 47.
✍ Secretary: Mr B. Whyte
472 Varkley Road, Kelowna.
V1W 1E3
☎ 1 604 764 8113

NANAIMO BURNS CLUB

Founded: 1974.
Aims & Activities: Social. Annual Gathering. To perpetuate the memory of Robert Burns.
Affiliations: The Burns Federation, No. 1041.
✍ Secretary: R. McWhirter
422 Dogwood Street, Parksville.
V9P 1C6

NANAIMO SCOTTISH COUNTRY DANCERS

Aims & Activities: See the RSCDS on page 47.
✍ Secretary: Dr A Berry
184 Crossbow Drive, Nanaimo.
V9T 1L3
☎ 1 604 756 1513

NANOOSE SCOTTISH COUNTRY DANCERS

Aims & Activities: See the RSCDS on page 47.
✍ Secretary: Bev Butler
396 Bass Avenue, Parksville.
V9P 1L6
☎ 1 604 248 9170

NELSON SCOTTISH COUNTRY DANCERS

Aims & Activities: See the RSCDS on page 47.
✍ Secretary: Edith Morgan
617 Third Street, Nelson.
V1L 2P8
☎ 1 604 352 3591

PORT ALBERNI SCOTTISH COUNTRY DANCERS

Aims & Activities: See the RSCDS on page 47.
✍ Secretary: Kay Houghton
4438 Adelaide Street,
Port Alberni.
V97 6N1
☎ 1 604 723 57

SONA SCOTTISH COUNTRY DANCERS

Aims & Activities: See the RSCDS on page 47.
✍ Secretary: Mrs H. Tulip
6036 Falaise Road, Duncan.
V9L 2N5
☎ 1 748 8767

VANCOUVER BRANCH OF THE ROYAL SCOTTISH COUNTRY DANCE SOCIETY

Aims & Activities: See the RSCDS on page 47.
Membership: 403.
✍ Secretary: Mrs A. E. Scott
2358 Darnell Court, Coquitlam.
V3J 6X5
☎ 1 604 461 0163

VANCOUVER ISLAND SCOTTISH COUNTRY DANCE SOCIETY

Aims & Activities: See the RSCDS on page 47.
✍ Secretary: Catherine Mick
385 Tamarack Road, Victoria.
V9B 4W8
☎ 1 604 478 9457

VICTORIA BRANCH OF THE ROYAL SCOTTISH COUNTRY DANCE SOCIETY

Aims & Activities: See the RSCDS on page 47.
Membership: 129.
✍ Secretary: Mrs D. Williams
19-4030 Lochside Drive,
British Columbia.
V8X 2C8
☎ 1 604 727 6395

VICTORIA ST ANDREWS AND CALEDONIAN SOCIETY

Founded: 1849.
Aims & Activities: Social and to encourage interest in Scottish her-itage, particularly in the works of Robert Burns. Annual Gathering.
Affiliations: The Burns Federation, No. 303.
✍ Secretary: Ms Jean Dey
820 Seamist Place, Victoria.
V8Y 2R4

MANITOBA

CLAN JARDINE SOCIETY WESTERN CANADA BRANCH

Aims & Activities: To strengthen over-seas links.
Affiliations: The Clan Jardine Society, Scotland.
Membership: Open to those with the name Jardine or connected by mar-riage or descent.
✍ Chairman: Archie Jardine
45 Magellan Bay, Winnipeg.
R3K 0P7

MANITOBA HIGHLAND GATHERING OR SELKIRK GATHERING

Founded: 1966.
Aims & Activities: To organise games generally held on the first Saturday in July in Selkirk Park on the Red River in the town of Selkirk, just north of Winnipeg. These claim to be, 'Western Canada's Finest Gathering'. The Games include. piping, Highland dancing and heavy events, sheep-shearing and sheep-dog work, also York-boat (the traditional Red River heavy transport boat propelled by oars and sail) racing on the Red River as well as a Highland cattle dis-play. Clan gathering participation.
✍ Secretary: Don Porter Box 59
Selkirk.
R1A 2B1

PRAIRIE PIPE BAND ASSOCIATION

Aims & Activities: Encouraging an interest in the formation and organisation of pipe bands and piping and drumming. Also participation in competitions and events in Highland Games.
Affiliations: The Royal Scottish Pipe Band Association, (page 59).
✍ Secretary: W. J. MacLeod
Box 473 Pine Falls.
R0E 1M0

WINNIPEG BRANCH OF THE ROYAL SCOTTISH COUNTRY DANCE SOCIETY

Aims & Activities: See the RSCDS on page 47.
Membership: 133.
✍ Secretary: Patricia Hill
34 McNulty Crescent, Winnipeg.
R2M 5H4
☎ 1 204 256 2888

WINNIPEG BURNS CLUB

Founded: 1907.
Aims & Activities: To perpetuate the memory and encourage the study of Burns and Scottish culture and heritage. Annual Gathering. Highland dancing. Overseas links. Charitable. Educational. Historical. Social.
Affiliations: The Burns Federation, No. 197.
✍ Secretary: Mrs Carolee King
PO Box 2584, Winnipeg.
RC3 4B3

NEW BRUNSWICK

FREDERICTON SOCIETY OF ST ANDREW

Aims & Activities: Social and to encourage interest in Scottish tradition, history and heritage.

✍ President: Barbara MacKinnon
PO Box 283, Fredericton.
E3B 4Z6

FREDRICTON SCOTTISH COUNTRY DANCE GROUP

Aims & Activities: See the RSCDS on page 47.
✍ Secretary: Ms J. McNeil
475 York Street, Fredericton.
E3P 3B9
☎ 1 506 455 4415
✆ 1 506 457 7633

NEW BRUNSWICK HIGHLAND GAMES

Founded: 1980.
Aims & Activities: To organise Games which usually take place on the last weekend in June at the Waasis Road Sports Field. Oromocto. They include piping, Highland dancing and the usual heavy events.
✍ Contact: The New Brunswick Tourist Board

ST JOHN SCOTTISH COUNTRY DANCE GROUP

Aims & Activities: See the RSCDS on page 47.
✍ Secretary: Mr G. W. Graham
13 Kenneview Drive, Rothesay.
☎ 1 506 847 4041

WOODSTOCK SCOTTISH COUNTRY DANCE GROUP

Aims & Activities: See the RSCDS on page 47.
✍ Secretary: Shelley Murray
PO Box 855, Woodstock.
E0J 2B0
☎ 1 506 325 9590

NEWFOUNDLAND

ST JOHN'S BRANCH OF THE ROYAL SCOTTISH COUNTRY DANCE SOCIETY

Aims & Activities: See the RSCDS on page 47.
Membership: 58.
✍ Secretary: Mr B. Hamilton
Box 23097, Churchill Square PO, St John's, Newfoundland.
A1B 4J9
☎ 1 709 753 8768

NORTH WEST TERRITORIES

YELLOWKNIFE SCOTTISH COUNTRY DANCE CLUB

Aims & Activities: See the RSCDS on page 47.
✍ Secretary: Mrs S. Lewis
873 Lanky Court, Yellowknife.
I1A 1Y7

NOVA SCOTIA

AMHERST SCOTTISH COUNTRY DANCERS

Aims & Activities: See the RSCDS on page 47.
✍ Secretary: Mrs J. Gosbee
54 Academy Street, Amherst.
B4H 3J2
☎ 1 902 667 1329

ANNAPOLIS VALLEY HIGHLAND GAMES

Founded: 1987.
Aims & Activities: Held annually on the last Saturday in August in the town of Middleton on the former race track. The Games include pipe band and heavy event championships, Highland dancing and piping, a hill run of eight miles, a kilted golf tournament and a ceilidh.
✍ Contact: Annapolis Valley Tourist Board

ANNAPOLIS VALLEY HIGHLAND SOCIETY

Founded: Annapolis Valley lays claim to the first landing of Scots in North America in 1598 and the first Scottish settlement in 1629.
Aims & Activities: To encourage interest in Scottish matters and Scottish heritage, also to organise annual Highland Games. The Society was formed because of the large number of people of Scots descent living in the area.
✍ Contact: Annapolis Valley Tourist Board

ANTIGONISH HIGHLAND GAMES

Founded: 1863.
Aims & Activities: Claiming to be 'the oldest Scottish Festival in North America' the games are held each July in Antigonish 'the Highland heart of Nova Scotia'. The Antigonish Highland Games Week, is one of Nova Scotia's notable tourist attractions. The Games week usually starts on the first weekend in July with a children's events, a Highland Ball and social events. Since 1984 the Games themselves have taken place over three days on a site at Columbus from the Friday over the second weekend in July. They include a pipe band competition, Highland dancing, solo piping and drumming, a 10,000 metre race and the usual heavy and track events. There is also a kilted golf tournament. They are closely associated with the St. Francis Xavier

University, which has an extensive collection of Celtic works.

✍ Secretary: c/o St Francis Xavier University
Box 80, Antigonish.
B2G 1C0

☎ 1 902 867 2473

CLAN DUNBAR SOCIETY OF NOVA SCOTIA

Aims & Activities: To collect clan genealogical and historical records. To strengthen Overseas links.
Affiliations: The Clan Dunbar, Scotland.
Membership: Open to those with the name Dunbar and to those related by marriage or descent.

✍ President: Murray H. Dunbar

✍ Secretary: Mrs Elsie Dunbar
124 Mackay Street,
New Glasgow.

☎ 1 902 752 7430

METRO SCOTTISH FESTIVAL AND HIGHLAND GAMES

Aims & Activities: Held in the Wanderer's Grounds in Halifax these Games last two days over the first weekend in July. They include the usual heavy and track events, also piping and Highland dancing.

✍ Secretary: c/o The North British Society
PO Box 5125, Station A, Halifax.
B3L 4M7

NORTH AMERICAN CLAN EWEN SOCIETY

Aims & Activities: To strengthen overseas links.
Affiliations: The Clan Ewen Society, Scotland.
Membership: Open to those bearing the names MacEwan, McEwan, Ewen, Ewing, etc. and to those connected with the clan by descent.

✍ Secretary: William H. MacEwen

PO Box 3, St Peters B0E 3B0

☎ 1 902 535 2167

NORTH BRITISH SOCIETY OF HALIFAX

Aims & Activities: To encourage interest in Scottish matters and Scottish heritage in Halifax and the surrounding area and organise annual Highland Games.

✍ Secretary: c/o North British Society
PO Box 5125, Station A, Halifax.
B3L, 4M7

NOVA SCOTIA BRANCH OF THE ROYAL SCOTTISH COUNTRY DANCE SOCIETY

Aims & Activities: See the RSCDS on page 47.
Membership: 72.

✍ Secretary: Ms M. Martin
6230 Oakland Road, Halifax.
B3H 1P2

☎ 1 902 422 2732

NOVA SCOTIA PIPERS AND PIPE BAND ASSOCIATION

Aims & Activities: Encouraging an interest in and the formation and organisation of pipe bands and piping and drumming, also participation in competitions and events in Highland Games.
Affiliations: The Royal Scottish Pipe Band Association, (page 59).

✍ Secretary: George A. Fowler
35 Lawson Avenue, Dartmouth.
B2W 2Z2

SOUTH SHORE SCOTTISH COUNTRY DANCERS

Aims & Activities: See the RSCDS on page 47.

✍ Secretary: Merril Heubach
RR1, Lunenburg B0J 2C0

☎ 1 902 634 3426

ONTARIO

ARDBRAE DANCERS OF OTTAWA

Aims & Activities: See the RSCDS on page 47.
✍ Secretary: Elaine Hoag
99 Glebe Avenue, Apt 4, Ottawa.
K15 2C2
☎ 1 613 233 8571

ARMSTRONG CLAN SOCIETY

Aims & Activities: To strengthen overseas links.
Affiliations: The Armstrong Trust, Ltd. The Armstrong Clan Society.
Membership: Open to all connected with the clan by descent or marriage.
✍ Convener: Kenneth G. Armstrong
58 Glenforest Road, Toronto.
M4N 1ZD
☎ 1 416 489 5266

BELLEVILLE SCOTTISH COUNTRY DANCERS

Aims & Activities: See the RSCDS on page 47.
✍ Secretary: Dr W. Cunningham
PO Box 22154, Belleville.
K8N 5U7
☎ 1 613 965 4212

BLAIR SCOTTISH COUNTRY DANCERS

Aims & Activities: See the RSCDS on page 47.
✍ Secretary: Mr E. Robertson
543 Queenston Road,
Cambridge.
N3H 3J9
☎ 1 519 653 6102

BRIG O' DOON BURNS CLUB

Aims & Activities: Social and to encourage interest in the works of Burns. Annual Gathering.

Affiliations: The Burns Federation, No. 1094.
✍ Secretary: James McMeekin
269 Mackenzie Crescent,
Caledonia.
N3W 2G7

BURLINGTON BRANCH OF THE ROYAL SCOTTISH COUNTRY DANCE SOCIETY

Aims & Activities: See the RSCDS on page 47.
Membership: 49.
✍ The Secretary
PO Box 52044, Burlington Mall, Postal Outlet 62044, Burlington.
L7R 4K2

BURLINGTON STRATHCONA SOCIAL AND SCOTTISH COUNTY DANCE CLUB

Aims & Activities: See the RSCDS on page 47.
✍ Secretary: Mrs J. B. Douglas
468 Bridgman Avenue (Apt 2),
Burlington.
L7R 2V2
☎ 1 905 632 6632

BURNS SOCIETY OF TORONTO

Founded: 1947.
Aims & Activities: Social. Annual Gathering. To perpetuate the memory of Robert Burns.
Affiliations: The Burns Federation, No. 710.
✍ Secretary: Mrs Stella V. Wyness
Apt: 203, 2181 Avenue Road,
Toronto.
M5M 4B8

CAMBRIDGE HIGHLAND GAMES

Aims & Activities: Generally held on the third Saturday in July in the Churchill Park, these Games include the Ontario Open Highland Dance Championships.

✍ Contact: Tourist Board
Cambridge, Ontario.

CLAN DONALD COUNCIL OF CANADA

Aims & Activities: To promote and control the activities of the Clan Donald Societies throughout Canada.
✍ Chairman: Lt. Col. Gordon D. Leggett. Secretary: Mrs Norma E. Henderson
60 Pleasant Boulevarde, 2207 Toronto.
M4T 1K1

CLAN DONALD SOCIETY OF CANADA GRAND RIVER VALLEY BRANCH

Aims & Activities: To strengthen overseas links.
Membership: Open to all bearing the name, or that of one of the septs, or connected with the clan by descent or marriage.
✍ President: Charles A. MacDonald. Secretary: Mrs W. Donald
173 Pinedale Drive, Kitchener.
N2E 1K2

CLAN DONALD SOCIETY OF CANADA TORONTO BRANCH

Aims & Activities: To strengthen overseas links.
Membership: Open to all bearing the name, or that of one of the septs, or connected with the clan by descent or marriage.
✍ President: Robert H. Macdonald. Secretary: Mrs Elizabeth Bryant
32 Wilfrid Avenue, Toronto.
M4S 2J2

CLAN HUNTER ASSOCIATION

Aims & Activities: To strengthen overseas links.
Affiliations: The Clan Hunter Association, Scotland.

Membership: Open to those with the name Hunter, or those connected to the clan by descent or marriage.
✍ John M. W. Hunter
Queen's Court 201 W, 460 Wellington St, London.
N6A 3P8

CLAN MACDOWELL

Aims & Activities: To strengthen overseas links.
Membership: Open to those bearing the name Macdowell, or variants of it, and those connected by descent or marriage.
✍ Secretary: Fergus D. H. Macdowell of Garthland
16 Tower Road, Nepean, Ontario.

CLAN MACKAY ASSOCIATION OF CANADA

Aims & Activities: To strengthen overseas links.
Affiliations: The Clan Mackay Society, Scotland.
Membership: Open to members of the clan or its septs, or those connected by descent or marriage.
✍ President: Grace Mackay Edgar
47 Edgemore Dr. Toronto.

CLAN MACMILLAN SOCIETY OF NORTH AMERICA

Aims & Activities: To strengthen Scottish and overseas links. Annual Gathering.
Membership: Open to those with the name MacMillan and those related by birth and descent. Historical. Genealogical.
✍ President: Dr. Charles B. McMillan
✍ Admin. Officer: John B. McMillan
5364 Salem Road, Burlington.
L7L 3X3
☎ 1 416 637 3395

COBOURG HIGHLAND GAMES

Aims & Activities: Usually held on the first Saturday in July in the Donegan Park in the town of Cobourg, on the shore of Lake Ontario and only an hour's drive from Ontario.

✍ Contact: Ontario Tourist Board

DEEP RIVER SCOTTISH COUNTRY DANCE CLUB

Aims & Activities: See the RSCDS on page 47.

✍ Secretary: Mr J. Christie
  Box 1038, Deep River.
  K0J 1P0

☎ 1 613 584 2271

DUTTON HIGHLAND GAMES

Aims & Activities: Usually held on the 2nd Saturday in June in the Sons of Scotland Highland Park.

✍ Contact: Ontario Tourist Board

FERGUS HIGHLAND GAMES AND SCOTTISH FESTIVAL

Founded: 1946.

Aims & Activities: Held in the town of Fergus, 10 miles north-west of Guelph, these Games are generally held on the second weekend in August in the Victoria Park. These Games claim to be the largest Highland Festival in North America. They include the North American and International Scottish Heavy Events Championships and the North American Tug-of-War Championships. They also include pipe band competitions, solo piping and Highland dancing.

✍ Contact: Ontario Tourist Board

GALT BURNS CLUB

Founded: 1907.

Aims & Activities: Social. To encourage interest in the works of Robert Burns. Annual gathering.

Affiliations: The Burns Federation, No. 501.

✍ Secretary: Mrs Greta Hanley
  448 Waterloo Street, Cambridge, Ontario.
  N3H 1N7

GEORGETOWN HIGHLAND GAMES

Founded: 1975.

Aims & Activities: Originally known as the Halton Hills Highland Games and Festival, they are usually held in the Georgetown Fairgrounds on the third Saturday in June. They include the usual heavy events, pipe band comptitions, solo piping and Highland dancing.

✍ Officers: Secretary: Chamber of Commerce
  PO Box 111, Georgetown.
  L7G 4T1

☎ 1 415 877 7119

GEORGINA HIGHLAND GAMES

Aims & Activities: Usually held on the third Saturday in June in the town of Keswick on the southern tip of Lake Simco. These small games are held in the Keswick Arena and include the usual heavy events, pipe bands and Highland dancing.

✍ Contact: Ontario Tourist Board

GLENGARRY HIGHLAND GAMES

Founded: 1948.

Aims & Activities: Generally held on the Saturday before the first Monday in August in the Agricultural Grounds of Maxville, Ontario. They also claim to be the world's largest Games. They include the North American Pipe Band Championships, solo piping and Highland dancing, both track and field events and a drum majors competition. A concrert, tatto and displays take place on the Friday evening before the Games.

✍ Contact: Ontario Tourist Board

GUELPH SCOTTISH COUNTRY DANCE CLUB

Aims & Activities: See the RSCDS on page 47.
✍ Secretary: Miss D. Cherry
25 Merion Street, Guelph.
N1H 2L9

HALIBURTON HIGHLAND GAMES

Aims & Activities: These Games are generally held in the Glebe Park on the fourth Saturday in June.
✍ Secretary: Haliburton Highland Games
PO Box 29, Haliburton.
K0M 1S0
☎ 1 705 457 3555

HAMILTON BRANCH OF THE ROYAL SCOTTISH COUNTRY DANCE SOCIETY

Aims & Activities: See the RSCDS on page 47.
Membership: 164.
✍ Secretary: Irene Mayhew
4-1460 Garth Street, Hamilton.
L9B IR6
☎ 1 416 387 2662

HOUSE OF GORDON

Aims & Activities: To strengthen overseas links.
Affiliations: The House of Gordon, Scotland.
Membership: Open to those bearing the name or one of the septs, also to those who have served in the Gordon Highlanders.
✍ Convener: C. Edwin Todd
10 Ottawa Avenue, Barrie.
L4M 2W7
☎ 1 705 728 0478

KINGSTON BRANCH OF THE ROYAL SCOTTISH COUNTRY DANCE SOCIETY

Aims & Activities: See the RSCDS on page 47.
Membership: 80.
✍ Secretary: Jill Wing
378 Chelsea Road, Kingston.
K7M 3Z4
☎ 1 613 389 2269

KITCHENER WATERLOO BRANCH OF THE ROYAL SCOTTISH COUNTRY DANCE SOCIETY

Aims & Activities: See the RSCDS on page 47.
Membership: 139.
✍ Secretary: Edith Harper
PO Box 40029, Waterloo Town Square, 75 King Street South, Waterloo N2J 4V1

LONDON BRANCH OF THE ROYAL SCOTTISH COUNTRY DANCE SOCIETY

Aims & Activities: See the RSCDS on page 47.
Membership: 118.
✍ Secretary: Mrs Ann Weese
70 Stevenson Avenue, London.
N5W 1Y5
☎ 1 519 455 6023

LONDON BURNS CLUB

Founded: 1938.
Aims & Activities: Social and to promote interest in the works of Robert Burns. Annual Gathering.
Affiliations: The Burns Federation, No. 561.
✍ Secretary: Ms Liz Auld
PO Box 1904, Station B, London.
N6A 5J4

MOLSON HIGHLAND GAMES

Founded: 1985.
Aims & Activities: These Games are

usually held on the fourth Saturday in July in the Molson Park, Barrie, which can cope with more than 30,000 spectators. The Games already claim to be one of the three largest in Ontario. They include the usual heavy events, pipe bands, solo piping and Highland dancing, also the 'Farmer's Walk', in which competitors have to carry 200lb in each hand as far as they can.
✍ Contact: Ontario Tourist Board

N. A. A. F. B.

Aims & Activities: Social and to encourage interest in Scottish heritage. Annual Gathering.
Affiliations: The Burns Federation, No.1024.
✍ Secretary: Mrs Janet A. Mann
    774 Wilkins Street, London.
    N6C 4Z9

NIAGARA FALLS BURNS CLUB

Founded: 1967.
Aims & Activities: Social. Annual Gathering. To perpetuate the memory of Robert Burns.
Affiliations: The Burns Federation, No. 980.
✍ Secretary: Ms Elizabeth Freeman
    277 Main Street, East Aurora.
    NY 14052

NORTH BAY ROBERT BURNS CLUB

Aims & Activities: Social and to promote interest in the works of Robert Burns. Annual Gathering.
Affiliations: The Burns Federation, No. 893.
✍ Ms Annie Coyne
    1559 Fraser Street, North Bay.
    P1B 3Z1

NORTH LANARK HIGHLAND GAMES

Founded: 1984.
Aims & Activities: Usually held on the fourth Saturday in August in the North Lanark Agricultural Society Fairgrounds on the banks of the Mississippi river. The games include the usual heavy events, piping and Highland dancing.
✍ Contact: Ontario Tourist Board

OAKVILLE SCOTTISH COUNTRY DANCE GROUP

Aims & Activities: See the RSCDS on page 47.
✍ Secretary: Sue Clark
    2144 Grand Boulevard, Oakville.
    L6H 5M2
☎ 1 905 849 4385

ORANGEVILLE SCOTTISH COUNTRY DANCE GROUP

Aims & Activities: See the RSCDS on page 47.
✍ Secretary: Cheryl Go.as
    RR1 Caledon East.
    L0N 1E0
☎ 1 519 941 9717

OTTAWA BRANCH OF THE ROYAL SCOTTISH COUNTRY DANCE SOCIETY

Aims & Activities: See the RSCDS on page 47.
Membership: 231.
✍ Secretary: Andree McDermott
    5421 Main Street, PO Box 318,
    Osgoode.
    K0A 2W0
☎ 1 613 826 30231 (home)
☎ 1 613 998 8865 (business)

OTTAWA BURNS CLUB

Founded: 1977.
Aims & Activities: Social. Annual gath-

ering. To perpetuate the memory of Robert Burns.

Affiliations: The Burns Federation, No. 957.

✍ Secretary: Bill Beaton
79 Meadowlands Drive West,
Nepean.
K2G 2R9

PETERBOROUGH SCOTTISH COUNTRY DANCE SOCIETY

Aims & Activities: See the RSCDS on page 47.

✍ Secretary: Mr I. M. Sandeman
PO Box 1982, Peterborough.
K9J 7X7
☎ 1 705 652 8754

PIPERS AND PIPE BAND SOCIETY OF ONTARIO

Aims & Activities: Encouraging an interest in and the formation and organisation of pipe bands and piping and drumming, also participation in competitions and events in Highland Games.

Affiliations: The Royal Scottish Pipe Band Association, (page 59).

✍ Secretary: Henry Roberts
1271 Roseberry Crescent,
Oakville.
L6M 1W2

ROBERT BURNS SOCIETY OF HAMILTON

Aims & Activities: Social, To perpetuate the memory of Robert Burns. Annual Gathering.

Affiliations: The Burns Federation, No. 842.

✍ Secretary: Ms Catherine Devay
270 Hunter Street West,
Hamilton.
L8P 1S3

SARNIA HIGHLAND GAMES

Aims & Activities: Usually held on the

third Saturday in August in the Centennial Park. These Games include the All-Ontario Heavy Events Championships, as well as the usual events and a sheepdog demonstration.

✍ Contact: Ontario Tourist Board

SARNIA SCOTTISH COUNTRY DANCE GROUP

Aims & Activities: See the RSCDS on page 47.

✍ Secretary: Donna Needham
2070 Gladys Street,
Brights Grove.
N0N 1C0
☎ 1 519 869 6897

SAULT STE. MARIE SCOTTISH COUNTRY DANCERS

Aims & Activities: See the RSCDS on page 47.

✍ Secretary: Mrs F. Ortiz
104 Bishop's Court,
Sault Ste Marie.
P6A 3V9
☎ 1 705 942 5709

SCOTTISH COUNTRY DANCING TEACHERS' ASSOCIATION

Aims & Activities: The Royal Scottish Country Dance Society.

✍ Secretary: Anne Harison
1232 Montclair Drive, Oakville.
L6H 1Z4
☎ 1 905 845 6718

SERTOMA HIGHLAND GAMES

Aims & Activities: Generally held on the holiday Saturday at the end of the May and usually the first Games to be held in Ontario.

✍ Contact: Ontario Tourist Board

SONS OF SCOTLAND BENEVOLENT ASSOCIATION

Founded: 1876.

Aims & Activities: Fraternal benefit life insurance society of Scots, their families and descendants. Seeks to cultivate an appreciation of Scottish literature, history, music and poetry. Social. Triennial meetings.

Publications: Scotia (quarterly). Annual directory.

✍ Secretary: Effie MacFie
90 Eglinton Ave. E. 4th Fl.,
Ste 411, Toronto.
M4P 2Y3
☎ 1 416 482 1250

ST CATHERINES BRANCH OF THE ROYAL SCOTTISH COUNTRY DANCE SOCIETY

Aims & Activities: See the RSCDS on page 47.

Membership: 83.

✍ Secretary: Mr G. Clarkson
c/o F. Franklin, 11 Sandy Cove,
St Catherines.
L2N 5Z3
☎ 1 905 834 0417

ST GEORGE SCOTTISH COUNTRY DANCERS

Aims & Activities: See the RSCDS on page 47.

✍ Secretary: Cynthia Ridley
41 Scott Avenue, St George.
N0E 1N0
☎ 1 519 448 3668

TORONTO BRANCH OF THE ROYAL SCOTTISH COUNTRY DANCE SOCIETY

Aims & Activities: See the RSCDS on page 47.

Membership: 828.

✍ Secretary: Mary Baldwin
278 Broadway Avenue, Toronto.
M4P 1VP
☎ 1 416 485 8280

WHITE COCKADE SOCIAL AND DANCE GROUP

Aims & Activities: See the RSCDS on page 47.

✍ Secretary: Mrs A. Kerr
285 Headon Road, Burlington.
L7M 1S3
☎ 1 905 335 6139

WINDSOR BRANCH OF THE ROYAL SCOTTISH COUNTRY DANCE SOCIETY

Aims & Activities: See the RSCDS on page 47.

Membership: 54.

✍ Secretary: Isobel Hunter
264 Hyde Park Road, RR3,
Amherstburg N9V 3R3
☎ 1 519 978 0091 (home)
☎ 1 519 978 0138 (business)
✆ 1 519 978 1511

PRINCE EDWARD ISLAND

CALEDONIAN CLUB HIGHLAND GAMES

Aims & Activities: Highland Games held annually.

✍ The Secretary
c/o Prince Edward Island Tourist Board

COLLEGE OF PIPING AND CELTIC PERFORMING ARTS OF CANADA

Aims & Activities: Offers a one-year internship programme on all aspects of piping. Summer programs on piping, drumming, dancing and specialist courses in Piobaireachd also available.

✍ Director: Scott MacAulay
College of Piping, 619 Walter St
East, Summerside C1N 4H8
☎ 1 902 436 5377
✆ 1 902 888 3860

PRINCE EDWARD ISLAND SCOTTISH COUNTRY DANCERS

Aims & Activities: See the RSCDS on page 47.

✍ Secretary: Miss K. Matthews
279 Richmond Street, Apt 3.,
Charlottetown.
C1A 1J7
☎ 1 902 892 3128

SUMMERSIDE HIGHLAND GATHERING

Aims & Activities: To organise an annual Highland Gathering on the last weekend in June.

✍ The College of Piping
619 Walter Street East,
Summerside C1N 4H8
☎ 1 902 436 5377
✆ 1 902 888 3860

QUEBEC

MONTREAL BRANCH OF THE ROYAL SCOTTISH COUNTRY DANCE SOCIETY

Aims & Activities: See the RSCDS on page 47.
Membership: 135.

✍ Secretary: Ena Doyle
432 Wakefield Road, Beaconsfield
H9W 3L7
☎ 1 514 695 2652

MONTREAL HIGHLAND GAMES

Aims & Activities: These Games are generally held at St. Lambert on the eastern side of the St. Lawrence river during the first weekend in August.

✍ Contact: Quebec Tourist Board

ROBERT BURNS ASSOCIATION OF MONTREAL

Aims & Activities: Social and to pro-
mote interest in the poetical work of Robert Burns. Annual Gathering.

Affiliations: The Burns Federation, No. 841.

✍ Secretary: Mr R. W. Jewkes
7215 Boyer Street, Montreal.
H2R 2R6

ST ANDREW SOCIETY OF MONTREAL

Aims & Activities: To encourage all social activities likely to promote an interest in Scotland and Scottish heritage throughout the world.

Affiliations: The St Andrew Society of Scotland.

✍ Secretary: Mrs Margaret Fordham
1195 Sherbrooke West, Montreal.
H3A 1H9

SASKATCHEWAN

CLAN HUNTER ASSOCIATION OF WESTERN CANADA

Aims & Activities: To strengthen overseas links.

Affiliations: The Clan Hunter Association (page 28).

Membership: Open to those with the name Hunter or connected by marriage or descent.

✍ Malcolm B. Hunter
2117 Haultaine Avenue,
Saskatoon S7J 1P5
☎ 1 306 343 1855

SASKATCHEWAN BRANCH OF THE ROYAL SCOTTISH COUNTRY DANCE SOCIETY

Aims & Activities: See the RSCDS on page 47.
Membership: 83.

✍ Secretary: Mr G. Ogilvie
805 Grace Street, Regina.
S4T 5M4
☎ 1 306 554 1131

SOUTH AMERICA

ARGENTINA

HIGHLAND THISTLE PIPE BAND SOCIETY

Aims & Activities: See the RSCDS on page 47.

✍ Secretary: Mr C. Ayling
Catamarca 2527, 1636 Olivos
Buenos Aires.

☎ 54 799146

✍ All correspondence to:
Mr J. Smith
Gloucester Lodge, 2 West Close,
Felpham, Bognor Regis, England.
PO22 7LQ

☎ 0243 582558

BOLIVIA

LA PAZ SCOTTISH COUNTRY DANCE GROUP

Aims & Activities: See the RSCDS on page 47.

✍ Secretary: Mr J. Cooper
Casilla 3511, La Paz.

☎ 591 350581 410452

BRAZIL

ST ANDREW SOCIETY OF RIO DE JANEIRO

Aims & Activities: Social. See the RSCDS on page 47.

✍ Secretary: Mr K. Cattley
Av Rio Branco, 45/4th Floor,
Andar, 20090-003, Rio de
Janeiro.

CHILE

ST ANDREW SOCIETY OF SANTIAGO

Aims & Activities: To encourage all social activities likely to promote an interest in Scotland and Scottish heritage throughout the world.

Affiliations: The St Andrew Society of Scotland and the Royal Scottish Country Dance Society.

✍ Secretary: Mrs Beatrice O. Cheyne
Casilla 13998, Santiago.

WEST INDIES

BARBADOS

SCOTTISH COUNTRY DANCE SOCIETY OF BARBADOS

Aims & Activities: See the RSCDS on page 47.
✍ President: Mr K. Thomson
The Happenings, 18 The Mount, St George, Barbados.
☎ 1 809 429 1752

ST ANDREW SOCIETY OF BARBADOS

Aims & Activities: Social. To encourage an interest in Scotland and Scottish heritage.
Affiliations: The St Andrew Society of Scotland, (page 48).
Membership: Open to those of Scottish descent.
✍ Secretary: Neil W. Thomson
41 Durants, Christchurch.

JAMAICA

SCOTTISH COUNTRY DANCE SOCIETY OF JAMAICA

Aims & Activities: See the RSCDS on page 47.
✍ Secretary: Mrs C. McDonald
1 St Lucia Avenue, Spanish Court.
Shop: No. 27, Suite 65, Kingston 10.

AUSTRALIA

AUSTRALIAN CAPITAL TERRITORY

BELCONNEN SCOTTISH COUNTRY DANCERS

Aims & Activities: See the RSCDS on page 47.
✍ Secretary: Ms J. Livingston
92 Mainwaring Rich Circuit, Palmerston.
ACT 2913
☎ 61 6 2429665

BURNS SCOTTISH COUNTRY DANCE GROUP

Aims & Activities: See the RSCDS on page 47.
✍ Secretary: The Secretary
18 Bangalay Crescent, Rivett.
ACT 2611
☎ 61 6 2885151

CANBERRA AND DISTRICT BRANCH OF THE ROYAL SCOTTISH COUNTRY DANCE SOCIETY

Aims & Activities: See the RSCDS on page 47.
Membership: 165.
✍ Secretary: Mrs Middlemiss
PO Box 9027, Deakin.
ACT 2600
☎ 61 62 733 482 (home)
☎ 61 062 824 674 (business)

CANBERRA HIGHLAND SOCIETY AND BURNS CLUB

Aims & Activities: Social and to promote interest in Scottish heritage, in particular the poetical works of Robert Burns. Annual Gathering.

Affiliations: The Burns Federation, No. 882.
✍ Secretary: Stephen Marks
PO Box 365, Erindale.
ACT 2903

CLAN MACAULAY

✍ Robert MacAulay
7 Rosentaal Street, Campbell.
ACT 2601

LIMESTONE PLAINS SCOTTISH COUNTRY DANCERS

Aims & Activities: See the RSCDS on page 47.
✍ Secretary: Mrs J. Fearon
42 Waller Crescent, Campbell.
ACT 2601

SCOTTISH COUNTRY DANCE CLUB OF CANBERRA

Aims & Activities: See the RSCDS on page 47.
✍ Secretary: Mr D. Dempster
PO Box 905, Canberra.
ACT

NEW SOUTH WALES

ARWON SCOTTISH COUNTRY DANCE GROUP

Aims & Activities: See the RSCDS on page 47.
✍ Secretary: Mrs V. Molyneux
170 St Anne's Street, Nowra.
NSW 2541
☎ 61 04 421 3561

AUBURN SCOTTISH ASSOCIATION

✍ Mr L Trainer
17 Norval Street, Auburn.
NSW 2144

BAIRD FAMILY ASSOCIATION

Membership: Open to anyone with the name Baird or related.
✍ Mr C. Price
47 Wilson Street, West Wallsend.
NSW 2286

BANKSTOWN SCOTTISH ASSOCIATION

✍ Secretary: Mrs Moyna Scotland
PO Box 236, Bankstown.
NSW 2200

BURNS CLUB OF NSW

✍ Miss M Dickie
26 The Crescent, Manly.
NSW 2095

CABRAVALE BURNS CLUB

✍ Mrs Janette George
21 Woodlands Crescent, Narallen.
NSW 2567

CAMPBELLTOWN AND DISTRICT SCOTTISH

✍ Mr Tom Hannah
PO Box 40, Campbelltown.
NSW 2560

CAMPSIE SCOTTISH SOCIETY

✍ Mrs D Keers
132 Mount Druitt Road, MT Druitt.
NSW 2770

CARINGBAH SCOTTISH COUNTRY DANCE CLUB

Aims & Activities: See the RSCDS on page 47.
✍ Secretary: Mr J. A. Anderson
9 Mercedes Place, Kareela.
NSW 2232
☎ 61 528 5159

CLAN ARMSTRONG

Membership: Open to all bearing the name Armstrong or related to it.
✍ Mr Jeffrey Armstrong
47 Eric St, Bundeena.
NSW 2230

CLAN BROUN OF COLSTOUN

Membership: Open to anyone bearing the name Broun and related.
✍ Mr W. W. Broun
23 Clanalpine St, Mosman.
NSW 2088

CLAN BUCHANAN

Membership: Open to all bearing the name Buchanan or variants.
✍ Mr J. McAusland
c/o McAusland & Co., PO Box 117, Kensington.
NSW 2033

CLAN CAMERON

Membership: Open to anyone bearing the name Cameron or variants.
✍ Mr A. M. Cameron
33 Cobran Road, Cheltenham.
NSW 2119

CLAN CAMPBELL OF AUSTRALIA

Membership: Open to anyone with the name Campbell or related to it.
✍ Mr C. Campbell
21 Morella Avenue, Sefton.
NSW 2162

CLAN CAMPBELL SOCIETY OF NSW

Membership: Open to anyone with the name Campbell ot related to it.
✍ Mrs B. Campbell
21 Morella Avenue, Sefton.
NSW 2162

CLAN CHISHOLM

Membership: Open to anyone of the name Chisholm.
✍ Miss E. Watson. 8 Parkham Road
Dundas.
NSW 2117

CLAN COCHRANE

Membership: Open to all beasring the name Cochrane or related.
✍ Maj D. Cochrane
1 Findley Road, Bringelly.
NSW 2171

CLAN COLQUHOUN

Membership: Open to all bearing the name or variants.
✍ Mr R. French
27 Barton Avenue, Haberfield.
NSW 2045

CLAN DAVIDSON

Membership: Open to all bearing the name or variants.
✍ Dr F. Davidson 23 Elizabeth St
Paddington.
NSW 2021

CLAN DONALD SOCIETY OF NSW

Membership: Open to all bearing the name Donald or variants.
✍ Mrs M. McConnell
45a Vermont St, Sutherland.
NSW 2232

CLAN DONNACHAIDH SOCIETY

Membership: Open to all bearing the name or connected to it.
✍ Mrs B. Robertson
294 Old Northern Road,
Castle Hill.
NSW 2154

CLAN DRUMMOND

Membership: Open to all with the name Drummond or variants.
✍ Mr G. Drummond
10 Elgin St, East Gordon.
NSW 2072

CLAN FARQUHARSON

Membership: Open to all bearing the name or variants.
✍ Mr S. E. Hardy
Villa 49 Maple Grove Village,
Pine Rd, Casula.
NSW 2170

CLAN FERGUSON AUSTRALIA

Membership: Open to all bearing the name Ferguson or related.
✍ Miss Naida Ford
78 Hampden Avenue,
East Wahroonga.
NSW 2076

CLAN FORSYTH

Membership: Open to all bearing the name Forsyth or related.
✍ The Secretary
PO Box 396, Roseville.
NSW 2069

CLAN FRASER

Membership: Open to those with the name Fraser and variants.
✍ Secretary: Mrs Judy Fraser-Byass
15 Birra Drive, Balarang.
NSW 2529

CLAN GRAHAM

Membership: Open to those named Graham in its various spellings or related.
✍ Mrs P. Birchall
6 Bates Drive, Kareela.
NSW 2232

CLAN GRANT

Membership: Open to all named Grant or related.
✍ Mrs D. H. Grant
10 Hill Street, Glenbrook.
NSW 2773

CLAN GREGOR

Membership: Open to all named Gregor and variants.
✍ Mr Sid Bowers
41 Boomerang Road,
Collaroy Plateau.
NSW 2098

CLAN GUNN

Membership: Open to all with the name Gunn or related.
✍ Mr Stuart Henderson
10 Delray Avenue, Wahroonga.
NSW 2076

CLAN HAY SOCIETY

Membership: Open to those with the name Hay, or connected to it.
✍ Mrs Helen Bate
PO Box 306, Newport Beach.
NSW 2106

CLAN HENDERSON SOCIETY OF AUSTRALIA

Membership: Open to all with the name Henderson and those related to them.
✍ Mr Ron Palmer
5 Coolabah Crescent, Forestville.
NSW 2087

CLAN HUNTER ASSOCIATION

Aims & Activities: To strengthen overseas links. Social. Annual Gathering.
Affiliations: The Clan Hunter Association, (page 28).
Membership: Open to all bearing the name Hunter, and those related by marriage or descent.
✍ Secretary: Albert S. J. Hunter
51 Albany St, Gosford.
NSW 2250
☎ 61 43 25 1588

CLAN INGLIS

Membership: Open to all with the name Inglis or variants.
✍ Mr J. Inglis
21 Cunliffe Road, Killara.
NSW 2071

CLAN JOHNSTON

Membership: Open to all with the name Johnston or variants.
✍ Judge H. P. Johnston
26 Terama Street, Bilgola Plateau.
NSW 2107

CLAN KEITH

Membership: Open to all bearing the name Keith or related to it.
✍ Dr William Marshall
423a Church St, North Parramatta.
NSW 2151

CLAN LAMONT

Aims & Activities: To collect genealogical and historical clan records. To promote overseas links. Social.
Membership: Open to those of the name Lamont, or connected by descent or marriage to the clan.
✍ Secretary: Mr J. Lamont
8 Wanjina Place, North Rocks.
NSW 2151

CLAN LUMSDEN

Membership: Open to anyone bearing the name Lumsden or related to it.
✍ Mr J. Lumsdaine
8/2 Woonona Avenue South,
Wahroonga.
NSW 2076

CLAN MACALISTER

Membership: Open to all connected with the clan name in any way.
✍ Mr P. C. Alexander CMG
OBE, D. Ua., GPO Box 5289,
Sydney.
NSW 2001

CLAN MACARTHUR

Membership: Open to anyone with the name Macarthur in its various spellings.
✍ Mr Robert Macarthur
41 Kiora St, Penania.
NSW 2213

CLAN MACDOUGALL

Membership: Open to all bearing the name or variants, or related to it.
✍ Mr A. K. McDougall
47 Thomas Street, North Manly.
NSW 2100

CLAN MACDUFF

Membership: Open to all with the name MacDuff or related to it.
✍ Mrs V. Sansom
5 Mons Road, Balgowlah North.
NSW 2093

CLAN MACFARLANE

Membership: Open to anyone of the name MacFarlane in its various spellings.
✍ Mrs B. MacFarlane
740 Forest Road, Peakhurst.
NSW 2210

CLAN MACFIE

Membership: Open to all bearing the name MacFie or related to it.
✍ Mr W. Tyrrell
8 Yeran Street, Sylvania.
NSW 2224

CLAN MACINTYRE

Membership: Open to all bearing the name Macintyre or variations of it.
✍ Mrs E. Storey
30 Fitzroy St, Kirribilli.
NSW 2061

CLAN MACIVER SOCIETY OF AUSTRALIA

Membership: Open to those of the name MacIver or variants.
✍ Mrs West
14 Mitchell Road,
West Strathfield.
NSW 2140

CLAN MACKENZIE

Membership: Open to all with the name Mackenzie or variants.
✍ Mrs May Armitage
144 Nerindah Road,
Baulkham Hills.
NSW 2153

CLAN MACKINTOSH SOCIETY OF AUSTRALIA

Membership: Open to all bearing the name Mackintosh in its varied spellings or related to it.
✍ Mr C. McIntosh
9/2C Jones Road. Kenthurst.
NSW 2156

CLAN MACLACHLAN

Membership: Open to any bearing the name Maclachlan or variants of it.
✍ Ms D. McLachlan
17/532 New South Head Road,
Double Bay NSW 2028

CLAN MACLAREN

Membership: Open to those bearing the name Maclaren or related to it.
✍ Mrs D. M. McLaren
108 Kildare Road, Blacktown.
NSW 2148

CLAN MACLENNAN

Membership: Open to all bearing the name or variations of it.
✍ Mr L. Vance
25 Nineteenth Street,
Warragamba.
NSW 2752

CLAN MACLENNAN – GRAFTON BRANCH

Membership: Open to all bearing the name or variations of it.
✍ Mrs M. Austen
Chambigne via Grafton.
NSW 2460

CLAN MACNEACAIL

Aims & Activities: To strengthen overseas links. To collect genealogical and historical records of the clan.
Membership: Open to those bearing the name Macneacail or variants of it, or to those related by marriage or descent.
✍ Secretary: Iain Macneacail
12 Fox Street, Ballina.
NSW

CLAN MACNICOL

Aims & Activities: To strengthen overseas links. Social.
Affiliations: The Clan MacNicol, Scotland.
Membership: Open to those of the name MacNicol, or its variants, and to those related to the clan by descent or marriage.
✍ Secretary: Councillor J. Nicholl
2 Cameron Avenue, Bass Hill.
NSW 2197

CLAN MACPHERSON

Membership: Open to all bearing the name or variations of it.
✍ Mr J. MacPherson
1 Alviston Street, Strathfield.
NSW 2135

CLAN MACQUEEN

Membership: Open to all bearing the name or variations of it.
✍ Miss Sandra MacQueen
47 Parklands Road, Mt Colah.
NSW 2079

CLAN MACRAE SOCIETY

Membership: Open to all bearing the name or variations of it.
✍ Kenneth McRae
136 Clifford Road, Goulbourn.
NSW 2580

CLAN MACTHOMAS

Membership: Open to all bearing the name or variations of it.
✍ Mr T. Thom
38 Scott Street, Kogarah.
NSW 2216

CLAN MAITLAND, AUSTRALIA

Membership: Open to all bearing the name or variations of it.
✍ Major General G. L. Maitland
37 Cherry Street, Warrawee.
NSW 2074

CLAN McLEOD SOCIETY OF NSW

Membership: Open to all bearing the name or variations of it.
✍ Mrs W. McLeod
15 Forest Way, French's Forest.
NSW 2086

CLAN MELVILLE

Membership: Open to all bearing the name or variations of it.

✍ Mrs M. England
   3 Canoon Road, Turramurra.
   NSW 2074

CLAN MENZIES

Membership: Open to all bearing the
name or variations of it.
✍ c/o Scottish Clan and Tartan
   Shop
   Birkenhead Point, Drummoyne.
   NSW 2047

CLAN MORRISON

Membership: Open to all bearing the
name or variations of it.
✍ Mr N. Morrison
   Level 44 MLC Centre,
   Martin Place, Sydney.
   NSW 2000

CLAN MUNRO

Membership: Open to all bearing the
name or variations of it.
✍ Mr A. Munro
   3 Mars Street, Padstow
   NSW 2211

CLAN ROBERTSON

Membership: Open to all bearing the
name or variations of it.
✍ Mr B. Robertson
   294 Old Northern Road,
   Castle Hill NSW 2154

CLAN ROSS

Membership: Open to all bearing the
name or variations of it.
✍ Mr Bruce Ross
   PO Box 83, Pennant Hills.
   NSW 2120

CLAN SHAW

Membership: Open to all bearing the
name or variations of it.
✍ Robert J. Shaw

Esq., Tintenbar Road, Tintenbar.
NSW 2480

CLAN SINCLAIR

Membership: Open to all bearing the
name or variations of it.
✍ Mr J. Sinclair
   33 Hame Avenue, Ermington.
   NSW 2115

CLAN SUTHERLAND

Membership: Open to all bearing the
name or variations of it.
✍ Mr W. Sutherland
   145 Cadgegong Road, Ruse.
   NSW 2560

CLAN TURNBULL

Membership: Open to all named
Turnbull.
✍ Mr S. J. Turnbull
   PO Box 375, St Mary's.
   NSW 2760

CLAN URQUHART

Membership: Open to those named
Urquhart and related to it.
✍ Mrs P. Urquhart
   1 Wolger Road. Mossman.
   NSW 2088

CLOSEBURN HOUSE BURNS CLUB

Aims & Activities: Social. To perpetu-
ate the memory of Robert Burns.
Affiliations: The Burns Federation,
No. 1116.
✍ Secretary: Peter J. Broome
   Closeburn Properties Pty Ltd.,
   44-48 Mt York Road,
   Mt Victoria.
   NSW 2786

COLLAROY LAKESIDE SCOTTISH COUNTRY DANCE CLUB

Aims & Activities: See the RSCDS on page 47.

✍ Secretary: A. R. Reyswood
42 Sunrise Road, Palm Beach.
NSW 2108
☎ 61 974 4752

COMBINED SCOTTISH SOCIETIES OF NSW

✍ Mrs Helen MacKenzie
80 Menzies Road, Eastwood.
NSW 2122

COOPER FAMILY ASSOCIATION

✍ Mr R Cooper
122 Osborne Street, Nowra.
NSW 2541

DRUMMOYNE AND DISTRICT SCOTTISH SOCIETY AND BURNS CLUB

Founded: 1932.
Aims & Activities: To promote Scottish culture and traditions. Social. Charitable.
Affiliations: The Burns Federation, No. 950.
Membership: Open to all interested in the aims of the society.
✍ Secretary: Mr R. C. Becker
12 Moir Avenue,
Northmead.
NSW 2152

EASTWOOD DENISTONE SOCIETY

✍ Mrs N Cowgill
4C Excelsior Avenue, Castle Hill.
NSW 2154

EPPING AND DISTRICT SCOTTISH SOCIETY

Aims & Activities: Social.
✍ Mr M. Pogson

23 Crowley Road, Browra.
NSW 2081

EPPING SCOTTISH COUNTRY DANCE CLUB

Aims & Activities: See the RSCDS on page 47.
✍ Secretary: Mrs A. Ure
13 Warrington Avenue, Epping.
NSW 2121
☎ 61 2 868 3778

ETTALONG CALEDONIAN CLUB

Aims & Activities: Social.
✍ Mr Cameron Bannerman
109 Broadwater Drive, Saratoga.
NSW 2250

FOOLISH-HOOLEY COMMITTEE

✍ Mrs G Gruzman
24 Hopetoun Avenue, Vaucluse.
NSW 2030

FORBES AND DISTRICT SCOTTISH SOCIETY

Aims & Activities: Social.
✍ Mrs J. Kerr
31 Clement St, Forbes.
NSW 2871

GLASGOW UNIVERSITY GRADUATES ASSOCIATION OF NSW

✍ Mr G R Stewart
PO Box 252, Roseville.
NSW 2871

GOSFORD RSL CALEDONIAN CLUB OF AUSTRALIA

Aims & Activities: Social.
✍ Mrs I Moon
26 Pacific Highway, Gosford.
NSW 2250

GRANVILLE CALEDONIAN SOCIETY

Aims & Activities: Social.
✍ Mrs J. Bracken
24 Emmetts Farm Road,
Rosemore.
NSW 2171

HIGHLAND SOCIETY OF NSW

Aims & Activities: Social.
✍ Mrs Gwen Stewart
Po Box 1130, Parramatta.
NSW 2150

HOUSE OF BROWNLEE

Membership: Open to those named
Brownlee or related to it.
✍ Mr Ian Brownlee
PO Box 378, Katoomba.
NSW 2708

HUNTER VALLEY SCOTS CLUB

Aims & Activities: Social.
✍ Mrs J. E. Bremner
PO Box 34, Kotara Fair.
NSW 2289

HUNTER VALLEY/NEWCASTLE BRANCH OF THE ROYAL SCOTTISH COUNTRY DANCE SOCIETY

Aims & Activities: See the RSCDS on
page 47.
Membership: 177.
✍ Secretary: Mr B. Cant
31 Cram Street, Merewether.
NSW 2302
☎ 61 49 691837

HURSTVILLE SCOTTISH

Aims & Activities: Social.
✍ Mrs Doris MacDonald
10 Seaforth Street, Bexley.
NSW 2207

LAKEMBA SCOTTISH

✍ Mrs Betty Corry
7 Young Street, Penshurst.
NSW 2222

MACLEAN – THE SCOTTISH TOWN IN AUSTRALIA ASSOCIATION

Aims & Activities: Social.
✍ PO Box 171
Maclean.
NSW 2463

MACQUARIE TOWNS SCOTTISH SOCIETY

✍ P O Box 457
Richmond.
NSW 2753

MACQUARRIE STEWART BURNS CLUB

Founded: 1970.
Aims & Activities: Social. Annual
Gathering. To perpetuate the memo-
ry of Robert Burns.
Affiliations: The Burns Federation,
No. 984.
✍ Secretary: D. G. Taylor
17 Callistemon Place, Epping.
NSW 2121

MONARO CALEDONIAN SOCIETY

Aims & Activities: See the RSCDS on
page 47.
✍ Secretary: Eileen Pevere
c/o PO Box 339, Cooma North.
NSW 2630
☎ 61 64 523078

NEPEAN DISTRICT ROBERT BURNS CLUB

Aims & Activities: Social. Annual
Gathering. To encourage interest in
the work of Robert Burns.

Affiliations: The Burns Federation, No. 1105.

✍ Secretary: Mrs I. McAulay
2 Chester Street, Mount Druitt.
NSW 2770

NEPEAN DISTRICT SCOTTISH

✍ Mrs M Cowie
26 Cutler Avenue, St Marys.
NSW 2760

NEW SOUTH WALES PIPE BAND ASSOCIATION LIMITED

Aims & Activities: Encouraging an interest in the formation and organisation of pipe bands and piping and drumming. Also participation in competitions and events in Highland Games.
Affiliations: The Royal Scottish Pipe Band Association, (page 59).

✍ Secretary: Mr David H. Scotland BEM, Box 3104, GPO Sydney.
NSW 2001

NOWRA SCOTTISH COUNTRY DANCE GROUP

Aims & Activities: See the RSCDS on page 47.

✍ Secretary: Mrs J. Meakin
PO Box 422, Nowra.
NSW 2541
☎ 61 44 213570

NSW PIPERS SOCIETY

Aims & Activities: To encourage piping.

✍ Mr Arthur Wright
17 Richmond Avenue, St Ives.
NSW 2075

ORANGE AND DISTRICT SCOTTISH ASSOCIATION

Aims & Activities: Social and to encourage iunterest in Scottish her-

itage including the works of Robert Burns. Annual Dinner.
Affiliations: The Burns Federation, No. 919.

✍ Secretary: Mrs Anne Brown
PO Box 497, Orange.
NSW 2800

ORKNEY AND SHETLAND ASSOCIATION

✍ Mr E Petri
8 Grafton Street, Balmain East.
NSW 2041

PARRAMATTA AND DISTRICT CALEDONIAN SOCIETY

✍ Ms Jennifer Quek
PO Box 535, Guildford.
NSW 2161

PEAKHURST SCOTTISH SOCIAL CLUB

✍ Mrs M Wild
28 Lugarno Parade
Lugarno.
NSW 2210

PRINCE OF WALES HOSPITAL SCOTTISH COUNTRY DANCE GROUP

Aims & Activities: See the RSCDS on page 47.

✍ Secretary: Mrs J. Wilson
61 Buckland Street, Alexandra.
NSW 2015
☎ 61 2 318 1802

QUEANBEYAN SCOTTISH ASSOCIATION

✍ P O Box 167
Queanbeyan.
NSW 2620

RED HACKLE ASSOCIATION

Aims & Activities: Social.

✍ Mr H. E. MacDonald
PO Box 123, Chester Hill.
NSW 2162

RICHMOND RIVER SCOTTISH SOCIETY

✍ Mrs E Wilson
32 Fenwick Drive, East Ballina.
NSW 2478

ROCKDALE AND DISTRICT SCOTTISH

✍ Mr R Moar
154 Caringbah, Road, Caringbah.
NSW 2229

ROYAL SCOTTISH COUNTRY DANCE SOCIETY

Aims & Activities: See the RSCDS on page 47.
✍ Dr Keith Napier
28 Pine Avenue, Fivedock.
NSW 2046

SCOTTISH CLANS COUNCIL OF AUSTRALIA

Aims & Activities: Organisational and advisory.
✍ Mr J. Fowler
PO Box 265, Drummoyne.
NSW 2047

SCOTTISH SOCIETY AND BURNS CLUB OF AUSTRALIA

Founded: 1939.
Aims & Activities: To promote Scottish culture and interest in Burns. To foster ties with Scotland and Scots abroad. Overseas links. Charitable. Educational. Historical. Social.
Affiliations: The Burns Federation, No. 566.
Membership: Membership open to all interested in the aims of the society.
✍ Secretary: Miss May Dickie
8/26 The Crescent, Manly.

NSW 2095

SOUTHERN HIGHLANDS SCOTTISH COUNTRY DANCERS

Aims & Activities: See the RSCDS on page 47.
✍ Secretary: Mr E. Barton
The Cedars, Wilson Drive,
Colo Vale.
NSW 2575
☎ 61 48 894 573

SYDNEY BRANCH OF THE ROYAL SCOTTISH COUNTRY DANCE SOCIETY

Aims & Activities: See the RSCDS on page 47.
Membership: 200.
✍ Secretary: Dr K. Napier
28 Pine Avenue, Five Dock.
NSW 2046
☎ 61 02 712 2918 (home)
☎ 61 02 352 2386 (business)

SYDNEY HERMITAGE SCOTTISH COUNTRY DANCE GROUP

Aims & Activities: See the RSCDS on page 47.
✍ Secretary: Mr B. Giri
38 Lavarack Street, Ryde.
NSW 2112

SYDNEY HIGHLAND GAMES

Founded: 1856.
Aims & Activities: Held annually on New Year's Day these are Australia's oldest and largest Highland Games They include massed pipe bands, the usual heavy events, athletic and track events, solo piping and Highland dancing and have an annual attendance of around 15,000.
✍ The Secretary
Sydney Highland Games, Sydney.
NSW

227

SYDNEY SCOTTISH COUNTRY DANCE CLUB

Aims & Activities: See the RSCDS on page 47.
✍ Secretary: Mrs J. Cook
Illabunda, Buckley's Road,
Winston Hills.
NSW 2153
☎ 61 2 624 5659

SYDNEY SOCIETY FOR SCOTTISH HISTORY

Aims & Activities: Promoting interest in Scottish history.
✍ Mrs N. Morrison
Martin Place, Sydney.
NSW 2000

ULSTER SOCIETY OF NSW

✍ Mrs D Orr
207 Holden Street, Canterbury.
NSW 2193

WAHROONGA ST JOHN'S SCOTTISH COUNTRY DANCE GROUP

Aims & Activities: See the RSCDS on page 47.
✍ Secretary: R. Reyswood
14 Wallis Street, Lawson.
NSW 2783
☎ 61 18 600779

WARINGAH SCOTTISH SOCIETY

Aims & Activities: Social.
✍ Mrs E. Tanare
1 Rowley Road, Guildford.
NSW 2161

NORTHERN TERRITORY

NORTHERN TERRITORY BRANCH OF THE ROYAL SCOTTISH COUNTRY DANCE SOCIETY

Aims & Activities: See the RSCDS on page 47.
Membership: 34.
✍ Secretary: Mrs P. Henry
PO Box 41176, Casuarina.
NT 0811
☎ 61 89 27 9203

QUEENSLAND

AYR AND LOWER BURDEKIN CALEDONIAN ASSOCIATION

Aims & Activities: See the RSCDS on page 47.
✍ Secretary: Mrs C. King
Box 928, Ayr.
QLD 4806

BRISBANE CALEDONIAN SOCIETY AND BURNS CLUB

Founded: 1947.
Aims & Activities: Social and to encourage an interest in Scotland and Scottish matters. Annual Gathering. To perpetuate the memory of Robert Burns.
Affiliations: The Burns Federation, No. 1038.
✍ Secretary: Mrs Wilma Ward
PO Box 46, East Brisbane.
QLD 4169

CLAN CLELLAND

✍ Mrs J C Hocknull
PO Box 1, Beaudesert.
QLD 4285

CLAN DOUGLAS ASSOCIATION OF AUSTRALIA

✍ Miss S Douglas
14 Fernlea Street, Geebung.
QLD 4034

CLAN HENDERSON

Aims & Activities: To collect genealogical and historical clan records. To strengthen overseas links.
Membership: Open to those bearing the name Henderson and those related by descent or marriage.
✍ Secretary: J. W. P. Henderson of Fordell
7 Owen Street, Toowoomba.
QLD

CLAN JARDINE

✍ Capt G L Jardine-Vidgeon
83 Terowi Street,
Sunnybank Hills.
QLD 4109

CLAN MACNICOL

Aims & Activities: To strengthen overseas links.
Affiliations: Clan MacNicol, Scotland; NSW; New Zealand.
Membership: Open to those bearing the name MacNicol and its variants, and to those related by descent or marriage.
✍ Peter Nicol
PO Box 284, Chernside.
QLD 4032
☎ 61 7 3502297

CLAN WALLACE

Membership: Open to all named Wallace or related to it.
✍ Mr James Wallace-Young
PO Box 598, Ipswich.
QLD 4305

MACFIE CLAN SOCIETY OF AUSTRALIA

Aims & Activities: To strengthen overseas links.
Membership: Open to those with the name Macfie (in its various spellings) or those related by descent or marriage.
✍ President: Alexander C. MacPhie
8 Panorama Crescent,
Toowoomba.
QLD 4350
☎ 61 76 32 3469

MACKAY AND DISTRICT BURNS CLUB

Aims & Activities: Social. Annual Gathering. Overseas links. To perpetuate the memory of Robert Burns.
Affiliations: The Burns Federation, No. 1086.
✍ Secretary: S. C. Young
Yaldeenie, 11 Orion Avenue,
North Mackay.
QLD 4740

QUEENSLAND HIGHLAND PIPERS SOCIETY

✍ President: Mr Maurice De Hays
PO Box 2, Brisbane, North Quay.
QLD 4002

QUEENSLAND PIPE BAND ASSOCIATION LTD

Aims & Activities: Encouraging an interest in the formation and organisation of pipe bands and piping and drumming. Also participation in competitions and events in Highland Games.
Affiliations: The Royal Scottish Pipe Band Association, (page 59).
✍ Vice Principal of Drumming: Mr D. Lowrie
PO Box 233, Asdley, Brisbane.
QLD

SCOTTISH CLANS CONGRESS OF QUEENSLAND

🖂 Mr Malcolm-Ferguson
Ross-shire, Daybord Road,
Samford.
QLD 4520

SOCIETY OF ST ANDREW OF SCOTLAND

Aims & Activities: Social and to encourage an interest in Scotland and Scottish heritage.
Affiliations: The St Andrew Society of Scotland, (page 48).
🖂 Secretary: Maurie de Hayr
PO Box 45, Carina.
QLD 4152

SOUTH-EAST QUEENSLAND BRANCH OF THE ROYAL SCOTTISH COUNTRY DANCE SOCIETY

Aims & Activities: See the RSCDS on page 47.
Membership: 173.
🖂 Secretary: Victoria Schofield
14 Rolex Terraces, 22 Mary Pleasant Drive, Birkdale.
QLD 4159
☎ 61 7 207 4280 (home)
☎ 61 7 268 7311 (business)

TOOWOOMBA CALEDONIAN SOCIETY AND BURNS CLUB

Founded: 1972.
Aims & Activities: Social. Annual Gathering. To perpetuate the memory of Robert Burns.
Affiliations: The Burns Federation, No. 1056.
🖂 Secretary: PO Box 20
Toowoomba.
QLD 4350

TOWNSVILLE SCOTTISH COUNTRY DANCERS

Aims & Activities: See the RSCDS on page 47.
🖂 Secretary: Mrs P. O'Shea
7 Burnett Crescent, Wulguru, Townsville.
QLD 4811
☎ 61 77 784338

SOUTH AUSTRALIA

ADELAIDE BRANCH OF THE ROYAL SCOTTISH COUNTRY DANCE SOCIETY

Aims & Activities: See the RSCDS on page 47.
Membership: 99.
🖂 Secretary: PO Box 508
North Adelaide.
SA 5006
☎ 61 8 268 3802

ADELAIDE SCOTTISH COUNTRY DANCE AND SOCIAL CLUB

Aims & Activities: See the RSCDS on page 47.
🖂 Secretary: Mrs B. Gray
5 Aranga Avenue, Ingle Farm.
SA 5098
☎ 61 8 262 5994

AGNEW FAMILY

🖂 Ray Agnew
PO Box 23, Stansbury.
SA 5587

BURNSIDE SCOTTISH COUNTRY DANCE GROUP

Aims & Activities: See the RSCDS on page 47.
🖂 Secretary: Mrs J. Lumsden
75 Dyott Avenue,
Hampstead Gardens SA 5086
☎ 61 8 261 5324

ELIZABETH SCOTTISH COUNTRY DANCE GROUP

Aims & Activities: See the RSCDS on page 47.

✍ Secretary: Mrs L. Davison
19 Chaddenwick Road,
Elizabeth Vale.
SA 5112
☎ 61 8 255 6857

GILLES PLAINS SCOTTISH COUNTRY DANCE GROUP

Aims & Activities: See the RSCDS on page 47.

✍ Secretary: Mrs M. Morris
26 Karingal Road,
Dernan Court.
SA 5075
☎ 61 8 261 8225

MOUNT GAMBIER CALEDONIAN

✍ Mrs Margaret Jordan
PO Box 265, Mt Gambier.
SA 5290

PORT ADELAIDE CALEDONIAN SOCIETY

✍ Ms Betty Pettman
189 Semophore Road, Exeter.
SA 5019

ROBERT BURNS SOCIETY OF SOUTH AUSTRALIA

Founded: 1945.
Aims & Activities: Social and to encourage an interest in the works of Burns. Annual gathering.
Affiliations: The Burns Federation, No. 1043.
✍ Secretary: Mrs M. Greig
23 Gurney Terrace, Enfield.
SA 5085

ROYAL CALEDONIAN SOCIETY OF SOUTH AUSTRALIA

Founded: 1881.
Aims & Activities: To cultivate Scottish culture and traditions. To encourage Scottish immigration. Highland games. Highland dancing. Charitable. Educational. Historical. Social. Annual Gathering. Overseas links.
Affiliations: The Burns Federation, No. 965. Close links with all Scottish organisations in South Australia.
Membership: Open to those of Scottish descent. Social membership open to all.
✍ The Secretary
379 King William Street,
Adelaide.
SA 5000

SOUTH AUSTRALIAN PIPE BAND ASSOCIATION

Aims & Activities: Encouraging an interest in the formation and organisation of pipe bands and piping and drumming. Also participation in competitions and events in Highland Games.
Affiliations: The Royal Scottish Pipe Band Association, (page 59).
✍ Publicity Officer: Bob Currie
1 Colwood Avenue, Fulham.
SA 5024

YORKE PENINSULA CALEDONIAN SOCIETY

Aims & Activities: Social.
✍ R. Brady
21 Snell Avenue, Port Hughes.
SA 5558

TASMANIA

BURNIE BURNS CLUB

Aims & Activities: Social and to promote interest in Scottish heritage,

particularly the poetry of Robert Burns. Annual Gathering.
Affiliations: The Burns Federation, No. 864.
✍ Secretary: Mrs Eric Tunbridge
147 David Street, East Devonport
TA 7310

BURNIE SCOTTISH COUNTRY DANCERS

Aims & Activities: See the RSCDS on page 47.
✍ Secretary: Mrs K. D. Woodward
14 Raglan Street, Somerset.
TA 7322
☎ 61 04 35 1493

LAUNCESTON CALEDONIAN SOCIETY SCOTTISH COUNTRY DANCERS

Aims & Activities: See the RSCDS on page 47.
✍ Secretary: Mrs M. Day. 250 Vermont Road
Mowbray, Launceston.
TA 7248
☎ 61 03 26 1987

ROSS HIGHLAND GAMES

Founded: 1958.
Aims & Activities: To organise Games which are held annually on the 2nd Saturday in March at the town of Ross in central Tasmania, between Launceston and Hobart. They include a pipe band contest, the usual heavy events, solo piping and Highland dancing.
✍ Secretary: Mrs D. Laverty
425 West Tamar Road, Riverside.
TA 7250
☎ 61 27 3180

SAINT ANDREW SOCIETY OF HOBART

Founded: 1960.
Aims & Activities: Encouraging an

interest in Scottish heritage and social events of like-minded people with an interest in Scotland.
Affiliations: The St Andrew Society of Scotland.
✍ Secretary: G. Livingstone
13 McGuinness Crescent, Lenah Valley, Hobart.
TA 7008

TASCAL SCOTTISH COUNTRY DANCE GROUP

Aims & Activities: See the RSCDS on page 47.
✍ Secretary: Mrs M. Peters
6 Hope Street, New Town.
TA 7008
☎ 61 02 282556

TASMANIAN CALEDONIAN COUNCIL

Aims & Activities: Co-ordinating, fostering and encouraging an interest in Scottish heritage and organising Highland Games and social events.
✍ Secretary: Mrs D. Laverty
425 West Tamar Road, Riverside.
TA 7250
☎ 61 27 3180

TASMANIAN CALEDONIAN SOCIETY

Founded: 1920.
Aims & Activities: Encouraging an interest in Scottish heritage and co-ordinating social events with a particular Scottish interest.
✍ Secretary: Miss G. F. Nichols
3 Benjafield Terrace, Mt Stuart.
TA 7000

TASMANIAN PIPE BAND ASSOCIATION

Aims & Activities: Encouraging an interest in the formation and organisation of pipe bands and piping and drumming. Also participation in

competitions and events in Highland Games.
Affiliations: The Royal Scottish Pipe Band Association, (page 59).
✍ Secretary: Mr Rod McGee
   1 Calder Crescent, Blackman's Bay.
   TA 7152

VICTORIA

AUSSIE SCOTS SCOTTISH COUNTRY DANCING GROUP

Aims & Activities: See the RSCDS on page 47.
✍ Secretary: Mrs D. Thomas
   63 Turner Road, Langwarrin.
   VIC 3910
☎ 61 3 9789 2462

AUSTRALIAN FEDERATION OF PIPE BAND ASSOCIATIONS

Aims & Activities: Encouraging an interest in the formation and organisation of pipe bands and piping and drumming. Also participation in competitions and events in Highland Games.
Affiliations: The Royal Scottish Pipe Band Association, (page 59).
✍ President: B. Neal
   1 Catherine Avenue,
   Mount Waverley.
   VIC 3149

BENDIGO AND DISTRICT CALEDONIAN

✍ Mr D K Keith
   PO Box 893, Bendigo.
   VIC 3550

BENDIGO ST ANDREW'S SCOTTISH COUNTRY DANCE GROUP

Aims & Activities: See the RSCDS on page 47.
✍ Secretary: Mrs I. Stables
   3 Finch Avenue, Eaglehawk.
   VIC 3556

CITY OF NEWTOWN HIGHLAND GATHERING

Founded: 1957.
Aims & Activities: To organise Games held on the weekend following the second Monday in March in the Queen's Park, Geelong. The events include pipe bands, solo piping, Highland dancing, the usual heavy events and competitions for the best dressed lad and lass; also Scottish dog breeds.
✍ Secretary: David Smith
   City Manager, City of Newtown,
   263 Pakington Street, Newtown.
   VIC
☎ 61 52 22 1033
✍ PO Box 1250
   Geelong.
   VIC 3220

CLAN CAMERON

✍ Mrs J Gibson
   42 Stuart Street, Armadale,.
   VIC 3143

CLAN ELLIOT

✍ Mr G H Elliot
   1 Wrendale Drive, Donvale.
   VIC 3111

CLAN FERGUSON

✍ Mr D Thomson
   'Worlingworth', 10-26 Banoon Road, Eltham.
   VIC 3095

CLAN MACGILLIVRAY

✍ Mr P McGillivray
1/27 Trafalgar Street,
Mount Albert VIC 3127

CLAN MACLEAN ASSOCIATION OF AUSTRALIA

✍ Mr Allen Pureell
62 King Street, Hamilton.
VIC 3300

DAYLESFORD HIGHLAND GATHERING

Founded: 1952.
Aims & Activities: To organise Games originally held on the first Saturday and Sunday in December in the Victoria Park of this well-known holiday and spa town. The main street is closed on the Saturday for the march of the massed pipe bands. The events include the usual heavy events, pipe band competitions, solo piping and Highland dancing.
✍ Secretary: Mrs Wendy Faulkhead
PO Box 36, Daylesford.
VIC 3460
☎ 61 053 48 3403

MELBOURNE AND DISTRICT BRANCH OF THE ROYAL SCOTTISH COUNTRY DANCE SOCIETY

Aims & Activities: See the RSCDS on page 47.
Membership: 398.
✍ Secretary: Mrs J. M. Reed
2 Meadowgate Drive, Chirnside
Park VIC 3116
☎ 61 3 97267431 (home)
☎ 61 3 92746471 (business)

MELBOURNE MASONIC BURNS CLUB

Aims & Activities: Social and to promote interest in the works of Robert Burns.

Affiliations: The Burns Federation, No. 874.
✍ Secretary: Mr Neil L. O'Connor
13 Quentin Way, Eltham.
VIC 3095

MELBOURNE SCOTS DANCING CIRCLE

Aims & Activities: See the RSCDS on page 47.
✍ Secretary: Mr G. Cooper
28 Moona Street, East Burwood.
VIC 3151

MITCHAM SCOTTISH DANCE SOCIETY

Aims & Activities: See the RSCDS on page 47.
✍ Secretary: Mrs L. Day
1 Lodge Court, View Bank.
VIC 3084
☎ 61 459 4353

MORNINGTON PENINSULA BRANCH OF THE ROYAL SCOTTISH COUNTRY DANCE SOCIETY

Aims & Activities: See the RSCDS on page 47.
Membership: 65.
✍ Secretary: Mrs J. Weeks
PO Box 4061, Frankston Heights.
VIC 3119
☎ 61 3 781 1908

ROBERT BURNS CLUB OF MELBOURNE

Founded: 1950.
Aims & Activities: To encourage interest in the works of Burns. Social. Overseas links. Annual Gathering.
Affiliations: The Burns Federation, No. 726.
✍ Secretary: Ron Johnston
PO Box 513, North Balwyn.
VIC 3104

SCOTSCRAIG SCOTTISH COUNTRY DANCE GROUP

Aims & Activities: See the RSCDS on page 47.
✍ Secretary: Marcia Perry
47 Athelstan Road, Camberwell.
VIC 3124
☎ 61 3 9889 4297

SCOTTISH GAELIC SOCIETY OF VICTORIA

✍ Mr R M Wills
102 Glenlyon Road, Brunswick.
VIC 3056

ST JOHN'S SCOTTISH COUNTRY DANCE GROUP

Aims & Activities: See the RSCDS on page 47.
✍ Secretary: Mrs M. Frolley
9 Amberley Court, Bulleen.
VIC 3105
☎ 61 850 2620

VICTORIAN HIGHLAND PIPE BAND ASSOCIATION

Aims & Activities: Encouraging an interest in the formation and organisation of pipe bands and piping and drumming. Also participation in competitions and events in Highland Games.
Affiliations: The Royal Scottish Pipe Band Association, (page 59).
✍ President: Mr Bruce Neal
12 Rutland Road, Box Hill.
VIC

VICTORIAN SCOTTISH GAELIC SOCIETY

✍ Mr R McIntosh
114 Vincent Street, Oak Park.
VIC 3046

WESTERN AUSTRALIA

ARMADALE HIGHLAND GAMES

Aims & Activities: To organise annual professional Highland Games and sports in the area.
Affiliations: The Scottish Games Association, (page 74).
✍ Secretary: Bill Tannock
11 Ewan Street,
Scarborough.
WA 6019
☎ 61 9 341 6764

INTERNATIONAL BELL SOCIETY

✍ Mrs June Bell Freeman
PO Box 598, Morley.
WA 6062

PERTH SCOTTISH COUNTRY SOCIETY

Aims & Activities: See the RSCDS on page 47.
✍ Secretary: Mrs S. Parker
43 Cowper Road, Sorrento.
WA 6020
☎ 61 447 4614

ST ANDREW SOCIETY OF WESTERN AUSTRALIA

Aims & Activities: Social and to encourage an interest in Scotland and Scottish heritage.
Affiliations: The St Andrew Society of Scotland.
✍ Secretary: Jack Turnbull
250 Beaufort Street,
Perth.
WA 6000

WESTERN AUSTRALIA BRANCH OF THE ROYAL SCOTTISH COUNTRY DANCE SOCIETY

Aims & Activities: See the RSCDS on page 47.
Membership: 132.

✍ Secretary: Mrs T. Dawn Cromb
27 Sedgeford Road,
North Beach.
WA 6020
☎ 61 447 7997

WESTERN PIPE BAND ASSOCIATION

Aims & Activities: To encourage the formation and organisation of Pipe bands and to encourage piping and drumming.

✍ Secretary: Mr Digby Claydon
1/10 MacLean Street, Melville.
WA 6156

NEW ZEALAND

NORTH ISLAND

AUCKLAND BURNS ASSOCIATION

Aims & Activities: Social. To promote interest in the works of Robert Burns. Annual Dinner.
Affiliations: The Burns Federation, No. 851.
✍ Secretary: Mrs Jessie Little
7/164 Blockhouse Bay Road, Avondale, Auckland 7.

AUCKLAND HIGHLAND GAMES

Founded: 1977.
Aims & Activities: Usually held on the Saturday nearest St. Andrew's Day. Includes pipe bands, piping, Highland dancing and the usual heavy events.
✍ Secretary: Mrs Tina Robertson
19 Larnoch Road, Henderson, Auckland.

AUKLAND PIPERS CLUB

Aims & Activities: Promotes and encourages solo piping and organises a programme of recitals and pipers' nights.
✍ Lewis Turrell
36 Balmoral Road, Balmoral, Auckland.
☎ 64 9 630 0502 (office)
☎ 64 9 638 8973 (home)

BRAEMAR SCOTTISH COUNTRY DANCE CLUB — AUCKLAND

Aims & Activities: See the RSCDS on page 47.
✍ Secretary: Mrs Y. Gray
34 Forrest Hill Road, Takapuna, Auckland 1310.
☎ 64 9 410 9126

CALENDAR OF PIPING AND DANCING COMPETITIONS

Aims & Activities: Produced annually by the Wellington Centre of the Piping and Dancing Association of new Zealand's Wellington Centre.
✍ Janet Hall
58 Fox Road, Wanganui.
☎ 64 6 344 6116

CELTIC CONNENCTIONS

Aims & Activities: Scottish interest radio programme in Wellington, broadcast on 783 Access AM on Saturday mornings.
✍ Ken Weir
6 Upper Main Drive, Porirua Hospital, Porirua City.
☎ 64 4 237 5947

CITY OF WANGANUI HIGHLAND PIPE BAND

Founded: 1920
Aims & Activities: A Grade two band.
✍ PO Box 911
Wanganui.

CITY OF WELLINGTON PIPE BAND

Aims & Activities: Grade one band.
✍ Secretary: Marion McVean
12 Loasby Crescent, Newlands, Wellington.
☎ 64 4 477 3991

CLAN CAMERON

Membership: Open to all who qualify by name, descent or marriage.
✍ Denis Cameron
Te Puna PDC, Te Puna, Tauranga.
☎ 64 7 552 42250
✍ Graeme Cameron

4 Karamu Street, Ngaio,
Wellington.
☎ 64 4 479 6250

CLAN DONALD NEW ZEALAND

Membership: Open to all who qualify
by name, descent or marriage.
✍ John Hawthorn
11 Seaview Road, Remuera,
Auckland.
☎ 64 9 524 2719

CLAN MACGREGOR SOCIETY

Membership: Open to all who qualify
by name, descent or marriage.
✍ Gregor MacGregor
86 Fitzherbert Avenue, Wanganui.
☎ 64 6 344 5833

CLAN MACLACHLAN SOCIETY

Membership: Open to all who qualify
by name, descent or marriage.
✍ Annette McLachlan
22 Hillcrest Road, Hamilton.

CLAN MACMILLAN

Membership: Open to all who qualify
by name, descent or marriage.
✍ President: Margaret Pool
39 Palmgreen Court,
Whangaparaoa, Northland.

CLAN MACNICOL

Aims & Activities: To strengthen overseas links.
Affiliations: Clan MacNicol, Scotland,
NSW, Queensland.
Membership: Open to those of the
name MacNicol and its variants, also
to those related by marriage and
descent.
✍ President: Harry Nicoll
51 Hinemoa St, Whakatane,
Bay of Plenty.
☎ 64 76 8597

COMUNN NA POIBAIREACHD

Aims & Activities: Promotes standards
of piobaireachd playing in New
Zealand.
✍ Iain Blakeley
PO Box 241, Wellington.

CORPS OF DRUM MAJORS

Aims & Activities: To promote the
skills of drum majors, marching
instructors and others interested in
maintaining the skills of drum major-
ship.
✍ David Bean
41 Monmouth Street, Tauranga.
☎ 64 7 578 1912
© 64 7 578 1912

GAIDHEALTACHD CELTIC STUDIES SUMMER SCHOOL

Aims & Activities: A unique five-day
Celtic interests summer school held
each year, 2-7 January, in spectacular
coastal surroundings at a historic
school near Whangerei Heads,
Northland. Programme includes
workshops on a range of topics by
day and evening ceilidhs. Numbers
limited and books essential.
✍ Douglas or Meg Chowns
MacKenzie Bay, RR4 Whangarei.
☎ 64 9 434 0819

HAMILTON HIGHLAND GAMES

Founded: 1984.
Aims & Activities: Usually held on the
31st December in the Fairlie
Showgrounds 31 kilometres west of
Timaru. Includes piping, Highland
dancing, caber tossing, tug-of-war
and a hill race, with a special prize for
the highest awards in the piping,
caber tossing and hill race. In the
event of a tie the best performer of
the Highland Fling to win. Wood
chopping and a rooster race.
✍ Mr R. Shand
PO Box 13, Fairlie.

HAMILTON SCOTTISH COUNTRY DANCE SOCIETY

Aims & Activities: See the RSCDS on page 47.
✍ Secretary: Mrs I. Polkinghorne Gwynyer, 20 Church Road, Church Hills, Hamilton.
☎ 64 7 8491845

HASTINGS HIGHLAND GAMES

Founded: 1950.
Aims & Activities: Held annually on the Saturday and Sunday before Easter. Includes pipe bands, piping and drumming, Highland dancing, heavy events and wood-chopping, athletics, tug-of-war etc.
✍ Secretary: K. McMillan 34 Scott Drive, Havelock North.

HAWKES BAY EASTER HIGHLAND GAMES

Aims & Activities: Organises annual two-day Highland games in Hastings, including piping, dancing and field events. Schedules for competitors mailed out in early December.
✍ The Secretary Hawkes Bay Highland Games, 57 Aukland Road, Napier.
☎ 64 6 844 4123

HIGHLAND GAMES HEAVY FIELD EVENTS

Aims & Activities: A group is in formation to co-ordinate and promote heavy field events at Highland games in New Zealand.
✍ Stephen Barry 508 Great South Road, Papakura, South Auckland.
☎ 64 9 297 7116

MACKENZIE HIGHLAND SHOW

Aims & Activities: Held annually at Fairlie, and organised by the Mackenzie County Agricultural and Pastoral Society. Piping and Highland dancing are included, but no other Scottish events. Wood chopping and horse and pony events are included.
✍ Secretary: Mrs A. Bell Hillcrest, 17RD, Fairlie.

NATIONAL BRANCH OF THE ROYAL SCOTTISH COUNTRY DANCE SOCIETY

Aims & Activities: To practise and preserve the Scottish country dances as danced in Scotland.
Membership: 1,445.
✍ Secretary: Mrs Beverley Young 84 Gossamer Drive, Pakuranga, Auckland.
☎ 64 9 5766685

PALMERSTON NORTH HIGHLAND GATHERING

Aims & Activities: Held on the second Saturday in December. Officially known as the Square Day because the gathering is held in the City Square. Includes pipe bands, piping and Highland dancing.
✍ Secretary: Mrs Jenny Mair 9 Glen Street, Palmerston North.

PARAPARAUMU AND DISTRICT CALEDONIAN SOCIETY

Aims & Activities: A lively and friendly Scottish social group with regular family events, ingleside, ceilidhs, etc.
✍ Chief: John MacAllister 5 Sunshine Avenue, Paraparaumu.
☎ 64 4 298 5294

ROTORUA ELECTRICITY HIGHLAND PIPE BAND

✍ PO Box 677 Rotorua.
☎ 64 7 345 5428
© 64 7 345 6913

ROYAL NEW ZEALAND PIPE BANDS ASSOCIATION

Founded: 1928
Aims & Activities: There are more than 100 pipe bands in New Zealand. The Royal New Zealand Pipe Bands Association is the umbrella body.
Publications: The New Zealand Pipeband (quarterly)
✍ PO Box 1835
 Wellington.

ROYAL SCOTTISH COUNTRY DANCE SOCIETY, NZ BRANCH

Aims & Activities: Organising body for Scottish country dancing in New Zealand. Most larger communities and many smaller centres have local clubs with weekly club nights and monthly district dances throughout the season.
✍ Mrs Beverley Young
 84 Gossamer Drive, Pakuranga, Auckland.

SCOTIA PACIFIC

Aims & Activities: Biannual (May and November) Scottish interest magazine published by the Piping and Dancing Association of New Zealand. The nearest thing New Zealand has to a general Scottish interest publication, Scotia Pacific accepts copy from various other organisations and groups and overseas and has a particular interest in piping and Highland dancing news and features. Copies and subscriptions are available ($NZ7.50 per year).
✍ Subscriptions: Carol Jahnke
 PO Box 33 191, Takapuna, Auckland.
✍ Advertising and editorial: Rae Matthews
 Abbey Caves Communication, 11 190 Ellerslie, Auckland.
☎ 64 9 579 6715

SCOTTISH FESTIVAL

Aims & Activities: First held in 1994 and being organised again for August 1996, the Festival consists of a range of cultural, social and performance events in and around Wellington.
✍ Frank MacKinnon
 68 Warwick Street, Wilton, Wellington.
☎ 64 4 801 6998 (day)
☎ 64 64 4 473 5314 (evening)

SHETLAND SOCIETY

Aims & Activities: Lively Shetland social group with a programme of familty events throughout the year.
✍ Gibby Inkster
 27 Margaret Road, Raumati Beach, Wellington.
☎ 64 4 297 3317

TAURANGA HIGHLAND GAMES

Aims & Activities: Generally held bi-annually on the third weekend in March. Includes pipe bands, piping, Highland dancing, heavy events, etc.
✍ Secretary: David Bean
 4 Cameron Road, Tauranga.

TAWA AND DISTRICTS HIGHLAND PIPE BAND

✍ Cheryl Austin
 PO Box 51 070, Tawa.
☎ 64 4 478 8250
✆ 64 4 473 7370

TURAKINA CALEDONIAN SOCIETY

Aims & Activities: Organising Annual Highland Games, etc.
✍ Secretary: Don J. Fitchet
 56A Fox Road, Wanganui.

TURAKINA HIGHLAND GAMES

Founded: 1865.
Aims & Activities: Organised by The

Turakina Caledonian Society. Generally held on the last Saturday in January and claiming to be the oldest Highland Games in New Zealand. Includes piping, Highland dancing, a pipe band contest and Scottish field events.
✍ Secretary: Don J. Fitchet
56A Fox Road, Wanganui.

TURAKINA HIGHLAND GAMES

Aims & Activities: New Zealand's oldest annual Highland games, a popular and friendly event held in late January in a rural setting.
✍ Don Fitchett
53a Fox Road, Wanganui.
☎ 64 6 344 5519

UNIVERSITY OF WAIKATO SCOTTISH STUDIES ASSOCIATION — TE ROPU WHAKAAKORANGA KOTIMANA

Aims & Activities: University-based group with particular interests and expertise in Scottish literature. The president is Professor Marshall Walker, commissioned author of a history of Scottish literature, and the secretary is Dr Alan Riach, a poet published in both New Zealand and Scotland, and an expert on Hugh MacDiarmid.
✍ Dr Alan Riach
English Department, University of Waikato, Private Bag 3105, Hamilton.
☎ 64 7 856 2889

VICTORIA UNIVERSITY OF WELLINGTON SCOTTISH INTEREST GROUP

Aims & Activities: A university-based social, activity and liaison group with wide interests. Holds monthly social gatherings, ceilidhs, etc.
✍ Dr Claire Toynbee
Department of Sociology, Victoria

University of Wellington, PO Box 600, Wellington.
☎ 64 4 471 5317
✆ 64 4 495 5117

VICTORIA UNIVERSITY OF WELLINGTON SCOTTISH INTEREST GROUP

Aims & Activities: To promote Scottish heritage, history and culture. Social. Monthly gatherings, ceilidhs.
Membership: Open to all who are keen to foster all facets of Scottish life.
✍ Les Allan
Marketing Group, Victoria University, PO Box 600, Wellington 6005.

WAIPU ANNUAL HIGHLAND GAMES

Founded: First in 1853, but officially in 1871.
Aims & Activities: Organised by the Waipu Caledonian Society. Always held on January 1 except when it falls on a Sunday. These Games were first started by the earliest settlers from Skye, who first emigrated to Nova Scotia led by Dr. Norman McLeod and then moved to Waipu in 1853, but the Games were only officially founded in 1873. Includes piping, dancing and the usual heavy events, also sheaf throwing, stone carrying and weight carrying.
✍ Secretary: Mrs J. Baxter
c/o Picketts, Police Station, Waipu.
☎ 64 89 432 0210

WAIPU CALEDONIAN SOCIETY

Aims & Activities: Organising annual Highland Games, etc.
✍ Secretary: Mrs J. Baxter
c/o Picketts, Police Station, Waipu.
☎ 64 89 432 0210

WELLINGTON GAELIC CLUB

Aims & Activities: Social group organising monthly ceilidhs and other activities.
✍ Alastair Bremner
   20 Black Rock Road, Newlands, Wellington.
☎ 64 4 478 8307

WELLINGTON PIPERS CLUB

Aims & Activities: Promotes and encourages solo piping and organises a programme of recitals and pipers' nights.
✍ Secretary: Marion McVean
   12 Loasby Crescent, Newlands, Wellington.
☎ 64 4 477 3991

WELLINGTON POLICE PIPE BAND

Aims & Activities: A Grade one band
✍ Alan Denham
   20 Leadley Lane, Tawa, Wellington.
✍ John Hanning
   42a Simla Crescent, Khandallah, Wellington.
☎ 64 4 479 5649

WELLINGTON SCOTTISH PIPES AND DRUMS

✍ Kevin Nelson
   10 Korokoro Road, Petone.

WHANGAREI AND COUNTY PIPE BAND

Aims & Activities: A Grade two band. A pipers' club is associated with the band.
✍ Bain McGregor
   RD # 2, Millbrook Road, Waipu.
☎ 64 9 432 0527

SOUTH ISLAND

CANTERBURY BURNS CLUB

Aims & Activities: Social and to perpetuate interest in the poetry of Robert Burns. Annual dinner.
Affiliations: The Burns Federation, No. 915.
✍ Secretary: Miss M. N. Hill
   PO Box 33119, Barrington, Christchurch 2.

CITY OF INVERCARGILL CALEDONIAN PIPE BAND

Founded: 1896
Aims & Activities: Based in a town with strong Scottish roots, the Caledonian Pipe Band of Southland was the first pipe band in New Zeland and is possibly the oldest civillian pipe band in the Southern Hemisphere. It was renamed the City of Invercargill Caledonian Pipe Band around 1970.
✍ Ian Mowat
   PO Box 1447, Invercargill.
☎ 64 3 218 9452

CLAN DONALD NEW ZEALAND

Membership: Open to all who qualify by name, descent or marriage.
✍ Rhondda Martin
   55 Oakland Street, Dunedin.
☎ 64 3 454 4009

COLLEGE STREET SCOTTISH COUNTRY DANCE CLUB

Aims & Activities: See the RSCDS on page 47.
✍ Secretary: Mrs J. Hurring
   18 Coughtrey Street, St Clair, Dunedin.
☎ 64 7 8550840

DUNEDIN BURNS CLUB

Founded: 1861.
Aims & Activities: To promote interest in Scottish literature and the work of Robert Burns. Social. Educational. Annual Gathering.
Affiliations: The Burns Federation, No. 69. The earliest Burns Club outside the UK to become affiliated.
Membership: Open to all.
✍ Secretary: Mrs Margaret Smith
　25 Munro Street, Maori Hill, Dunedin.

NELSON SCOTTISH COUNTRY DANCE CLUB

Aims & Activities: See the RSCDS on page 47.
✍ Secretary: Mrs D. Emeny
　15 Brougham Street, Nelson.
☎ 64 3 5489534

NEW ZEALAND PIPE BAND ASSOCIATION

Aims & Activities: To encourage an interest in and the formation and organisation of pipe bands and piping and drumming, also participation in competitions and events in Highland Games.
Affiliations: The Royal Scottish Pipe Band Association, (page 59).
✍ President: Mr Ross Wilson
　PO Box 3992, Christchurch.

PIPING AND DANCING ASSOCIATION OF NEW ZEALAND

Aims & Activities: Organises competitive solo piping and Highland dancing activities nationally.
✍ President: Frank MacKinnon
✍ Secretary: Helen Brown
　PO Box 1175, Nelson.
☎ 64 3 548 6756

ROYAL NEW ZEALAND PIPE BANDS ASSOCIATION COLLEGE OF PIPING

Aims & Activities: Organises annual pipers' retreats and other initiatives to promote piping skills.
✍ Lester Flockton
　25 Moana Crescent, Dunedin.
☎ 64 32 455 1816

SOUTH BRIGHTON SCOTTISH COUNTRY DANCE CLUB

Aims & Activities: See the RSCDS on page 47.
✍ Secretary: Mr D. Jenkinson
　403 Pine Avenue, Christchurch 7.
☎ 64 3 3888570

SOUTH CANTERBURY CALEDONIAN GAMES

Founded: 1875.
Aims & Activities: Organised by the South Canterbury Caledonian Society and held annually on January 1 in the Caledonian Grounds. Concentrates on Highland dancing and piping, and includes amateur athletics, cycling events and wood chopping.
✍ Secretary: Mr M. Thin
　Langridge Road, Temuka.

SOUTH CANTERBURY CALEDONIAN SOCIETY

Founded: 1875.
Aims & Activities: To promote interest in Scotland and Scottish heritage. Social. Annual gathering. Includes holding annual Highland Games.
✍ Secretary: Mr M. Thin
　Langridge Road, Temuka.

ST ANDREW'S SCOTTISH SOCIETY

Founded: 1915.
Aims & Activities: To foster interest in Scottish heritage.

✍ Secretary: G. M. McLennan
PO Box 1236, Invercargill,
Southland.

ST ANDREW'S SCOTTISH SOCIETY AND BURNS CLUB OF SOUTHLAND

Aims & Activities: Social and to foster interest in Scottish heritage including the works of Robert Burns. Annual Gathering.
Affiliations: The Burns Federation, No. 860.
✍ Secretary: Mrs E. L. Thomson
PO Box 255, Invercargill,
Southland.

TEMUKA CALEDONIAN GAMES

Founded: 1887.
Aims & Activities: Usually held on the January 2 annually. These Games include Highland dancing and piping, also amateur athletics and amateur and professional cycling.
✍ Secretary: Mrs R. Hix
PO Box 116, Temuka.

WAIMATE CALEDONIAN SOCIETY GAMES

Founded: 1875.
Aims & Activities: Includes Highland dancing and piping with athletic and cycling events.
✍ Secretary: Mrs W. Todd
31 Rugby Street, Waimate.

AFRICA

GHANA

CALEDONIAN SOCIETY OF GHANA

Aims & Activities: To encourage all social activities likely to promote an interest in Scotland and Scottish heritage.
Affiliations: The St Andrew Society of Scotland, (page 48).
✍ Secretary: W. D. Lobban
   PO Box 669, Accra.

KENYA

CALEDONIAN SOCIETY OF KENYA

Aims & Activities: To encourage all social activities likely to promote an interest in Scotland and Scottish heritage.
Affiliations: The St Andrew Society of Scotland, (page 48).
✍ Secretary: L. M. Gardner
   PO Box 40755, Nairobi.

LIBYA

CALEDONIAN SOCIETY IN TRIPOLI

Aims & Activities: Social.
Affiliations: The Royal Scottish Country Dance Society, (page 47).
✍ Secretary: Mr J. Bone
   c/o Waha Oil Company, PO Box 395, Tripoli.
☎ 218 21821 600074

NIGERIA

LAGOS CALEDONIAN SOCIETY

Aims & Activities: Social.
Affiliations: The Royal Scottish Country Dance Society, (page 47).
✍ Secretary: Mr Murdo Orr
   c/o Rank Xerox, Nigeria Ltd.,
   Faja Atere Way, Mator cheme,
   OSaodi, RMB21314, Ikeia, Lagos.
☎ 234 1 526012

SOUTH AFRICA

BERGVLIET SCOTTISH COUNTRY DANCE CLUB

Aims & Activities: See the RSCDS on page 47.
✍ Secretary: Miss K. Aaschenborn
   1 Celita Joy, Main Road, Hout Bay 7800, Cape Town.
☎ 27 21 7902321

BLOEMFONTEIN SCOTTISH COUNTRY DANCE SOCIETY

Aims & Activities: See the RSCDS on page 47.
✍ Secretary: P. D. McLeod
   Scotch Corner, 102 Dan Pienaar, Bloemfontein.

CALEDONIAN SOCIETY OF JOHANNESBURG AND THE FEDERATED CALEDONIAN SOCIETY OF SOUTHERN AFRICA

Founded: 1891, when it held its first Highland Games.
Aims & Activities: The games continued until 1918/19 when the various Caledonian Societies joined together

and formed the Federated Caledonian Society of Southern Africa. This body then organised the various Highland Games including the Johannesburg Gathering. Since 1932 the Annual Scottish Gathering has been permitted to use the title Royal. Today the Gatherings are mostly restricted to pipe bands, Highland dancing and solo piping. The traditional dates for the events are listed, but both dates and venues are subject to alteration.

Eastern Cape Gathering — second Saturday in April, Port Elizabeth; Irish Pipe Band Gathering — first Saturday in May, St. John's college, Johannesburg; Natal Scottish Gathering — first Saturday in April, Hoy Park, Durban; Natal South Coast Gathering — last Saturday in May, Amanzimtoti; Northern Johannesburg Caledonian Society Gathering — third Saturday in May, Guide Dog Training Centre, Johannesburg; Pretoria Caledonian Society — 6 June, Christian Brothers College, Pretoria; Southern Johannesburg Caledonian Society — 16 June, St Martin's School, Rosettenville; The Royal Scottish Gathering — first weekend in September, Johannesburg.

🖎 Charles Wilson
   Federation Secretary, The
   Federated Caledonian Society of
   Southern Africa, UCS Centre,
   103 Simmonds Street,
   Braamfontein, Johannesburg,
   2001.
   Or, Box 31424, Braamfontein,
   2017.
☎ 27 11 403 1837

CALEDONIAN SOCIETY OF PRETORIA

Founded: 1892.
Aims & Activities: Social, also to foster an interest in Scottish heritage.
🖎 Chieftain: S. Gibson

PO Box 971, Pretoria.

CAPE TOWN BRANCH OF THE ROYAL SCOTTISH COUNTRY DANCE SOCIETY

Aims & Activities: See the RSCDS on page 47.
Membership: 49.
🖎 Secretary: Mr W. Jervis
   7 The Park, Lingen Street,
   Gardens, Cape Town 8001.
☎ 27 21 23938

CLAN DUNDAS

Aims & Activities: To promote the clan spirit around the world. To strengthen overseas links. To collect and preserve genealogical and historical clan records. Social.
Membership: Open to members of the Dundas clan and those related by marriage and descent.
🖎 David D. Dundas of Dundas
   8 Derna Road, Kenwyn, 7700.

COMPASS SCOTTISH COUNTRY DANCERS

Aims & Activities: See the RSCDS on page 47.
🖎 Secretary: Mr R. Marais
   21 Sixth Street, Northmead,
   Benoni, 1501.

DURBAN SCOTTISH COUNTRY DANCERS

Aims & Activities: See the RSCDS on page 47.
🖎 Secretary: Mrs R. B. Burrows
   108 Atterbury Road,
   Rosehill, 4051.
☎ 27 31 847663

EAST LONDON CALEDONIAN SOCIETY SCOTTISH COUNTRY DANCE CLUB

Aims & Activities: See the RSCDS on page 47.
✍ Secretary: Mr R. B. Largue
127 Beach Road, Nahoon,
East London, 5241.
☎ 27 431 352823

GRAHAMSTOWN SCOTTISH COUNTRY DANCE GROUP

Aims & Activities: See the RSCDS on page 47.
✍ Secretary: Mrs W. Simpson
18 Milner Street,
Grahamstown, 6140.
☎ 27 461 26082

JOHANNESBURG BRANCH OF THE ROYAL SCOTTISH COUNTRY DANCE SOCIETY

Aims & Activities: See the RSCDS on page 47.
Membership: 97.
✍ Secretary: Mrs M. I. van Warmelo
PO Box 727, Auckland Park,
2006.
☎ 27 11 7261252

MIDRAND SCOTTISH COUNTRY DANCERS

Aims & Activities: See the RSCDS on page 47.
✍ Secretary: Mrs J. Dyer
16 Quintos Van Der Walt Drive,
Norkern Park, Kempton Park
1619.
☎ 27 11 3152165

PIETERMARITZBURG BRANCH OF THE ROYAL SCOTTISH COUNTRY DANCE SOCIETY

Aims & Activities: See the RSCDS on page 47.
Membership: 22.
✍ Secretary: Mrs S. Nesbitt

16 Walsh Crescent, Fairmead,
Pietermaritzburg, 3200.
☎ 27 331 62523 (home)
☎ 27 331 454341 (business)

PINELAND CALEDONIAN SOCIETY SCOTTISH COUNTRY DANCERS

Aims & Activities: See the RSCDS on page 47.
✍ Secretary: Mrs G. R. Lofthouse
8 The Bend, Edgemead,
Cape Town, 7441.
☎ 27 21 58 1595

PIPE BAND ASSOCIATION OF SOUTHERN AFRICA

Aims & Activities: To encourage the formation and organisation of pipe bands and an interest in piping and drumming, and also participation in competitions and events in Highland Games.
Affiliations: The Royal Scottish Pipe Band Association, (page 59).
✍ Secretary: Glynn Sanders
124 Bayley Street,
Farrarmere,
Benoni. 1500.

PORT ELIZABETH SCOTTISH ASSOCIATION COUNTRY DANCE CLUB

Aims & Activities: See the RSCDS on page 47.
✍ Secretary: Mrs A. C. Kennedy
Culzean, 10 Northcliff Avenue,
Walmer,
Port Elizabeth, 6070.
☎ 27 41 51 1582

PRETORIA BRANCH OF THE ROYAL SCOTTISH COUNTRY DANCE SOCIETY

Aims & Activities: See the RSCDS on page 47.
Membership: 23.

✍ Secretary: The Secretary
PO Box 99, Groenkloof, Pretoria,
0027.
☎ 27 12 47 6321

SOMERSET WEST SCOTTISH COUNTRY DANCE CLUB

Aims & Activities: See the RSCDS on page 47.
✍ Secretary: Miss B. J. Rendle
12 Weavers Way, Somerset West,
7130.
☎ 27 24 514216

ST ANDREW SOCIETY OF LESOTHO

Aims & Activities: To encourage all social activities likely to promote an interest in Scotland and Scottish heritage throughout the world.
Affiliations: The St Andrew Society of Scotland, (page 48).
✍ Secretary: Mrs Wilma Fulton
PO Box 894, Maseru.

THISTLE COUNTRY DANCE CLUB

Aims & Activities: See the RSCDS on page 47.
✍ Secretary: Miss M. R. Vance
19 Sparrow Avenue, Walmer,
6070.

WELKOM SCOTTISH COUNTRY DANCE GROUP

Aims & Activities: See the RSCDS on page 47.
✍ Secretary: Mrs B. Earl
31 Village, Harmony, Virginia.
☎ 27 57 2171735

THE GAMBIA

GAMBIA CALEDONIAN SOCIETY

Aims & Activities: Social. To promote interest in Scottish heritage.
Affiliations: The Royal Scottish Country Dance Society, (page 47).
✍ Secretary: Mrs A. Clifford
ITC, PMB 14, Banjul.

ZIMBABWE

BULAWAYO CALEDONIAN SOCIETY COUNTRY DANCE GROUP

Aims & Activities: See the RSCDS on page 47.
✍ Secretary: Mrs H. Jansen
125 Matopos Road, PO Famono,
Bulawayo.

HARARE CALEDONIAN SOCIETY COUNTRY DANCE SECTION

Aims & Activities: See the RSCDS on page 47.
✍ Secretary: Mr I. M. Thomson
156 Coronation Avenue,
Greendale, Harare, 492276.

ST COLUMBA'S PRESBYTERIAN CHURCH COUNTRY DANCE CLUB

Aims & Activities: See the RSCDS on page 47.
✍ Secretary: Mr G. B. Howell
22 Carrington Road, Mutare,
60940.

ST MARY'S SCOTTISH COUNTRY DANCE GROUP

Aims & Activities: See the RSCDS on page 47.
✍ Secretary: Mr M. Gillespie
PO Box 3486, Harare.
☎ 263 4 744315

MIDDLE EAST

KUWAIT

KUWAIT CALEDONIANS

Aims & Activities: Social. Annual Gathering.
Affiliations: The Burns Federation, No. 1021.
Membership: Open to all of Scots descent.
✍ Secretary: George Reid
PO Box 5226, Salmiya 22063.

QATAR

QATAR SCOTTISH COUNTRY DANCING GROUP

Aims & Activities: See the RSCDS on page 47.
✍ Secretary: Mr G. Miller
QTEL, PO Box 217, Doha, Qatar.
☎ 974 685675

SAUDI ARABIA

DHAHRAN SCOTTISH COUNTRY DANCE GROUP

Aims & Activities: See the RSCDS on page 47.
✍ Secretary: Mr C. Martin
c/o British Aerospace, CBT, PO Box 987, Dhahran, 31932.
☎ 966 3 8571242 ext 2195

JEDDAH SCOTTISH COUNTRY DANCE GROUP

Aims & Activities: See the RSCDS on page 47.

✍ Secretary: Mrs C. Hart
PO Box 13682, Jeddah 21414.
☎ 966 6910041 ext 506

RIYADH SCOTTISH COUNTRY DANCE CLUB

Aims & Activities: See the RSCDS on page 47.
✍ Secretary: Mrs E. Robinson
British Aerospace plc, PO Box 3843, Riyadh 11481.
☎ 966 1 248 0101 ext 121

SULTANATE OF OMAN

CALEDONIAN SOCIETY OF OMAN

Aims & Activities: Social. See the RSCDS on page 47.
✍ Secretary: Mrs Briggs–Watson
HQ Sultan of Oman's Navy, PO Box 1723, CPO SEEB, Sultanate of Oman.
☎ 968 618881

UNITED ARAB EMIRATES

DUBAI CALEDONIAN SOCIETY

Aims & Activities: Social. See the RSCDS on page 47.
✍ Secretary: Mrs M. Soar
c/o McDermott International, PO Box 18961, Jebel Ali, Dubai.

INDIAN SUBCONTINENT

BANGLADESH

DHAKA CALEDONIAN SOCIETY

Aims & Activities: Social and to encourage an interest in Scotland and Scottish heritage.
Affiliations: The St Andrew Society of Scotland, (page 48).
✍ Chieftain: Mr Maurice Cairns
c/o Ewbank Preece, Ltd., PO Box 331 (A), Dhaka 1000.

NEW DELHI SCOTTISH COUNTRY DANCE SOCIETY

Aims & Activities: See the RSCDS on page 47.
✍ Secretary: Ms J. Campbell
c/o Timex Watches, 7 Ansal Baran, K. G. Marg, New Delhi.

INDIA

MADRAS SCOTTISH COUNTRY DANCE GROUP

Aims & Activities: See the RSCDS on page 47.
✍ Secretary: K. K.Vijaykumar
24 Sivaganga Road, Madras 600034.
☎ 91 44 8271284

BRUNEI

ST ANDREW SOCIETY OF BANMDAR SERI BEGAWAN

Aims & Activities: To encourage all social activities likely to promote an interest in Scotland and Scottish heritage throughout the world.
Affiliations: The St Andrew Society of Scotland.
✍ Secretary: Mr Peter D. Nimmo
   PO Box 1219, Bandar Seri Begawan 1912, Negara Brunei, Darussalam.

INDONESIA

JAKARTA HIGHLAND GATHERING

Founded: 1974.
Aims & Activities: To hold an annual Highland Gathering and Games. The Jakarta Highland Games include the usual heavy events, pipe bands, solo piping, Highland dancing, rugby, football, athletics, children's events and local teams of dancers and pipe bands are encouraged to participate.
✍ Chairman: Norman Campbell
✍ Secretary: C. M. F. Birkett
   c/o F. Elliott, J1 Banga Vii/2 Kemang, Jakarta.

JAVA ST ANDREW SOCIETY

Aims & Activities: Social and to promote interest in Scotland and Scottish heritage including organising Burns celebrations and an annual Jakarta Highland Gathering.
Affiliations: The Royal Scottish Country Dance Society, (page 47).

✍ Chieftain: Kenneth Threipland.
   Chairman: Norman Campbell.
✍ Secretary: Mrs A. McLeod
   PO Box 7948, JKSKM, Jakarta 12079.
© 62 7491109

MALAYSIA

PETALING JAYA SCOTTISH COUNTRY DANCE GROUP

Aims & Activities: See the RSCDS on page 47.
✍ Secretary: Mr C. Chong
   No. 1 Jalan TK1/13, Taman Kinrara, Batu 7, Jalan Puchong, 58200 Kuala Lumpur.
☎ 60 5704994

SELANGOR ST ANDREWS SOCIETY

Aims & Activities: See the RSCDS on page 47.
✍ Secretary: Mr M. Lyons
   PO Box 6210, Pudu Post Office, 55720 Kuala Lumpur.

YMCA SCOTTISH DANCE CLUB

Aims & Activities: See the RSCDS on page 47.
✍ Secretary: The General
   YMCA-KL, 95 Jalan Padang Belia, 50470 Kuala Lumpur.
☎ 60 3 2741439

PHILIPPINES

MANILA REEL CLUB

Aims & Activities: See the RSCDS on page 47.

✍ Secretary: Mrs H. Price
JA Batac Sr St, BF Homes,
Executive Village Las Pinas, Metro Manila.

SINGAPORE

SINGAPORE ST ANDREW'S SOCIETY

Aims & Activities: To encourage all social activities likely to promote an interest in Scotland and Scottish heritage throughout the world.

Affiliations: The St Andrew Society of Scotland and The Royal Scottish Country Dance Society.

✍ Secretary: Ms Kathryn McMullan
c/o The Royal Bank of Scotland plc., Six Battery Road 27-01, Singapore, 0104.

✍ Dancing Secretary: Lesley Jennings
PO Box 049, Taman Warna Post Office, Singapore, 1027.

THAILAND

BANGKOK ST ANDREWS SOCIETY

Aims & Activities: Social. See the RSCDS on page 47.

✍ Secretary: Mrs E. Evans
25 Thai Village, Soonvichai 7, Petchburi Road, Bangkok.

FAR EAST

HONG KONG

BUDLET FOLK DANCE CLUB

Aims & Activities: See the RSCDS on page 47.

✍ Secretary: Mr K. S. Lui
   GPO Box 13303, Hong Kong.

HONG KONG REEL CLUB

Aims & Activities: See the RSCDS on page 47.

✍ Secretary: Mr A. McNeill
   Flat 6016, Cape Mansions, 60
   Mount Davis Street, Hong Kong.
☎ 852 28171113

HONG KONG ST ANDREW SOCIETY

Aims & Activities: Social. To encourage friendship between expatriate Scots. Annual Gathering. To perpetuate the memory of Robert Burns.

Affiliations: The Burns Federation, No. 1048.

✍ Secretary: c/o Price Waterhouse
   23rd Floor, Prince's Building
   Central, Hong Kong.

PACIFIC RIM

FIJI

SCOTTISH COUNTRY DANCE GROUP OF FIJI -ARTS CLUB

Aims & Activities: See the RSCDS on page 47.

✍ Secs: Mr & Mrs Murray Mackenzie
PO Box 2344, Government Buildings, Suva.

JAPAN

GIFU SCOTTISH COUNTRY DANCE CLUB

Aims & Activities: See the RSCDS on page 47.

✍ Secretary: Mrs Arita
18 Fudou-cho, Gifu City, Gifu 500.

☎ 81 582 62 1656

JAPAN FOLKLORE DANCE ASSOCIATION, SCOTTISH DIVISION

Aims & Activities: See the RSCDS on page 47.

✍ Secretary: Mr Y. Oyama
0-4-5-404, Shimorenjaku, Mitaka-shi, Tokyo 181.

☎ 81 422 44 3406

KANSAI ST ANDREW SOCIETY

Aims & Activities: To encourage all social activities likely to promote an interest in Scotland and Scottish heritage throughout the world.

Affiliations: The St Andrew Society of Scotland, (page 48).

✍ Secretary: Mrs Anna G. Pearks

c/o KSAS Kobe Club, 4-15-1 Kitano-cho, Chuo-Ku, Kobe 650.

KANSAI WHITE HEATHER DANCERS

Aims & Activities: See the RSCDS on page 47.

✍ Secretary: Dr Y. Ohta
4, Tajikano-cho, Apt. 1-502, Nishihomiya, Hyogo 663.

☎ 81 798 54 5981

MYASHIRO SCOTTISH COUNTRY DANCE GROUP

Aims & Activities: See the RSCDS on page 47.

✍ Secretary: S. Kakegawa
3-4-14 Myashirodai, Myashior, Machie, Saitama.

☎ 81 33 3494

SCOTTISH BLUE BELL CLUB - TOKAI

Aims & Activities: See the RSCDS on page 47.

✍ Secretary: Mrs N. Nakamura
285-8-4-801, Terajima-cho. Hamamatsu-shi, Shizuoka-Ken, 430.

☎ 81 53 458 2646

SENDAI SCOTTISH COUNTRY DANCE CLUB

Aims & Activities: See the RSCDS on page 47.

✍ Secretary: Mr K. Watanabe
92 Minamzaimoku-Cho, Wakabayashi-Ku, Sendai-city, Miyagi-Ken 982.

☎ 81 22 227 1136

ST ANDREW SOCIETY OF YOKOHAMA AND TOKYO

Aims & Activities: To encourage all social activities likely to promote an interest in Scotland and Scottish heritage throughout the world.
Affiliations: The St Andrew Society of Scotland.
✍ Secretary: Alan Proudfoot
Royal Bank of Scotland plc., Dai-Ichi-Seimei SogoKhan, 7-1 Kyobashi 3-chome, Chuo-ku, Tokyo 104.

TOKYO SCOTTISH BLUE BELL CLUB

Aims & Activities: See the RSCDS on page 47.
✍ Secretary: Mrs M. O. Naitoh
1-9-10-304 Yushima, Bunkyo-Ku, Tokyo 113.
☎ 81 3 3814 0771

TOKYO SCOTTISH DANCE CLUB

Aims & Activities: See the RSCDS on page 47.
✍ Secretary: Mr K. Miyakawa
3-4-1, 4-103 Segasaki, Urawa-City, Saitami-Ken Zc 336.

URAWA SCOTTISH COUNTRY DANCE GROUP

Aims & Activities: See the RSCDS on page 47.
✍ Secretary: Hitomi Sato
2000, Daitakubo, Urawa-City, Saitama 336.
☎ 81 488 885 1894

Index

Details for inclusion/amendment in forthcoming editions of
The World Directory of Scottish Associations

Name of body/association ....

Address ....
....
....Zip/post code ....

Founded: ....
....

Aims and activities: ....
....
....
....
....
....

Affiliations: ....
....
....

Membership details: ....
....
....

Publications: ....
....

Principal office-bearers: ....
....

Contact name: ....

Address: ....
....
....Zip/post code ....

Tel: ....Fax: ....E-mail: ....
Date completed:........................

Send completed forms to:
Neil Wilson Publishing Ltd,
303a The Pentagon Centre Ltd,
36 Washington Street
GLASGOW G3 8AZ
United Kingdom
   Or fax to 0141 221-5363, E-mail to nwp@cqm.co.uk

OFFICE USE ONLY
RECEIVED: ....UPDATED: ....

Details for inclusion/amendment in forthcoming editions of
The World Directory of Scottish Associations

Name of body/association ....

Address ....
....
....Zip/post code ....

Founded: ....
....

Aims and activities: ....
....
....
....
....
....

Affiliations: ....
....
....

Membership details: ....
....
....

Publications: ....
....

Principal office-bearers: ....
....

Contact name: ....

Address: ....
....
....Zip/post code ....

Tel: ....Fax: ....E-mail: ....
Date completed:........................

Send completed forms to:
Neil Wilson Publishing Ltd,
303a The Pentagon Centre Ltd,
36 Washington Street
GLASGOW G3 8AZ
United Kingdom
    Or fax to 0141 221-5363, E-mail to nwp@cqm.co.uk

OFFICE USE ONLY
RECEIVED: ....UPDATED: ....

Details for inclusion/amendment in forthcoming editions of
The World Directory of Scottish Associations

Name of body/association ....

Address ....

....

....Zip/post code ....

Founded: ....

....

Aims and activities: ....

....

....

....

....

....

Affiliations: ....

....

....

Membership details: ....

....

....

Publications: ....

....

Principal office-bearers: ....

....

Contact name: ....

Address: ....

....

....Zip/post code ....

Tel: ....Fax:.........................E-mail:.....................
Date completed:.........................

Send completed forms to:
Neil Wilson Publishing Ltd,
303a The Pentagon Centre Ltd,
36 Washington Street
GLASGOW G3 8AZ
United Kingdom
    Or fax to 0141 221-5363, E-mail to nwp@cqm.co.uk

OFFICE USE ONLY
RECEIVED: ....UPDATED: ....